HILLS AND VALES

OF THE

BLACK MOUNTAIN DISTRICT.

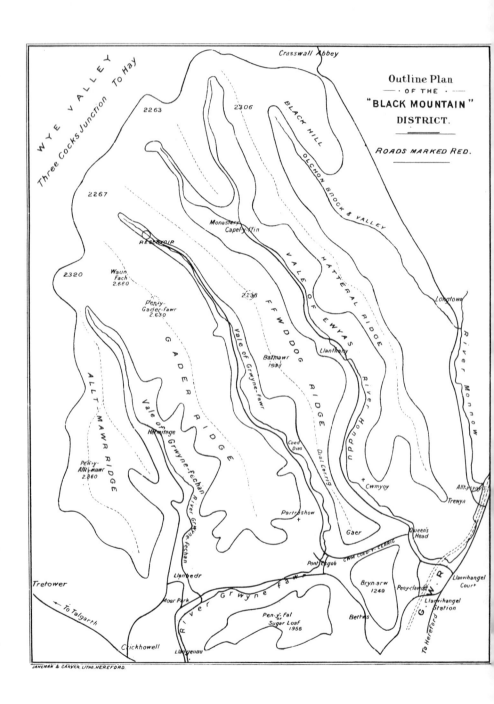

Outline Plan
OF THE
"BLACK MOUNTAIN"
DISTRICT.

ROADS MARKED RED.

WYE VALLEY

Three Cocks Junction To Hay

Crasswall Abbey

BLACK HILL

OLCHON BROOK & VALLEY

2263

2306

2267

Monastery
Capel-y-ffin

RESERVOIR

2320

Waun
Fach
2660

Pen-y-
Gader-fawr
2630

2238

Batimawr
1997

VALE OF EWYAS

HATTERAL RIDGE

Llanthony

Longtown

River Monnow

FFWDDOG RIDGE

Vale of Grwyne-fawr

ALLT MAWR RIDGE

GADER RIDGE

Hermitage

Pen-y-
Allt-mawr
2360

Vale of Grwyne-fechan River Grwyne-fechan

Coed
Dias

Dial Carreg

River Honddu

Cwmyoy

Alltyrynys

Trewyn

Partrishow

Gaer

Queen's
Head

CWM COED-Y-CERRIG

Pont Esgob

Tretower

+ To Talgarth

Llanbedr

Moar Park

RIVER GRWYNE FAWR

Crickhowell

Llangenau

Pen-y-fal
Sugar Loaf
1955

Bettws

Bryn-arw
1249

Pen-y-clandy

Bettws

G. W. R.

Llanvihangel
Court

Llanvihangel
Station

To Hereford

JAKEMAN & CARVER, LITHO. HEREFORD.

HILLS AND VALES

OF THE

BLACK MOUNTAIN DISTRICT,

ON THE BORDERS OF

BRECON, MONMOUTH AND HEREFORD,

BY

RICHARD BAKER-GABB,

THE CHAIN,

ABERGAVENNY

HEREFORD:

JAKEMAN AND CARVER, PRINTERS, HIGH TOWN.

Originally published in 1913
by Jakeman and Carver, Hereford

Reprinted 1976

This edition © 1993 Lapridge Publications

0 9518589 3 9

Printed and bound by
Redwood Books, Trowbridge, Wiltshire
for
Lapridge Publications
25 Church Street, Hereford HR1 2LR
Telephone 0432 353586

CONTENTS.

ILLUSTRATIONS.

PREFACE.

The construction of a road into the heart of the Black Mountains, where a rough track only had previously been, seems an occasion for making the beauty and historical interest of the District better known. This the writer has endeavoured to do, his reason for attempting the task being that he has spent a large part of many years in exploring these lovely hills and vales, with ever-increasing delight.

The road has been constructed by the Abertillery and District Water Board through the Vale of Grwyne-fawr, in connection with a Reservoir to be there formed, for the purpose of supplying Abertillery, Abercarn and the adjoining mining district with an urgently-needed water supply.

The writer is indebted to the Woolhope Naturalists' Field Club and to Mrs. Ley, for their kind permission to make use of an article on " The Botany of the Honddu and Grwyne Valleys," written by the late Rev. Augustus Ley, M.A., in 1885 ; to the Rev. John Davies, Pandy, near Abergavenny, for some kindly corrections and valuable suggestions ; to Mr. William Leycester Lyne, Maes-y-ffin, Llanthony, adopted son of Father Ignatius, for kind assistance in preparing the short account of the late reverend Father ; to Mr. Baldwin Latham, M.Inst.C.E., M.Inst.M.E., F.G.S., F.R.Met.Soc., for details of the Water Scheme, of which he is the Engineer ; to Mr. Walter Baker-Gabb, son of the writer, for much assistance in the " Bird-life " and in the general preparation of the work ; to Mr. W. D. Reynolds, B.Sc., Assoc.M.Inst.C.E., for the photograph of " Site of Reservoir," and to Miss Baker-Gabb, daughter of the writer, for the rest of the photographs, with the exception of the Portraits.

May-Day, 1913.

HILLS AND VALES

OF THE

BLACK MOUNTAIN DISTRICT.

GENERAL DESCRIPTION OF THE DISTRICT.

I stood upon the hills, when heaven's wide arch
Was glorious with the sun's returning march,
And woods were brightened, and soft gales
Went forth to kiss the sun-clad vales—
The clouds were far beneath me ;—bathed in light,
They gathered mid-way round the wooded height.

*   *   *   *   *

The veil of cloud was lifted, and below
Glowed the rich valley, and the river's flow
Was darkened by the forest's shade
Or glistened in the white cascade.

LONGFELLOW.

THE BLACK MOUNTAINS on the borders of Brecon, Monmouth and Hereford, consist of four principal parallel ridges, having a general direction of S.E. and N.W., and all connected into a single plateau, over 2,200 feet in height, at their N.W. extremity. Here they suddenly cease, giving place to the valley of the Wye, as it flows for 5 miles N.E. from Three Cocks Junction to Hay. The slope into this valley is the finest and most abrupt in the whole range, and the view obtained from the edge of the plateau is very extensive, embracing several counties.

The easternmost of the four ridges, which lies partly in Hereford and partly in Monmouth, separates the Olchon valley and that portion of the Monnow valley which lies between Longtown and Allt-yr-ynys—where the Honddu flows into the Monnow—from the Vale of Ewyas. This ridge rises to a height of some 2,300 feet and is known as Hatteral Hill. The next ridge is commonly known as Ffwddog Ridge, the name being a corruption of "Ffawyddog" or "Beech Tree Country," for which tree the Ffwddog valley was formerly celebrated, but comparatively few of such trees now remain there, the greater part having been cut down and made into charcoal in the early days of the Iron Industry. This ridge, partly in Brecon and partly in Monmouth, rises to a height of over 2,200 feet, and its most prominent—although not the highest—point is called Bal-mawr or Great Hill. The next ridge is called Gader ridge, having as its most prominent feature the cairn-crowned "Pen-y-gader fawr,"

A BLACK MOUNTAIN DINGLE.

(Head of the great Chair) and rising at Waun-fach to a height of 2,660 feet. This ridge is wholly in Brecon, as is the last and westernmost ridge called " Allt-mawr " (Great Cliff or Eminence), the highest point of which—Pen-allt-mawr—rises above the Crickhowell-Talgarth road to a height of 2,360 feet.

The Geological structure of the Range is Old Red Sandstone, and according to Sir Roderick Murchison, it is—with the Brecon Beacons—the grandest exhibition of that strata to be seen in England and Wales. He writes " In no other " tract of the world which I have visited is there " seen such a mass of red rock (estimated at a " thickness of 8,000 to 10,000 feet) so clearly " intercalated between the Silurian and Carbon-" iferous strata."

These ridges—more especially the Gader and Ffwddog—form a true Grouse Country, the mountain sides being covered with heather or ling, and riven with delightful dingles, down which flow sparkling streams and in which mountain ash, birch and thorn trees grow.

Each ridge is about 10 miles in length and between them lie three main valleys, the Vale of Ewyas ; the Vale of Grwyne-fawr ; and the Vale of Grwyne-fechan.

Down each valley flows a river, all taking their rise in the high plateau on the N.W. extremity of the range; the Honddu through the Vale of Ewyas, and then N.E. to join the Monnow at Allt-yr-ynys and thence to the Wye; the Grwyne-fawr through the Vale of Grwyne-fawr and then S.W. to join the Usk at Glangrwyne; and the Grwyne-fechan through the Vale of Grwyne-fechan to join the Grwyne-fawr below the village of Llanbedr.

Theophilus Jones in his History of the County of Brecknock (1805) — writing of the derivation of the word "Grwyne"—says "for this stream "the etymologist has his choice of definitions; "Carw-ne, as flowing from a forest where the "bucks feed; Grwyn-aw, from grwy, hollow— "the murmuring stream; Grone, the pebbly "stream; and Gerwyne, the vats, from the round "deep holes made in the rocks in its falls." Another suggested derivation is "Chwyrn-wy," rapid stream. The English pronunciation is 'groyney'; 'fawr' means 'great,' and 'fechan' means 'little.'

THE VALE OF EWYAS.

Take proper care of your monuments   *   *   *
Watch an old building with an anxious care   *   *   *
Count its stones as you would jewels of a crown ;
Bind it together with iron where it loosens ;
Stay it with timber where it declines ;
Do not care about the unsightliness of the aid ;
Better a crutch than a lost limb ;
And do this tenderly and reverently and continually
And many a generation will still be born
And pass away beneath its shadow.—

RUSKIN,
" The Seven Lamps of Architecture."

THE largest and most important of the three valleys is the Vale of Ewias, in which stand the picturesque ruins of Llanthony Abbey. This valley, with its adjacent hillsides, forms the Manor and parish of Cwmyoy, one of the numerous Manors at one time subject to the great Lordship of Ewyas Lacy, the Lord of which at the time of the foundation of the Abbey was a Norman knight, Hugh de Lacy, whose castle was at Long-town. According to some writers the word " Ewyas " denotes the strife and turbulence which

long prevailed over the district owing to it being
part of the Marches, the disputed frontier between
England and Wales; but Welsh scholars are of
opinion that the word is probably derived from
" Yw-as," meaning Yew Land, from the number
of Yew trees formerly growing throughout the
Lordship. It is well known that the best bows
were made of yew, and that the tree was extensively planted for that purpose. In the time of
Edward III. every able-bodied man was, for the
purpose of national defence, obliged by law to
practise archery after church on Sundays, and, by
a statute of Edward IV., to have a bow of his own
height for his own use.

Llanthony is a corruption from Llan-
Honddu (the Church on the Honddu), or, more
fully, Llan-Ddewi-Nant-Honddu (the Church of
St. David on the river Honddu) the first Church
there, according to tradition, having been erected
by St. David in the sixth century.

The particulars usually given of the parentage
and life of St. David are necessarily very legendary
from the remoteness of the age in which he lived.
He appears to have been for a short time, Bishop
of the ancient, but long since extinct, See of
Caerleon, and he subsequently founded the See of
Menevia in Pembrokeshire, named after him, " St.
David's," of which he became the first Bishop,

THE SHRINE OF ST. DAVID, 1913.

sometime in the sixth or beginning of the seventh
century. In the early part of the 12th century he
was canonized by Pope Calixtus II. and raised to
the distinction of Patron Saint of Wales. His
Shrine at St. David's—a photograph of which is
here given—became famous and an object of
pilgrimage. Henry II. is said to have visited it
in 1173, and Edward I. and Queen Eleanor in
1284. The shrine is said to have been embellished
with frescoes; St. David in the centre arch in full
Episcopal robes, with St. Patrick in the arch on
his right, and St. Denis on his left, but no vestige
of these now remains. The low arches support a
stone table on which rested a portable shrine
with the relics of the Saint, which was carried in
procession on special occasions ; but this shrine,
with the relics, has long since disappeared.

According to tradition, being much attached
to solitude and religious contemplation, St. David
retired during some period of his career, to the
Vale of Ewyas, and there erected a small chapel
or cell on the banks of the Honddu. It is said to
have been " a poor building, covered with moss
and ivy and surrounded with thickets, scarcely
habitable for man or beast."

The tradition appears to have gained credence
in early times; Giraldus (1188) mentions it, and
Michael Drayton in the poem called " Polyolbion,"
written 300 years ago (1613), thus refers to it :—

" The Britons, alike devout, their messengers direct
" To David, that he would their ancient right protect.
" 'Mongst Hatterills loftie hills, that with the clouds are
   crowned
" The Valley Ewias lies, immersed so deep and round,
" As they below that see the Mountains rise so hie,
" Might think the straggling Herds were grazing in the
   skie;
" Which in such a shape of solitude doth beare,
" As Nature at the first appointed it for pray'r:
" Where in an aged cell, with mosse and Ivie growne,
" In which, not to this day the sunne hath ever showne,
" That reverend British Saint in zealous ages past,
" To contemplation lived; and did so truly fast,
" As he did onlie drink what crystal Hodney yields,
" And fed upon the leeks he gathered in the fields.
" In memorie of whom, in the revolving yeare,
" The Welshmen on his day that sacred herbe do
   weare."

It will be seen from this quotation, that
Drayton, like Shakespeare, does not support the
modern contention that the daffodil, and not the
leek, is the true national emblem of Wales.

Robert Southey (Poet Laureate, 1813,) also
refers to the tradition in an " Inscription for a
Monument in the Vale of Ewyas ":—

" Here was it, stranger, that the Patron Saint
" Of Cambria, pass'd his age of penitence
" A solitary man: and here he made
" His Hermitage; the roots his food, his drink
" Of Honddy's Mountain Stream.

The story of Llanthony Abbey is as follows :—

For some centuries St. David's chapel or cell
was deserted and lay in ruins. In the reign of
William Rufus, a Knight (kinsman and retainer
of Hugh de Lacy, Lord of Ewyas Lacy) whose
simple name " William " is only preserved, found
his way during the chase, into the secluded and
wild Vale of Ewyas. Inspired by the example
set by St. David and impressed by the thought of
the heavenly peace of days spent in religious contemplation amongst those rocks and woods, he
renounced the world and its pleasures, repaired
the cell of St. David in such a manner as to make
it habitable and there dwelt, giving himself up to
contemplation and prayer. The fame of the hermit
knight soon travelled far, and at last it reached
the ears of the Court ; Henry I., with his Queen,
Maud, being then on the throne. Ernesius, the
chaplain of the Queen, was so moved by the
recital that he resolved to visit the hermit, and in
1103 the journey to the Vale of Ewyas was undertaken, with the result that he persuaded William
to receive him as a companion and partner in
St. David's cell. Together they there dwelt and
built a small and homely church in the place of
their hermitage. In 1108 this church was duly
consecrated and dedicated to St. John the Baptist,
the patron saint of hermits. Hugh de Lacy,

who had not lost sight of his kinsman and former knight—and possibly was present at the consecration—offered to endow the church with lands and other wealth, with a view to the erection of a larger and more handsome building. This offer was for a time refused, but at length it was accepted, whereupon, with the sanction of Anselm Archbishop of Canterbury, the erection of the magnificent Abbey, the ruins of which we now see, was commenced. The work was probably completed, or mainly completed, not later than 1120, and the Order selected to occupy the Abbey was the Canons Regular of St. Augustine. The building was soon filled with 40 brethren of that Order, and Ernesius was chosen the first Prior. He was succeeded by Robert de Betun, who, however, remained but a short time, having been, much against his will and inclination, removed to the See of Hereford, where he was consecrated Bishop in 1131. About this time Walter de Gloucester, father of Milo, Earl of Hereford and High Constable of England, is said to have joined the Community and to have there died and been buried, and it has been conjectured that the stone lid of a coffin now to be seen at the Abbey, was that of Walter de Gloucester. Robert de Braci became third Prior, but almost immediately on his accession, the peace and tranquillity of the Abbey was so completely destroyed by the con-

tinual incursions and depredations of the natives
and neighbouring Welsh, that residence there
became almost insupportable, and the main body
of the Brethren were removed to Hereford under
the protection of their late Prior, the Bishop. In
consequence of these disturbances application was
made, through the intercession of the Bishop, to
Milo, Earl of Hereford and High Constable of
England, to found a new Priory, and, with his
aid, a site was found at Hyde on the banks of
the Severn near Gloucester. There a spacious
Church and Monastery were so speedily built
that the Church was consecrated in 1136 and
dedicated to the Virgin Mary, the Priory being
named after the Mother House, " Llanthony."
Milo and his family richly endowed the new
Priory, and William of Wycombe was made
Prior over both Houses. William of Wycombe
appears to have borne no good will towards
Llanthony in the Vale of Ewyas, and to have
done all that lay in his power to enrich the new
Priory, largely—according to the record given
below—at the expense of the Mother House. He
was succeeded by Clement, who is said to have
retained a great affection for the Mother Church,
and attempted to raise her from her prostrate
condition. Every year, therefore, he obliged the
whole community—13 monks excepted who were
left at Gloucester—to migrate with him to Llan-

thony in the Vale of Ewyas and spend several months in that retirement.

In the Cottonian Library is a Latin MS. purporting to have been written by a monk of the Mother House of Llanthony. In it he describes —somewhat bitterly—the state of that House after the founding of the new Priory :—

" When the storms were blown over and
" peace was restored to Church and State and
" everyone might go safe about their own business
" then did the sons of the Church of Llanthony at
" Gloucester tear up the bounds of their Mother
" Church and refuse to serve God there, as their
" duty required. For they used to say there was
" much difference between the City of Gloucester
" and the wild rocks of Hatyrel; between the river
" Severn and the brook of Hodeni; between the
" wealthy English and the beggarly Welsh; there
" fertile meadows; here barren heaths; therefore
" elated with the luxuries of their new situation
" and weary of this, they declaimed against it as
" a place unfit for a reasonable creature, much less
" for the religious ✳ ✳ ✳ There they have
" built lofty and stately offices; here they have
" permitted our plain ancient buildings to go to
" ruin ✳ ✳ ✳ They send hither their old and
" useless members who can be neither profitable
" to themselves or others; who might say with

"the Apostle, 'We are made the scum and
"outcast of the brethren.' They permitted the
"Monastery to be reduced to such poverty that
"the Friars were without surplices. ❊ ❊ ❊
"Sometimes they had no breeches and could not
"attend divine service; sometimes one day's bread
"must serve for two, whilst the monks of Glou-
"cester enjoyed superfluities. Our remonstrances
"either excited their anger or ridicule, but pro-
"duced no alteration; if these complaints were
"repeated, they replied, 'Who would go and sing
"to the wolves? Do the whelps of wolves delight
"in loud music? They even make sport, and when
"any person was sent hither would ask, What
"fault has he committed? Why is he sent to
"prison?' Thus was the Mistress and the Mother
"House called a dungeon and a place of banishment
"for criminals. Notwithstanding the Church was
"thus shamefully and cruelly oppressed, many
"respected her with the affection of a son; yet
"none ventured to stand up in her behalf. None
"dared to open their mouths or to complain; if
"anyone presumed to murmur he was punished as
"a heinous delinquent; all therefore acquiesced,
"while God by His just will, although unaccount-
"able to us, permitted the Library to be despoiled
"of its books. the storehouse of its silk vestments
"embroidered with gold and silver; of its Deeds
"and Charters and the Treasury of all its precious

" goods. Whatever was ornamental or valuable
" in the Church of St. John was carried away to
" Gloucester without remonstrance; even the bells,
" which from their great weight were difficult of
" removal, were transported to the same place."

Giraldus (1188) commenting on these monasteries, writes :—

" In the deep Vale of Ewyas, which is about
" an arrow-shot broad, encircled on all sides by
" lofty mountains, stands the Church of St. John
" the Baptist, on the very spot where the humble
" Chapel of David the Archbishop had formerly
" stood, decorated only with moss and ivy. A
" situation truly calculated for religion and more
" adapted to Canonical discipline than all the
" Monasteries of the British Isle. It was founded
" by two hermits, in honour of the retired life, far
" removed from the bustle of mankind, in a solitary
" Vale watered by the river Hodeni. ⁜ ⁜ ⁜
" Owing to its mountainous situation the rains are
" frequent, the winds boisterous and the clouds
" in winter almost continual. The air, though
" heavy, is healthy, and diseases are so rare, that
" the brotherhood, when worn out by long toil
" and affliction during their residence with the
" daughter [at Gloucester] retiring to this Asylum
" and their Mother's lap, soon regained their long
" wished for health. ⁜ ⁜ ⁜ Here the Monks

"sitting in their Cloisters, enjoying the fresh air,
"when they happen to look up towards the
"horizon, behold the tops of the mountains as it
"were touching the heavens and herds of wild deer
"feeding on their summits; The body of the sun
"does not become visible above the heights of the
"mountains, even in serene weather, till about the
"first hour or a little before. A spot truly fitted
"for contemplation, a happy and delightful spot,
"fully competent from its first establishment, to
"supply all its own wants, had not the extrava-
"gance of English luxury [at Gloucester], the
"pride of a sumptuous table, the increasing growth
"of intemperance and ingratitude, added to the
"negligence of its Patron and Prelates, reduced
"it from freedom to servility; and if the step-
"daughter, no less enviously than odiously, had
"not supplanted her mother."

Such briefly told, is the story of Llanthony
up to the close, or nearly the close, of the 12th
century. Few particulars concerning the life of
the Community from the close of that century
to the reign of Edward IV., have been handed
down; but it is evident that during that period
a separation took place between Llanthony in the
Vale of Ewyas and Llanthony in Gloucester, each
Priory having its own Community, and each Community appointing its own Prior; and it seems

also evident that Llanthony in Gloucester remained, in effect, the principal House, although the Church of St. John the Baptist had been, it is said, authoritatively pronounced "Superior" to the Church of St. Mary at Gloucester.

In the reign of Edward IV. a Royal Licence was issued (1481) "To unite the Priory of Llanthony the first in Wales and the Priory of Llanthony, near Gloucester." It states that John Adams, Prior of Llanthony in Wales, has wasted and destroyed the profits, revenues, and emoluments of the said Priory, and daily more and more does waste and destroy the same and does keep and sustain in the said Priory not above four Canons besides himself, who lead no very good lives ; and all divine worship, hospitality, and other works of piety and charity which ought and were heretofore performed and observed according to the intention of the first foundation, are now wholly neglected and omitted. * * * And we, observing the prudent government of those religious Men, the Regular Canons, the Prior and Convent of the Priory and Monastery of the Blessed Mary of Llanthony, near Gloucester, have given and granted to our beloved in Christ, Henry Deen, Prior. * * * All the Lands and Estates of Llanthony the first and also that the Church Conventual of St. John the Baptist of Llanthony

EAST END OF LLANTHONY ABBEY.

(*From Wyndham's " Tour through Monmouthshire and Wales," 1777.*)

the first in Wales may be united and annexed to Llanthony, near Gloucester. And also that the said Prior of Llanthony, near Gloucester shall for ever appoint and sustain in the said Priory of Llanthony the first in Wales, one Prior donative and four Canons, to perform Masses and other divine Offices for ever in the said Priory of Llanthony the first in Wales, and to administer the Sacrament to the Parishioners in that place, if not disturbed or hindered from it by any rebellion or open breach of the peace.

Henry Deen, the Prior of Llanthony in Gloucester at the time of this Charter, subsequently became Bishop of Bangor, where he commenced to rebuild the Cathedral, but had only completed the Choir when he was removed to the See of Salisbury. At Salisbury he only remained one year, when he was made Lord Chancellor of England, and in 1501-2 Archbishop of Canterbury.

On the dissolution of Monasteries, the lands and site of the Abbey in the Vale of Ewyas were granted to Sir Nicholas Arnold, then Lord Chief Justice of Ireland. The buildings fell into decay, and Sir Richard Colt Hoare, writing in 1806, says—" When my friend and countryman " Mr. Wyndham made the Tour in Wales in 1777, " the Eastern Front of the Abbey was standing, " but has since fallen, and its design is only now

" preserved by the view of it engraven in his book.
" When I accompanied Mr. Coxe in the year 1800
" to make drawings for his Historical Tour through
" Monmouthshire, the Western Front still retained
" its exterior elegance. In the year 1801 one of
" the fine windows gave way, and in 1803 I was
" a mournful eye witness of the total downfall of
" the three windows which then composed the
" principal ornament of that Front."

The engraving in Mr. Wyndham's book " A
Tour through Monmouthshire and Wales," is here
reproduced. It is called " A View of the Abbey
" Church at Llanthony from within the West Door."
The drawing of the West Front from Coxe's " An
Historical Tour in Monmouthshire," is also repro-
duced ; and a photograph, showing the present
state of the west front, is added.

The late Professor E. A. Freeman, Regius
Professor of Modern History at Oxford, and a
recognised authority on all archæological, anti-
quarian, and architectural subjects, visited Llanthony in or about 1855, and thus records his
impressions.* " I will not enlarge on its wonder-
" ful situation, further than to place on record a
" passing expression of my own feelings of admira-
" tion as I first approached it on a September
" evening, winding my way along the utterly

* Archæologia Cambrensis, Vol. I., Third Series, 1855.

Sir Rich. Hoare Bart. del.t

W. Byrne sculp.t

WEST VIEW OF LLANTHONY ABBEY.

(From Coxe's "Tour in Monmouthshire," 1800).

"unknown Valley, till the dark mass of ruins
"burst on me, with the full light of the moon
"streaming through its shattered windows and
"bringing it into still more perfect harmony with
"the scene around.   Tintern is nothing to Llan-
"thony.   With less actually to offend, with no
"actual desecration, Tintern is almost too perfect,
"too neat and trim, and bears too palpably the
"stamp of a show place. Llanthony, an utter ruin,
"its Prior's house an Inn, which intrudes into the
"South West Tower of the Church itself, its
"Cloister a Farmyard, its Chapter House a Calf
"pen, seems more, so to speak, in a state of
"nature.   One can wander in and out unre-
"strained, and the fact of being actually lodged
"in the building itself, adds something to the
"romantic character of the whole." He then
describes in great detail the architectural features
of the Church, and it will be of interest, in view
of the drawing and photograph, to repeat what
he says of the West Front:

" In this Front the style may fairly be called
" Early English, though one or two round arches,
" the use of the square and octagonal abacus, and
" a general squareness of section, show that the
" Romanesque leaven has not been quite worked
" out.   The aisles are terminated by two equal
" Towers which must have been, or at any rate

" have been designed to be, at least a stage higher
" than at present, as they now reach only to the
" level of the clerestory wall. This gives the whole
" front an appearance of much greater breadth and
" massiveness than it could have possessed in the
" days of its perfection. * * * The lowest stage
" of the central compartment contains the great
" western doorway. This is pointed, a circumstance
" somewhat remarkable, for ordinarily the round
" arch is preserved in doorways, as long as it is
" preserved anywhere, as we see very conspicuously
" in the Early English work at Llandaff, where
" the round arch is retained in the doorways and
" nowhere else. The doorway is not very richly
" ornamented, its chief decorative feature being
" boultins without capitals. On each side of the
" doorway is a large blank arch of analogous
" character, and two smaller ones in each of the
" Towers range with them, there being, as at
" Llandaff, no doorways in the aisles. These
" arches form a kind of a niche being slightly
" hollowed. The great West Window is gone, the
" central compartment being broken down at the
" string above the doorway. * * * The tall,
" banded jamb-shafts of the outer lights still re-
" main. Two stages of the Towers range with
" the West Window ; the string dividing them
" ranges with the bands of the jamb-shafts of the
" West Window, so that the upper stage is very

WEST FRONT—LLANTHONY ABBEY, 1912.

" much the higher of the two. The lower one
" contains the west windows of the aisles, which
" are thus set very high in the wall; they are
" round-headed lights, plain and rather broad.
" ⁂   ⁂   ⁂   The upper stage is panelled with
" two very long and slender blank pointed arches
" on each side, resting on shafts with octagonal
" abaci, except a single square one to the south.
" The flat turret nearest the centre on each side
" have two pointed arches from boultins in each
" stage, sharing their respective proportions. The
" outer turrets have merely slits to light the stair-
" case."

He then proceeds : " Llanthony exhibits the
" transition state of Norman into Early English
" in a very advanced stage, developing in the
" West Front into nearly confirmed Lancet Work.
" ⁂   ⁂   ⁂   Llanthony belongs to the same class of
" Church as St. David's and Llandaff and evidently
" comes between the two in date. Now we know
" the date of St. David's, it was commenced in
" 1180, it was finished not many years before 1220.
" Llanthony must be placed after the first of those
" dates. Llandaff must be later than Llanthony.
" ⁂   ⁂   ⁂   I feel convinced that these three
" Churches were built in the order I have named,
" by architects each of whom had diligently
" studied the works of his immediate predecessor.

" Llanthony took some hints from St. David's and
" Llandaff looks very like an improvement upon
" Llanthony. ❊ ❊ ❊ Internal evidence then
" asserts a rebuilding of Llanthony about the
" year 1200. It is clear that the work was done
" gradually, the West front being the last of the
" Church finished."

It will thus be seen that Professor Freeman
contends that we are not looking at the ruins of
the first Abbey Church, but at the ruins of that
Church as rebuilt. As, however, he places the
rebuilding not later than the close of the 12th
century and the Abbey was only commenced in
the early part of that century, it appears improb-
able that the short interval which had elapsed
between those dates—some 70 or 80 years only—
could have made a rebuilding necessary; unless
indeed the original Church had been ruthlessly
destroyed, of which there is no record. Is it not
more probable that the Church was in fact not
completed until about the end of the century?
The flight of the monks to Hereford ; the building
of the Priory at Gloucester ; and the turbulent
state of the kingdom upon the death of Henry I.,
may have arrested the building, which was probably resumed when the state of the country
became more settled, and possibly when Clement
was Prior, he having, as recorded, retained " a

great affection for the Mother Church." Moreover the work in Professor Freeman's opinion "was done gradually "; so that, for these reasons, it seems more probable that the ruins we look at are those of the only Abbey Church erected there, commenced in the early part of the 12th century and completed at or about the close of that century.

The Church of Llanthony in which Divine Service is held (Chapel-of-Ease to the parish Church at Cwmyoy), is supposed to stand upon or near the site of St. David's cell. The Church is dedicated to St. David, and is oriented for March 1st, *i.e.* the axis of the Church directly points to that part of the heavens where the sun rises on St. David's Day. The axis of the Abbey Church is not parallel with St. David's, having been oriented, it is supposed, for a different day, namely that of St. John the Baptist, June 24th. Professor Freeman says of this Church: "A little "to the South of the Priory, just outside the "Cloister, but within the general precincts, lies "the small Parish Church evidently contemporary "with the Priory. It consists of a nave and "chancel only, with a north porch and a wooden "bell-cote at the west end. As an example of "style it may rank among the most interesting "of the smaller buildings in Monmouthshire, its "character being so completely identical with that "of its magnificent neighbour."

It may be as well to mention that this small Church was "restored" in or about 1893.

As regards the Priory at Gloucester; whilst the ruins of the Mother Church are still considerable and greatly beautify the Vale of Ewyas, the only part of her arrogant daughter which remains is the Gateway, a photograph of which is here given. The Priory at Gloucester had many powerful supporters and amongst the greatest of these was the noble family of Bohun, whose battered shield is still to be seen on the Gateway. Earl Milo, the founder; his son-in-law Humphrey de Bohun, Earl of Hereford and Lord of Brecknock; Henry de Bohun, Earl of Hereford, and Humphrey de Bohun the fifth of that name, who died in 1275, are, amongst others, said to have been buried within the precincts of the Priory, but their monuments have been entirely demolished together with the rest of the building.

The remains of the Priory Church were destroyed in the 18th century, on the construction of the Ship Canal from Gloucester to Sharpness. The site of the Priory is on low, swampy ground close to the City of Gloucester, within the purlieus of the Docks.

In the early part of the 18th century the site of the Abbey in the Vale of Ewyas and the lands then held with it in and about Cwmyoy, were sold

GATEWAY OF LLANTHONY, GLOUCESTER, 1913.

to the Harley Family, Earls of Oxford, and in 1799 these Estates were offered for sale by public auction, when Sir Mark Wood became the purchaser of the greater part of them, as well as of the site of the Abbey. A few years later these were re-sold by him to Walter Savage Landor, Prose Writer and Poet, who had conceived the idea of building himself a handsome residence near the Abbey.

It is generally believed that this intention was not carried out, and that, in consequence of disputes with his Tenants and other causes, he abandoned the house in an unfinished state. From letters however written by him in the years 1813 and 1814, and from a diary kept during those years by Captain Thomas Morgan, of the Royal Monmouth and Brecon Regiment, who resided at the Hill near Abergavenny, it would conclusively appear that the house was completed and for a time occupied by Walter Savage Landor.

Frequent reference is made in these letters— written from "Lantony," as he spells it—to his house, to his servants, and one even mentions the wine he has stored in his cellar. On 5th April, 1813, he invites Mr. Baker Gabb, father of the writer of this account, to see him, adding "I "trust I shall have the pleasure of your company "at dinner. We can give you a bed."

In the diary of Captain Morgan is the entry, under date October 28th, 1814. "Went to Llan-"thony coursing, killed 2 Hares; had 5 Courses. "Dined at Landor's new house."

These letters also afford abundant evidence of the unsatisfactory relationship which existed between him and his tenants. He was in a constant state of litigation with them; for recovery of rent; for trespass of various kinds; for poaching, and in one letter he complains of the timber having been carried away from his sawpit and the sawpit itself wrecked. He appears to have abandoned the house and valley after a very short residence, when the house was taken down and the materials sold. In 1857, when residing at Bath, he re-visited the valley—although evidently retaining no pleasant memories of it—and after the visit, wrote "Sad scene! sad remembrances! Forty "three years have passed since I saw the place, "and never had I wished to see it again."

After leaving Llanthony (in 1814 or 1815) Walter Savage Landor resided abroad, ultimately settling at Fiesole, near Florence, until 1835, when he returned to England and made his home at Bath. In 1858 he went back to Florence. "I "think I will go and die in Italy, but not in my "old home. It is pleasant to see the sun about "one's death-bed" he wrote; and in Florence he died on 17th September, 1864, in his 90th year. He lies buried in the English Cemetery at Florence.

The Estate still belongs to the Landor Family, the present owner being Charles Savage Landor, son of the Poet and Father of the well known traveller who has experienced so many adventures in Thibet, South America and elsewhere.

The Valley possesses a good road as far as the Abbey; from there to the head of the Valley, at Capel-y-ffin—near which place the late Father Ignatius erected his plain Monastic Buildings—the road is somewhat narrow and rough, and from there cart tracks extend over the north-west extremity of the range to Hay and the Wye Valley.

As the career of Father Ignatius is of much interest, a short outline of it is here given.

The real name of Father Ignatius was Joseph Leycester Lyne, and he was born in November, 1837, at Trinity Square, in the parish of All Hallows, Barking. He was the second son of Mr. Francis Lyne, who married Miss Louisa Leycester, a lady claiming descent from the ancient family of Leycester, of Tabley, in the County of Chester; and he was a cousin of Dean Stanley. At an early age he was sent to St. Paul's School, then close to the Cathedral, but being, it is said, a delicate and emotional boy, he was soon removed to a private

school in the country. Later on, he entered
Trinity College, Glenalmond, and after some lay
work in Scotland, he obtained a title for Holy
Orders from the Reverend G. R. Prynne, whose
noble work, on extreme lines, will always be
associated with St. Peter's, Plymouth. He was
ordained Deacon in 1860 by Lord Auckland, then
Bishop of Bath and Wells, with the conditions
imposed that, not being a graduate of a University,
he should remain a Deacon for 3 years, and abstain
from preaching in the Diocese until he had received Priest's orders. His efforts at St. Peter's
were thus somewhat limited, but he started a
Guild for men and boys, with himself as "Superior,"
and was about to open a Community house when
his engagement with Mr. Prynne came to an end.
He next joined "Father" Lowder (as he was
usually called) the famous and saintly Vicar of
St. Peter's, London Docks, and was by him
attached to St. Saviour's, a Mission Church, where
he worked for some time with his accustomed
zeal and eccentricity; but by adopting the Benedictine habit, he brought upon himself the serious
displeasure of his Vicar, and so they parted. In
1863 he acquired some premises on a site in
Norwich, formerly occupied by Dominicans and
there he started work, being still in Deacon's
orders, but soon got into trouble with the Bishop,
and an Appeal to Dr. Wilberforce, the Prelate,

only resulted in "complete obedience to the Bishop" being enjoined upon him, which did not accord with his views. In 1866 and the subsequent year he preached in several of the City Churches, but in 1868, Dr. Tait, as Bishop of London, thought fit to suspend him from preaching in the Diocese, whereupon he took the Portman Rooms and various public halls for his London ministrations. About this time the Community he had founded at Norwich, having left its Norwich home, found a temporary refuge at Laleham Priory, near Chertsey, and in the autumn of 1869, land was purchased at the head of the Vale of Ewyas, 4 miles above Llanthony Abbey, and there Father Ignatius erected the present Monastic Buildings. Various friends gave him sums of money towards the cost of construction, to which he added largely out of the monetary results of his preaching up and down the country.

At an Eisteddfod held at Brecon in August, 1889, he is said to have been elected a Member of the Druidic Circle of Wales, the ceremony having been performed before the Gorsedd and the title of Dewi Honddu—David of the Honddu—conferred upon him. In June, 1890, he visited the United States of America and there remained for 13 months, preaching in nearly every city of importance between New York and Florida. The

Mission and career of the preacher thus became known to one Joseph Vilatte, a Syrian Archbishop (claiming to be Metropolitan for the Old Catholics in America) who, on visiting England in 1898, offered to confer the "Priesthood" upon Father Ignatius, and the ceremony was duly performed at Llanthony in July of that year. When, or by what means Father Ignatius became—or claimed to have become—an Anglican Benedictine Monk, is not clear. At Llanthony he remained, with his small community, for some 38 years—varied by frequent preachings and missions both at home and abroad—and there, in his beloved Monastery, he was buried on Thursday, 22nd October, 1908, having died on the previous Friday at his sister's house in Camberley.

It is, in many respects, a sad story, for Father Ignatius was undoubtedly a good and earnest man, with marked abilities as a preacher and great powers of riveting the attention both of men and women.

By his will dated 21st November, 1906, Father Ignatius—therein described as Joseph Leycester Lyne, in Religion Ignatius of Jesus, of Llanthony Monastery, Abbey of St. Mary and St. David, in the County of Brecon—gave devised and bequeathed the Monastery of Llanthony, the Convent and Monastery Church thereof, with the garden and other lands held or enjoyed therewith unto Alfred Harris (in religion Father Asaph) and Jennie Dew (in religion Mother Tudfil) absolutely as joint Tenants, and on the same day he signed the following "wish" addressed "To Father Asaph " and Mother Tudfil of the Monastery and Convent "of Llanthony." Whereas in my last Will and Testament I have devised the Monastery, Convent and Church at Llanthony to you absolutely as joint Tenants in full confidence that you will, as long as you can, carry on the work there according to the rules, customs and observances of the Order of St. Benedict as I have done during the last 36 years. Now I declare it to be my most earnest and sincere wish that in the event of your being unable at any time after my decease to continue such work for any reason, you or the survivor of you should convey the premises so devised to you unto the Abbot for the time being of the Monastery of St. Mary, at Buckfastleigh, in the County of Devon, for an estate of inheritance in fee simple for his own absolute personal use and benefit. This wish is expressed simply to guard our beloved Monastery from the " Higher Criticism" supported as it is by the traitorous Bishops of our beloved and cruelly wronged English Church.

Upon the death of Father Ignatius in 1908, Father Asaph and Mother Tudfil took possession under the Will, and after trying for a year to keep

together the same Community which was in the
Monastery at the time of their Superior's death,
they found that the money which he had left for
the purpose, as well as a small endowment, had
been expended; whereupon application for help
was made to the Abbot of a Community of Anglican Benedictine Monks settled at Caldy Island, near
Tenby. The outcome of this application was that
Mother Tudfil made over her share of the property
to Father Asaph, who subsequently conveyed the
whole to the Abbot of Caldy Island. An action
at law was thereupon brought by the Abbot of
the Monastery, at Buckfastleigh, to recover the
property in accordance with the "Wish," but
such action failed, on the ground that the "Wish"
by itself was not of sufficient legal force to pass
the property to him. The Abbot of Caldy Island
therefore remains in possession.

The account of Father Ignatius and his Monastery would not be complete without some allusion to the apparition of our Lady of Llanthony,
as the anniversary of that event was made one of
the principal Feast Days of the Monastery and
called "Apparition Festival." The vision is said
to have first appeared on Monday, August 30th,
1880. In the evening of that day about 8 o'clock
and still light, although getting dusk, four boys
were playing in the Abbot's field adjoining the
Monastery, when one of them suddenly saw a

OUR LADY OF LLANTHONY.

bright dazzling figure gliding across the meadow
towards him. A halo of glory shone out from the
figure all round in an oval shape. The form was
of a woman with a veil hung over the head and
face, the hands being raised as if in blessing. The
boy called out to the other boys to look, and they
all saw the form enter the hedge of the meadow,
and after remaining there in the light for a few
moments it passed through the bush and vanished.
After that a careful watch was kept each evening
about the same time by the Inmates of the Monastery, and on the following Saturday the bush became all aglow with light, and the form again
appeared. On the 8th September, the Feast of the
Nativity of the Blessed Virgin, the vision again
appeared, and once again on the 15th September.
Such—very shortly—is the purport of the official
statement published in August, 1881. The "bush,"
a holly, has been removed, and a life size marble
statue of our Lady of Llanthony has been erected
on the spot.

It has been announced (February, 1913) that
the Abbot of Caldy Island was for some time in
correspondence with the Archbishop of Canterbury and the Bishop of Oxford, with a view to
electing the latter as Episcopal Visitor to the
Community and that the correspondence ceased,
because the Community could not conscientiously
submit to the conditions the Bishop found it

necessary to impose before consenting to accept the office of Visitor. The Community therefore decided to ask to be received into the Roman Church and to seek admission into the Benedictine Order, and they have since been so admitted.

F. J. MATTHEWS.
Chairman of "The Abertillery and District Water Board."
Deputy-Chairman "Abercarn District Council."

THE VALE OF GRWYNE-FAWR.

If thou art worn and hard beset
With sorrows, that thou wouldst forget ;
If thou wouldst read a lesson, that will keep
Thy heart from fainting and thy soul from sleep ;
Go to the woods and hills !—No tears
Dim the sweet look that Nature wears.
            —LONGFELLOW.

A short distance up the Vale of Ewyas, the road begins, which has been constructed by the Abertillery and District Water Board, through the Vale of Grwyne-fawr to a reservoir about to be constructed in the heart of the Black Mountains. It first passes through Cwm-Coed-y-cerrig (the valley of wood and stones) which lies between the Gaer Hill—the termination of the Ffwddog ridge —on the right hand and the Bryn-arw Hill on the left. About half way through this valley, the road enters the Manor and Hamlet of Ffawyddwg or Ffwddog, which once formed part of the Lordship of Ewyas Lacy, and continues through that Hamlet until the river Grwyne-fawr is reached.

By a Provisional Order of the Local Government Board made in 1893 and confirmed by Act of Parliament 56 and 57 Vict., after reciting that the Hamlet of Ffwddog now forms part of the County of Hereford, but is surrounded partly by the County of Brecknock and partly by the County of Monmouth, it was ordered that the boundary between the Counties of Hereford and Monmouth shall be altered so that the Hamlet of Ffwddog shall, for the purpose of the Act, cease to be within the Administrative County of Hereford, and shall form part of the Administrative County of Monmouth. The Parliamentary Vote of the Hamlet however continues to be cast for the South Hereford Division of that County. The Manor now belongs to Mr. Baker-Gabb, by purchase from the Most Honorable the Marquess of Abergavenny, K.G., the present Lord of Ewyas Lacy. It lies between the water-shed of the Ffwddog ridge and the river Grwyne-fawr and forms the right hand side of the Vale of Grwyne-fawr—as the road is ascended—for a distance of about 5 miles. The left hand side of the vale is formed by the Eastern slope of the Gader ridge, in the Parishes of Partrishow and Grwyne-fawr, in the County of Brecon. Until this road was constructed there was practically no access to the Vale of Grwyne-fawr; steep and narrow lanes ascend on the right to the Ffwddog ridge, and on the left to the Gader ridge, the latter passing over the bridge called Pont Esgob or the Bishop's Bridge; but neither are really fit for wheel traffic. In fact the roads or tracks hitherto used in the valley appear to be little better now than they were in the 12th century, when Baldwin, Archbishop of Canterbury, with his faithful companion Giraldus, Archdeacon of Brecon, travelled through the valley on their return from preaching the 3rd Crusade in Wales, and of which journey Sir Richard Colt Hoare in his translation and comments gives the following account:

"From Talgarth, climbing up a steep ascent "now (and still) called Rhiw Cwnstabl or the " Constable's Ascent, he (the Archbishop) crossed " the Black Mountains to the source of the Gronwy- "fawr river, which rises in that eminence and pur- "sues its rapid course into the Vale of Usk. From "thence a rugged and uneven tract descends sud- "denly into a narrow glen, formed by the torrent " of the Gronwy, between steep impending Moun- "tains, bleak and barren for the first 4 or 5 miles, " but afterwards wooded to the very margin of the "stream. A high ledge of grassy hills on the left "hand, of which the principal is called the Bal, "divides this formidable pass from the Vale of " Ewyas, in which stands the Noble Monastery of " Llanthoni, encircled by its Mountains. The road " at length emerging from this deep recess of Coed

"Grono or Gwm Gronwy (the Vale of the River
" Gronwy) crosses the river at a place called Pont
"Esgob or the Bishop's Bridge, probably so called
"from the very circumstance of its having been
"now passed by the Archbishop and his suite."

Though—like the writer—many may regret
the hum and hoot of the motor in this narrow and
secluded valley, where the sound of the distant
train rarely penetrates, and where the chuckle of
grouse, the cry of Curlew and Plover, the bleating
of sheep and the bark of the shepherd's dog are
the sounds most frequently heard; yet this coming
of a 20th century road must materially improve
the condition of the valley and bring it into line
with modern appliances and ideas; indeed, up to
the present time, there is some truth in the obser-
vation made by a navvy—at work in the upper
part of the valley—"Things don't seem to have
"changed much here, sir, since the days of
"Adam."

A short distance from the bridge called "Pont
Esgob," the new road crosses the river by an iron
girder bridge, and soon afterwards—before the
Homestead of Gwern-y-bustach Farm is reached—
passes through, what appears to the writer to be,
the terminal moraine of a glacier which probably
in one of the glacial periods, flowed from the
Gader ridge. The Gaer Hill, the termination of

PONT ESGOB.

the Ffwddog ridge, is very conspicuous from this part of the road. Gaer means Camp, and the one in question is a fine example of a strongly fortified British Camp. It is of a long oval shape divided into three compartments and altogether enclosing an area of $4\frac{1}{2}$ acres. The main entrance is approached by a sunken passage, and it is strongly protected by a double embankment. It forms one of a line of British encampments in direct signal communication with Trewyn Camp to the East, and a Camp above Crickhowell to the West.

Beyond the homestead of Gwern-y-bustach, the road crosses by an embankment, the glen and brook called " Nant Mair " or Mary's Brook, and the Bal or Bal-mawr on the Ffwddog ridge comes into view. A short distance up Nant Mair glen stands the hermit-founded Church of Partrishow, the way to which is by a short lane on the left—about a quarter of a mile beyond the embankment —and then through fields. This small Church, with its Norman Font, Stone Altars, magnificent Rood Screen and Loft, and Inscriptions on Walls, is believed to be unique of its kind. It stands on a small piece of ground artificially levelled out of the hillside and is called the Church of Ishow the Martyr. Theophilus Jones, in his History of the County of Brecknock, states that the name was " so called from a saint of the name of ' Ishaw' " or ' Ishow,' of whom nothing is now known, save

" from the tradition of the neighbourhood, where
" it is said that he was a holy man who led a re-
" ligious life in this retired spot, and had his little
" Oratory upon the bank of a small rivulet called
" ' Nant Mair ' or ' Mary's Brook,' which runs at
" the bottom of the hill on which the Church is
" built ; that having long lived in high estimation
" among the natives, whom he instructed in the
" principles of Christianity, he was at length mur-
" dered by an ungrateful traveller, who had been
" hospitably received and entertained by him in
" his humble cell." The name of the parish,
" Partrishow," is probably a corruption of " Par-
thaw-yr-Ishow," the District of Ishow. Near the
Church is a 15th century dwelling house, now a
farm house called " Tyn-llwyn " (the House in the
Grove) where the key of the Church is kept, and
where copies of a pamphlet " A short account of
" the Church of Ishow the Martyr " are sold. This
house was once, it is said, the residence of a branch
of the Herbert Family, and it is conjectured that
the Rood Screen and Loft were presented to the
Church by one of that Family about the reign of
Henry VII. The Family was a very powerful one
in the neighbourhood during the 15th and 16th
centuries. The ancestor was Sir William ap
Thomas, whose ancestral seat was at Werndu (now
a farmhouse) near Abergavenny ; he married (as
his second wife) Gwladys, commonly called

GENERAL VIEW OF CHURCH AND " TYN-LLWYN " HOUSE.

Gwladys Gam, daughter of Sir David Gam, and widow of Sir Roger Vaughan, of Bredwardine Castle, Herefordshire. Both Sir David Gam and Sir Roger Vaughan fell at Agincourt whilst defending the person of Henry V., and were knighted on the battlefield. Sir William ap Thomas died in 1446, leaving two sons, William the elder who was summoned by Edward IV. to his first Council as Sir William Herbert, and Richard the younger who also took the name of Herbert, and founded a branch of the family at Coldbrook, near Abergavenny. Sir William Herbert was created in 1461 Baron Herbert of Chepstow, Raglan, and Gower, and in 1468 was also made Earl of Pembroke. In 1469, when leading the Yorkist army, he was totally defeated near Banbury by the Lancastrians, under the command of the great Earl of Warwick, the Kingmaker; was, with his brother Richard, taken prisoner, and both were beheaded at Northampton. In St. Mary's Church, Abergavenny, are handsome monuments to Sir William ap Thomas and Lady Gwladys his wife; to Sir Richard Herbert, of Coldbrook, and Lady Margaret his wife; and to Sir Richard Herbert, of Ewyas, who was a natural son of Sir William Herbert, Earl of Pembroke. The eldest son of this Sir Richard Herbert, of Ewyas, became Governor of Calais, and in 1551 was made Baron Herbert, of Cardiff, and also re-created Earl of

Pembroke, and from him are descended the present Earls of Pembroke and Carnarvon.

Partrishow Church is in the patronage of His Grace the Duke of Beaufort, who also owns a large portion of the original Herbert Estates, including the Castle and Barony of Raglan and the Baronies of Chepstow and Gower, those Estates having passed into the possession of the Beaufort Family at the end of the 15th century, through the marriage of Sir Charles Somerset with Elizabeth Herbert, grand-daughter of Sir William Herbert, first Earl of Pembroke.

After leaving the lane which leads to Partrishow Church, the road passes through the Coed Farm and its picturesque wood, and—a short distance beyond—Coed Dias Wood on the slope of the Ffwddog ridge comes into view. Near this Wood occurred an ancient tragedy, the following particulars of which are taken from Giraldus. Richard, Earl of Clare, whose chief seat was at Tunbridge, but who was also Lord of Usk, and had a Castle in Cardiganshire, as well as property at Talgarth and Builth, was, shortly after the death of Henry I. (1135), passing from Abergavenny (where he had been entertained at the Castle by Brian Fitzcount, the then Lord) into Wales, by way of the Vale of Grwyne-fawr, then called "the bad Pass of Coed Grono or

"COED DIAS" HOUSE AND WOOD.

Gronwy." Brian Fitzcount having accompanied him to the mouth of the Pass, there took leave of him and the Earl, with a few attendants, proceeded on his way ; when as he arrived opposite a wood a short distance up the Pass, he was attacked by Morgan-ap-Owen, the Welsh Lord of Caerleon, with a band of followers, who lay in ambush in the Wood, and the Earl and his party were slain. Private revenge is said to have prompted the murder.

Hoare, in his comments on the tragedy, says "about a mile above Pont Esgob there is a wood "called Coed Dias or the Wood of Revenge. Here " by the modern name of the place we are enabled to " fix the very spot on which Richard de Clare was " murdered. The name Coed Dias, or the Wood " of Revenge, the deep retirement and situation of "the place, close upon the banks of Gronwy, all "conspire to point out this very wood as the lurk-"ing place from whence the assassins issued to "complete their barbarous purpose." Hoare's translation of Coed Dias as " Wood of Revenge" is not correct, " Dial" and not " Dias" being Welsh for revenge, but immediately above the wood by the side of the hill road on the summit of the ridge, is a stone—said to be the remains of a once much larger memorial—called " Dial Cerrig," the Revenge Stone, placed there according to tradition to mark the scene of the murder.

When nearly opposite Coed Dias the road crosses the small stream called "Cwmffrwd," the boundary between the parishes of Partrishow and Grwyne-fawr, and between the Manor of Crickhowell, of which His Grace the Duke of Beaufort is Lord, and the Manor of Talgarth belonging to The Right Honble. Lord Glanusk, through whose land the road runs for the remainder of its length; the Reservoir also being on his land. The upper part of the valley and the Gader ridge now come more prominently into view; cultivation soon becomes scant, and after traversing the winding and narrow valley for a further 4 miles, the Grwyne-fawr river is again crossed by a girder bridge and the bare hill reached, along which the road runs for another two miles to the site of the Reservoir, in the parish of Llanelieu, and within about two miles of the N.W. extremity of the range.

The first turf of the road was cut on the 14th February, and of the Reservoir on the 16th October, 1912. The following account of the work, written on the occasion of the cutting of the first turf of the Reservoir, is principally taken from the "Monmouthshire Evening Post," of 17th October, 1912.

How human agency can triumph over nature was seen by the members of the Abertillery Water Board, when they journeyed up the Vale of

RIVER GRWYNE-FAWR AT COED DIAS,

Grwyne-fawr, among the majestic Black Mountains to take part in the ceremony of cutting the
first turf for the proposed Reservoir of their great
undertaking. The valley lying quiet in its secluded beauty has hitherto been practically inaccess-
ible, and as the site of the proposed Reservoir lies
a good ten miles up the valley, it was imperative
that the first work undertaken should be the construction of a road of that length. The difficulty
of such an engineering feat could only be realised
by one who has walked the valley from end to
end. The roadway which starts at Lower Cwmyoy has, for the most part, had to be constructed
on the side of the hills or mountains. In one
place—in Cwm-Coed-y-cerrig—a bog a quarter
of a mile long had to be crossed and the road
constructed on brushwood fascines. The Grwyne
stream is crossed in two places, and bridges for
this purpose have had to be constructed at Pont
Esgob and Blaen-y-cwm. Another bridge is being
constructed at Coed Dias, but this is being built
for Mr. Baker-Gabb, who has property on both
sides the stream, and will enable his property to
be joined up with the new road. A large number
of retaining walls have had to be erected in order
to keep the road up in difficult places, and one
portion of the road goes through a deep rock
cutting, where considerable difficulty was experienced in removing the rock. Huge trunks of

trees on the side of the road also gave some little
evidence of the obstacles which have been success-
fully overcome. The party, which numbered some
150, noted with admiration, if not wonder, the
engineering triumph of Mr. Baldwin Latham, the
Engineer, with the aid of the Contractors and
Navvies. A number of motors were present, but
most of the party made the journey by brake from
Llanvihangel Station. It was a charming, if at
times a somewhat slow and rocky ride. The
richly wooded slopes of the mountains, with the
beautiful and wonderful autumn tints of the trees
and foliage were a subject of continual admiration.
It was indeed a veritable feast of colour which
would rejoice the heart of one who had any love
at all for the beautiful. The new road, besides
adding to the value of property in the valley, has
opened up a new beauty spot—new in the sense
that it is now made easily accessible—and there
is no doubt that it will be a favourite resort in the
future. The site of the Reservoir is a fine one,
and the Water Board will have the distinction of
owning a Reservoir, not only the highest in elevation, but the greatest in depth of any in the
country. The Dam forming the Reservoir is to
be built of stone on a curve. The top water of
the Reservoir will be 1790 feet above sea level,
and the depth of water above lowest draw-off is
120 feet. The capacity will be 376 million gallons.

BALDWIN LATHAM.

M. Inst. C.E., M. Inst. M.E., F.G.S., F.R. Met. Soc., &c.

The height of the Dam above the stream will be 146 feet, and the length 974 feet, and it will have a foundation of 24 feet below the stream. The bottom width of the wall will be 128 feet and the top width 16 feet. The pipes which are being laid to convey the water to Abertillery and adjoining district appear to the uninitiated to be rather thin to withstand the tremendous pressure in conveying water from so great an elevation. They vary in thickness from $\frac{3}{16}$ inch to $\frac{3}{4}$ inch, but are made of the best wrought steel. A few years ago, before steel pipes were made, the scheme, it is said, would have been impossible, as cast iron pipes to withstand the pressure would require to have been in some cases $3\frac{1}{2}$ inches thick; a thickness most difficult to cast and almost impossible to handle, and would have greatly increased the cost. There are 32 miles of pipes included in the scheme, to which additional pipes will have to be added in order to distribute the water within the district. The track of the main pipes is down the new road to the mouth of the valley at Pont Esgob, and round the east side of the Sugar Loaf Mountain to Abergavenny; thence under the river Usk at Llanwenarth; through Govilon; by Waunavon and (by means of a tunnel) through the Coity Mountain to Abertillery. Two service reservoirs are being constructed, one at Abertillery, with a top water level of 1318 feet above sea level, and one at Abercarn, with a top water level of 1068 feet above sea level, and the water is further conveyed into the Nant-y-draenog reservoir of the Risca Council, which reservoir has a top level of 715 feet above sea level.

SITE OF RESERVOIR, 1913.

THE VALE OF GRWYNE-FECHAN.

Straight mine eye hath caught new pleasures
Whilst the landscape round, it measures ;
Russet lawns and fallows gray,
Where the nibbling flocks do stray,
Mountains on whose barren breast
The labouring clouds do often rest.

MILTON.

THE Vale of Grwyne-fechan, the shortest of
the three valleys within the Black Mountain
range, lies between the eastern slope of Alt-mawr
ridge and the western slope of Gader ridge. It is
of great beauty, the surface being extremely uneven, and although this feature—as Theophilus
Jones says—"adds greatly to the labours of the
" husbandman, yet, whatever inconveniences these
" inequalities may occasion to the farmer, the
" painter will be enraptured with the view." The
several spurs coming down to the valley from Gader ridge and the side valleys opening out between
them, also add greatly to the variety and beauty of
the scenery. From Abergavenny the approach to
the Vale of Ewyas and the best approach to the
Vale of Grwyne-fawr, either by rail or road, is by

way of Llanvihangel on the Hereford Road; but
the approach to the Vale of Grwyne-fechan is by
the Crickhowell Road as far as the village of Glangrwyne—where the Grwyne river empties into the
Usk—and thence along the course of the Grwyne
river through the charmingly situated village of
Llangenau, or more correctly Llancenau (St.Cenau),
until the village of Llanbedr is reached. St. Cenau
was the Patron Saint of the Parish of Llangenau,
and near the village is St. Cenau's Well, which—in
common with the spring she caused to flow near
Liskeard, in Cornwall, where she was known as
St. Keyne or St.Keyna—is said to have, in addition
to the usual medicinal virtues, the remarkable effect
that the first of a newly married couple who drinks
of the water, obtains the command of the house-
hold for life. In Carew's Survey of Cornwall (1602),
in the description of the Well there, this quality
of the water is thus referred to,

> The quality, that man or wife
> Whom chance or choice attains,
> First of this sacred streame to drink,
> Thereby the mastery gaines.

Southey amplifies and further perpetuates the
legend in the ballad of "The Well of St. Keyne."

> "St. Keyne" quoth the Cornish-man, "many a time
> Drank of this crystal Well,
> And before the Angel summoned her,
> She laid on the water a spell.

" If the husband, of this gifted Well
　　Shall drink before his wife,
A happy man thenceforth is he,
　　For he shall be master for life.

" But if the wife should drink of it first,
　　God help the husband then ! "
The stranger stoopt to the Well of St. Keyne
　　And drank of the water again.

You drank of the Well I warrant betimes ?
　　He to the Cornish-man said,
But the Cornish-man smiled as the stranger spoke,
　　And sheepishly shook his head ;

I hastened as soon as the Wedding was done,
　　And left my wife in the porch,
But i' faith she had been wiser than me,
　　For she took a bottle to Church.

St. Cenau or St. Keyna was a daughter of Bry-
chan, Lord of Breconshire during the first half of
the 5th century, and from him the county obtained
the name of Brecon. He is said to have had three
wives, "of names unintelligible and uncouth even
" to a Welshman whose powers of swallowing con-
" sonants are supposed to be equal to those of an
" Ostrich in devouring and digesting iron," and by
these wives to have had upwards of 40 sons and 25
daughters. St. Cenau was the 24th daughter, and
although sought in marriage by many nobles, she
utterly refused that state, having consecrated herself to the Lord by a perpetual vow. As already

stated, she visited Cornwall (besides Keynsham, near Bristol, and other places), but afterwards, by the admonition of an Angel, she returned to her native county there to build "on the top of "a hillock at the foot of a high mountain," an Oratory and small habitation for herself. The spot she selected upon which to build the Oratory, is within the beautiful grounds of " Pen-y-daren" (summit of a rocky knoll) at the foot of the Sugar-Loaf Mountain ; she also, by her prayers, caused a spring to flow near the Oratory which, besides having the remarkable effect already described, brought "health to divers infirmities." She is said to have died in 490, and to have been buried in her own Oratory.

The Well is on the right hand side of Pen-y-daren drive, a short distance beyond the Lodge Gate, and the Oratory is said to have stood on the high ground immediately behind the Well; a charming situation, strongly testifying to the good taste of the virgin saint. No vestige of the Oratory remains, but in or about 1809, a bell of quaint design and of a kind used for calling a congregation to prayer, was dug up on the supposed site. In Lewis' Topographical Dictionary of Wales (1849) under the head of Llangeney—after relating the discovery of the bell—it is stated "this curious " piece of antiquity was in the possession of the " late Venerable Archdeacon Payne, by whose per-

" mission it was exhibited before the Society of
" Antiquaries in London in the year 1809." What
has now become of the bell is not known ; the late
Mr. Doyle endeavoured to trace it but without
success.   Pen-y-daren is now the residence of Mr.
W. T. Rees, the present owner of the estate; but
recently (until his death in 1907) it was the
residence of that many-sided man Mr. John A.
Doyle, M.A., Fellow of All Souls College, Oxford;
author of "The English in America," and other
historical works; Chairman of Crickhowell Bench
of Magistrates; member of the Council of the
University College of Wales; Master of Harriers;
member and trustee of the Kennel Club; member
of the Council of the National Rifle Association,
and breeder of Shire Horses and Blood Stock.

It is a delightful 6 miles drive from Abergavenny through Llangenau to the village of Llanbedr (St. Peter), at the entrance to the Vale of
Grwyne-fechan, the views of the Sugar Loaf
Mountain, with its foothills and of Allt-mawr
and Gader ridges, being especially fine. At Llanbedr—immediately opposite the Church—the road
to the left towards Crickhowell should be followed
(about half a mile) until the road on the right,
which leads up the valley, is reached.   This road
runs for about 2 miles along the slope of Allt-
mawr ridge, overlooking the valley and the
western slope of Gader ridge, thus commanding

charming views; it then descends into and crosses
a side valley and rounds the opposite slope, forming an elbow bend, after which it rapidly descends
into the main valley until the river Grwyne-fechan
is reached at the Hermitage, a house belonging to
Lord Glanusk, beautifully situated in a well-
wooded glen. Here the high road ceases, about
4 miles from Llanbedr, and, a short distance beyond, the bare slope of the hills—that of Allt-
mawr ridge being especially steep—comes down
to the river and so continues to the head of the
valley.

In the parish of Llanbedr, stands a house of
some interest, especially to the writer, "Moor
Park," recently restored and added to by Mr.
Arthur Beckwith, the present owner and representative of the Vales of Grwyne on the County Council.
It was built about the middle of the 18th century
by John Powel, grandson of William Powel, who
was Rector of Llangattock Crickhowell in 1675.
John Powel married Anne, the only child and heiress
of Joshua Parry, of Tretower Court, near Crickhowell, who was a descendant of the ancient
Family of Parry, of New Court, in the Golden
Valley, in the County of Hereford. The pros-
perity of this Family was at its height during the
reign of Queen Elizabeth, when Blanche Parry
was chief Gentlewoman of the Queen's Privy
Chamber and Keeper of Her Majesty's Jewels, and

THE HERMITAGE.

James Parry was Master of the Royal Buckhounds. To Moor Park John Powel brought his bride, and in 1780 a daughter of the marriage, Anne, became the wife of Baker-Gabb, of Abergavenny, the grandfather of the writer. Blanche Parry, by her Will, dated 21st June, 1588, bequeaths "My Soul "into Thy hands O God, Father, Son and Holy "Ghost, and my body to be buried in the Parish "Church of St. Margarets, within the City of "Westminster, near unto my nephew John "Vaughan, if it please God to call me near Lon- "don. Item—I give to the Queen's Most Excellent "Majesty my Sovereign Lady and Mistress, my "best diamonds. Item—I give to the Right "Honourable my very good Lord Sir Christopher "Hatton, Knight, Lord Chancellor of England, "one table diamond. Item—I give to the Right "Honourable my very good Lord the Lord Burgh- "ley, Lord High Treasurer of England, my second "diamonds ＊ ＊ ＊ and I do humbly desire "my said good Lord, the Lord Burghley, to be "supraivisor of this my said last Will, and that it "will please his Lordship to see the same per- "formed according to the meaning of me set down "in this my Will, for charity's sake, and towards "his Lordship's charges herein I give his Lord- "ship Fifty Pounds." Blanche Parry was buried in St. Margaret's Church, Westminster, as she directed, and the Inscription to her memory reads as follows: "Hereunder is entombed Blanche "Parry, daughter to Henry Parry, of New Court, "within the County of Hereford, Esquire, Chiefe "Gentlewoman of Queen Elizabeth's Most Honour- "able Privy Chamber and Keeper of Her Majesty's "Jewels, whom she faithfully served from Her "Highness' birth; beneficiall to her kinsfolk and "countrymen ; charitable to the Poore, inso- "much that she gave to the Poore of Bacton and "Newton, in Herefordshire, seven score bushels of "wheat and rye yearly for ever, with divers sum- "mes of money to Westminster and other places "for good uses. She died a Maid in the 82nd "yeare of her age, the 12th of February, 1589." In the Chancel of Bacton Church, in the Golden Valley, is a handsome Monument, with a quaint inscription, to her memory.

SOME SUPERSTITIONS AND CUSTOMS.

Old legends of the monkish page,
Traditions of the Saint and Sage ;
Tales that have the rime of age,
And chronicles of eld.

—LONGFELLOW.

I N such a secluded District, and amidst such sur-
roundings, it is not a matter for surprise that
some superstitions still linger and some interesting
customs remain.   Many operations in the district
are carried out according to the waxing or the
waning of the moon. Pigs should be killed during
the waxing of the moon, otherwise the bacon will
waste in the boiling.   Peas and beans should be
sown during the waning of the moon, otherwise
he who soweth, soweth too soon.   "Cock's Eggs"
should always be thrown over the house in order
to avert ill luck.   When cabbages are cut in the
garden, the stalks should be marked with the sign
of the cross, in order to make them sprout better.
Apparitions both beneficent and evil are not un-
common.   Of the former, a phantom guide on one

part of the mountains puts lost travellers in the right path; whilst in other parts, travellers are led astray and landed in a bog. In one valley a dead man is said to have "appeared" so persistently that a remedy was sought by turning the body face downwards in the coffin, but without success.

The "Charmer" still largely takes the place of the Doctor and Veterinary Surgeon. With his aid many ailments are cured; and bones, broken or dislocated, are repaired or put in place.

    ❈   ❈   ❈   ❈   ❈

————when the level ray
Of some mild eve's descending sun
Lights on the village pastor, grey
In years ere ours had well begun.

As there—in simplest vestment clad,—
He speaks, beneath the churchyard tree,
In solemn tones—but yet not sad,—
Of what man is—what man shall be!

And clustering round the grave, half hid
By the same quiet churchyard yew,
The rustic mourners bend, to bid
The dust they loved, a last adieu.

BARHAM.

The funeral customs are interesting and impressive. The body is almost invariably carried to the grave—often several miles distant—by the neighbours, who assemble in considerable numbers, without any invitation being necessary or expected. A few of the more intimate friends are invited to act as "special bearers," their duty being to carry the body from the house to the bier; from the Churchyard gate to the Church and from the Church to the Grave. Over the remaining distance the body is carried by those not so specially invited, who are told off by the Undertaker from time to time for the purpose, in parties of four, so that every one present may, if possible, bear his share. Before leaving the house a meal is provided, of which a home-cured ham is usually the staple dish, and care is taken in many farm houses to have a ham always in readiness for such an occasion. After the meal the company are invited to take a last look at the deceased before the coffin lid is fastened down, then the body is carried by the special bearers out of the house and placed upon the bier, around which the company stand. Cake and wine, both of which have been especially reserved for this part of the ceremony, are then produced, and care is taken to hand them round from east to west, "the way of the sun," as this is considered to be of the greatest importance. Everyone present is expected to partake, and this is called " The Last Sacrament." Hymns are usually sung at the house and by the grave. When necessary to use a hearse in order to cross a stream—where only a narrow footbridge is available—the hearse is usually dispensed with after the stream is crossed, and the coffin is then placed upon the bier and carried the remaining distance.

BOTANY.

Boon Nature scattered, free and wild,
Each plant or flower, the mountain's child—
Here eglantine embalmed the air,
Hawthorn and hazel mingled there ;
The primrose pale and violet flower,
Found in each cliff a narrow bower.

SCOTT.

THE Botany of the Hills and Vales is varied and interesting.

One of the shrubs—indeed trees—most likely to claim attention during a walk in the district in Spring, is the Bird Cherry, with its long pendant white blossoms. It adorns many of the hedges and grows in great luxuriance up to a limit of about 1,000 feet. In summer, unfortunately, it is invariably stricken with the caterpillar blight and its beauty quite destroyed. The Mountain Ash, another tree belonging to the same natural order, is common throughout the district, and a great ornament both in Spring and Autumn. It fills the glens and clings to the rocky sides of the hills, up to at least 1,800 feet. The fruit of this tree is the favourite food of the Ring Ouzel, and the frequency of this rare bird in the district may well be connected with the frequency and luxuriance there of this tree. The Mountain or Wych Elm, the Oak and the Ash flourish well, and the Holly is very partial to the hillside woods, growing luxuriantly and becoming quite a large tree. The Birch silvers the hillsides everywhere, but the variety is more the rigid upright one than the more graceful Birch with pendent branches, which is usually planted. The hills during the month of August and September—especially the Gader and Ffwddog ridges—are rendered beautiful by the Heather or Ling, with its rich pink bloom and by the Cross-leaved Heath with its bells of rose, and on these ridges there are as fine and extensive beds of Heather as on any hills of South Wales. It is curious however that the fine-leaved Heath with its bells of deep purple, so common on the sandy ranges of southern England, is totally absent from these hills. The Crowberry and the Bilberry or Whinberry are very abundant; the red Whortleberry or Cowberry somewhat less so, and both Bilberry and red Whortleberry are extensively collected by women and children during the months of July and August. During that season also, the sweet Mountain Fern and Borrer's Fern abound, and are a great ornament to the hills. Both these Ferns grow in tufts, many fronds springing in a ring from one root. Another Fern, rare in many counties, the Scaly Hart's Tongue, reaches a very fine development in these vales, and will be found on walls and elsewhere in large quantities. The Shining Crane's Bill is also a great ornament to the old walls, and the Foxglove and Golden Rod to the hanging woods and banks. The rocks and their debris are covered with the mossy saxifrage where also the three Ferns, Oak, Beech, and Limestone grow, in some places in abundance. The crannies of the mossy walls, as well as those of the rocks, teem with the Brittle Fern in various forms, and also with many varieties of the prickly Shield Fern. Along the damp shady lanes and river banks, the alternate-leaved Golden Saxifrage is abundant and very fine, and the Marsh Willow-herb is common in damp spots, both in the vales and on the hillsides. The meadows in the higher parts of the vales are. in the Spring, bright with the Meadow Orchis, and in some places a meadow will be met with, filled with the rarer Globe Flower, while the smaller Butterfly Orchis and the Water Avens will be occasionally found, often in company with the Globe Flower.

In the small thickets along the course of the Grwyne-fawr river grows a rare Umbellifer, the Sweet Cicely, which at once reveals itself by its enormously large seeds and by the strong spicy odour of its crushed leaves; on rocks and by the river side, also grows the Welsh Poppy.

Many of the meadows in Autumn are bright with the Autumn Crocus, much to the detriment—as the farmers believe—of the stock depastured there. On the tops of the hills the Little Club Rush is found; the boggy parts produce the Cotton Grasses in abundance, and the spring heads are full of a water Crowfoot. Here too, in Spring, the Butterwort spreads its flat greasy leaves and lifts its beautiful violet-like blooms, while, at a later season of the year, the same spots are carpeted with the Creeping Forget-me-not, distinguished from all others of its tribe by the intense azure-blue of its flowers.

In addition to those above named, many other plants are to be found, but sufficient have been given to show the general botanical interest of the district.

BIRD LIFE.

Birds ! birds ! ye are beautiful things,
With your earth-treading feet and your cloud-cleaving
    wings ;
Where shall man wander, and where shall he dwell,
Beautiful birds, that ye come not as well ?

      *   *   *   *

Ye hide in the heather, ye lurk in the brake,
Ye dive where the sweet flags shadow the lake.

      *   *   *   *

Beautiful birds ! ye come thickly around
When the bud's on the branch, and the snow's on the
    ground,
Ye come when the richest of roses flush out,
And ye come when the yellow leaf eddies about.

ELIZA COOK.

THE Bird life of the district is also varied and interesting. On the hills, amongst the beds of Ling or Heather, are Red Grouse in fair numbers; Black Grouse (black cock and grey hen) are also occasionally met with, and in the more boggy parts Snipe are frequently flushed. In the early Spring the Ring Ouzel and Wheatear arrive, the former to nest, later on in the year, amongst the Heather; and the latter amongst the boulders and old walls. The wild note of the Curlew is also then heard, a weird note inseparably associated with the life of these hills. Peewit or Green Plover are frequently seen, and Golden Plover, although rare, are to be found. Meadow Pipits abound, and Tree Pipits swiftly and frequently rise from the thorn trees on the mountain side and then sink slowly back to their perch upon the trees, singing all the while. A few pairs of Stonechats and Whinchats are also usually to be seen. Overhead a hovering Kestrel may almost always be noticed, and the Sparrow Hawk, Merlin, and even an occasional Peregrine Falcon and Buzzard may be seen. The croak and sight of a Raven are not infrequent, and in the still Summer nights the whirr of the Nightjar or Fern Owl is heard.

On the streams the Dipper or Water Ouzel and the Grey Wagtail are the typical birds, but the Wagtail does not equal the Dipper in that exclusive attachment which seems to make him a very part of the stream itself. The Wagtail deserts the stream when the rigour of winter begins, returning in the early Spring to its accustomed nesting places, but the Dipper is constant for life and still haunts its usual beat when icicles hang on the rock faces and the banks are torn by the winter flood. The Dipper is usually seen either whizzing down the stream with its bolt-like flight or perched upon a stone in mid-stream curtseying and bowing in the curious manner which has given it the name of Dipper. The curtseying of the Dipper is the equivalent of the Wagtail's habit of flirting its tail, and both seem to be expressions of natural alertness. Another bird occasionally seen on the streams is the common Sandpiper, which arrives in April to lay its eggs in a bare hollow on the shingle, but before Summer is over has again taken its departure. A constant visitant to the streams is the Heron, and almost daily one can be seen standing (apparently in deep meditation) on the edge of the water, or winding its slow flight along the river course. The Kingfisher is another visitant, but very rare, as it seems to prefer the sluggish streams of the low country to these noisy torrents. In the trees and bushes by the river, numerous representatives of five of the British Tits are met with, namely— Great, Cole, Marsh, Blue and Longtailed, and in the woods and small brakes are heard Whitethroats, Blackcaps, Garden Warblers, Willow Warblers, Wood Warblers and Chiffchaffs. Another bird which is fairly plentiful is the Brown Owl, and it may, in this district, almost be called a bird of the river, as it so frequently nests in the old stumps and hollow trees on the river bank. The White Owl haunts the barns and old buildings.

Of the Woodpeckers the Green is fairly common, and the Great Spotted may occasionally be seen. As there is very little game preserving in the district, Carrion Crows, Jays and Magpies are very common.

The following incident may be of interest. In August or early September a few years ago, a lady, who was walking with a shooting party on the Ffwddog ridge, becoming rather tired lay down on the Heather to rest. She had not been there long when a Kestrel, with a freshly caught mouse in its claw—apparently mistaking her skirt for a rock— alighted upon her and commenced tearing the mouse to pieces.

SOME ANCIENT HOUSES IN THE VICINITY.

LLANVIHANGEL COURT AND PEN-Y-CLAWDD MANOR HOUSE.

A PART from the Hills and Vales themselves, there are many places of much interest in the immediate vicinity. At Llanvihangel—near the entrance to the Vale of Ewyas—stands Llanvihangel Court, an Elizabethan Mansion, rebuilt in its present form about the middle of the 16th century. Early in the 17th century it became the property of Nicholas Arnold—grandson of Sir Nicholas Arnold, to whom the grant of the Priory and Lands of Llanthony was made by Henry VIII.—and during the latter part of that century it belonged to and was occupied by his son John Arnold, a Justice of the Peace and Member for the County of Monmouth. A Justice of the Peace at that time combined in his own person the characters of Prosecutor, Magistrate, Detective and often Policeman. He could issue a warrant for the arrest, conduct the search himself, effect the capture, examine the accused, commit him and finally give evidence against him at his trial, and all these powers John Arnold seems to have employed to the uttermost in his persecution of Roman Catholics.

To the Government reward of £50, at that time offered for the apprehension of a Jesuit, he is said to have added £200 from his own resources for each capture; he procured the Priest's own dependents to give evidence against them and kept armed bodies of servants to assist him in his expeditions. As to the unfortunate accused, as soon as he was committed for trial, he was kept in close confinement until brought to the bar. Unless by extraordinary favour, he was allowed neither Counsel nor Solicitor to assist in his defence, and was not allowed to see his Witnesses before they came into Court.

England was at that time ringing with the pretended Roman Catholic plot, schemed by the infamous Titus Oates, and in March, 1678, a Committee of the House of Commons was appointed, to consider " The danger the Nation is in by the "growth of Popery and the remedies to prevent "the same," and at this enquiry John Arnold was one of the principal witnesses. His evidence is interesting, as showing that at that time a Chapel with a stone altar stood on the summit of the

Great Skirrid or Holy Mountain (in the evidence
called St. Michael's Mount) near Llanvihangel,
"where (as stated in the evidence) are frequent
" meetings, eight or ten times in the year, and
" Mass is said and sometimes Sermons are preached
" there." Through the exercise by John Arnold
of his extensive powers as a Justice of the
Peace, David Lewis alias Charles Baker, a native
of Abergavenny and a Roman Catholic Priest,
was arrested, committed for trial and brought to
the scaffold. David Lewis seems to have been a
man of great piety; indefatigable in his labours
amongst the poor; patient and charitable, and to
have been known by those amongst whom he
ministered for 30 years, as "The Father of the
" Poor."

He was arrested at Llantarnam, near New-
port, on 17th November, 1678, by six armed men
sent by John Arnold; was conducted to the
"Golden Lion" Hotel, Abergavenny, where he
was examined by John Arnold and committed.
He was taken from there to John Arnold's house
at Llanvihangel, and the next day was sent under
an armed escort to Monmouth gaol. He has left
a most interesting account of his arrest, imprison-
ment and trial, and the following short extracts
from it, as to impanelling the Jury and sentence
at the trial, may be of interest as showing the
mode of administering justice at that time.

" The 28th March, 1679, the Assizes began at
" Monmouth, Sir Robert Atkins being the sole
" Judge. A Grand Jury of gentlemen was returned
" by the Sheriff and called, against several of whom
" Mr. Arnold excepted, and so put by, as such he
" conceived might befriend me   *   *   *   At last
" a Jury was sworn and an Indictment drawn up
" against me upon the Statute of the 27th
" Elizabeth and preferred to the Grand Jury.
" That evening being Friday I was arraigned
" upon that Bill, to which I pleaded 'Not Guilty.'
" The next day about 10 of the clock in the
" morning, the Judge came from the Nisi Prius
" side and sat at the Crown side, and I, at the
" same time, being brought to the Bar, the Crier
" made proclamation for silence that a Jury for
" life and death might be impanelled; presently a
" Jury from the other Bar was called which was
" not usual and I to challenge, the Judge telling
" me I might challenge; by guess I challenged
" three; but out of that Nisi Prius Jury called to
" the Crown Bar, and that by Mr. Arnold's own
" suggestion (who had a strong influence upon the
" Judge as being his kinsman and sitting at his
" right) divers were excepted by Mr. Arnold * * *
" At last with much difficulty a Jury was im-
" panelled, a Jury now contrived of none but such
" as pleased Mr. Arnold, principal Prosecutor

" against me, which was very hard and an ignor-
" ant Jury it was withal."

The trial of course resulted in the prisoner
being found " Guilty " of High Treason, and the
close of the trial and sentence he describes as
follows:—

> " Clerk—Are you agreed of your verdict ?

> " Jury—Yes.

> " Clerk—Who shall speak for you ?

> " Jury—Foreman.

> " Clerk—Prisoner, hold up thy hand.   Do
> you find prisoner guilty or not
> guilty ?

> " Jury—Guilty.

" Judge—Give me my cap.   David Lewis,
" thou shalt be led from this place to the place
" from whence thou camest, and shalt be put upon
" a hurdle and drawn with thy heels forward to
" the place of execution, where thou shalt be
" hanged by the neck and be cut down alive, thy
" body to be ripped open and thy bowels plucked
" out ; thou shalt be dismembered and thy mem-
" bers burnt before thy face, thy head to be divided
" from thy body, thy four quarters to be separated
" and to be disposed of at His Majesty's will.   So
" the Lord have mercy on thy soul."

" I made a low bow to the Judge and the
" Court rose.   Soon after, the Judge sent for the

"Sheriff, and told him it was His Majesty's
"pleasure I should be reprieved until further
"orders."

David Lewis suffered death at Usk on the
27th August, 1679. From the scaffold he delivered
a most touching address, a copy of which, said to
have been written by him whilst in prison, is still
extant. In consequence of his persecution of
Roman Catholics, an attempt to murder John
Arnold (who was severely wounded) was made by
John Giles, a native of Usk.

John Arnold's son, Nicholas Arnold, sold
Llanvihangel Court and Estate to the Harley
(Earl of Oxford) family, from whom it was purchased in 1801 by Hugh Powell, Treasurer of St.
Bartholomew's Hospital. On the death of Hugh
Powell in 1821, it passed by his Will to his god-
son, the Honble. William Powell Rodney, grandson
of Admiral Lord Rodney, and in the Rodney
family it remained until 1904, when the Mansion
House, with a small portion of the Estate, was
sold to Mr. Attwood Mathews, whose widow is
the present owner and occupier. An avenue of
fine Scotch Fir and another of Spanish Chestnut
trees of great girth adorn the grounds.

Another house of some interest, close to
Llanvihangel Railway Station, is the 15th century Manor House (now a farmhouse) of Peny-

LLANVIHANGEL COURT.

clawdd (head of the Dyke) with its double Moat and oak timbering. In the reign of Edward III., the Manor of Pen-y-clawdd formed part of the possessions of Lawrence de Hastings, 13th Lord of Abergavenny, and was held under him by the service of one Knight's Fee, which entailed upon the holder the obligation of attending upon his Lord for 40 days in each year in time of peace and in troublous times of attending him to the war. The Manor afterwards came into the hands of a branch of the "Cecil" family, and passed from them by marriage to Sir John Herbert, of Neath Abbey; and subsequently—also by marriage—to Robert Greville, 4th Lord Brooke, who died in 1676. In that family it remained until the middle of the 18th century, when it was sold by Francis Greville, 8th Lord Brooke and 1st Earl of Warwick, to Henry Wilmot, whose son and heir Valentine Henry Wilmot, sold it in 1799 to Hugh Powell, and under his Will it passed, with the Llanvihangel Court Estate, to the Honble. William Powell Rodney. The Manor comprises the greater part of Bryn-arw hill, the remaining portion of the hill being within the Manor of Stanton (formerly a possession of Llanthony Abbey) which Manor adjoins and is now held with Pen-y-clawdd. Both these Manors are now the property of Mr Baker Gabb, by purchase from the Rodney family.

TRE-WYN AND ALLT-YR-YNYS.

About two miles from Llanvihangel, at the foot of the eastern slope of the Hatteral ridge, stand two houses of much interest, the Manor Houses of Tre-wyn and Allt-yr-ynys; the latter now a farmhouse. The Hamlet or Township of Tre-wyn or Bwlch Tre-wyn formed a Manor called " Castell Coch " (Redcastle) also formerly a possession of Llanthony Abbey. It was part of the County of Hereford until early in the reign of Queen Victoria, when it was incorporated with the County of Monmouth. It is said to have derived its name Tre-wyn (Wyn's House or Home) from Sir John Gwyn or Wyn, the original owner, who also owned Allt-yr-ynys. The name of the family afterwards became Wynston, a younger scion of which migrated into Gloucestershire, and from this branch, through the marriage of Sarah, daughter of Henry Wynston, with a Churchill in the early part of the 17th century, the name Wynston or Winston became annexed to that of Churchill.

In "The Historie of Cambria now called Wales "—written in 1584 by Dr. David Powell— in the part which relates to "The Historie of the Winning of Glamorgan," some particulars of which were (as he states) " delivered unto me by " the Right Worshipfull Mistress Blanch Parry,

" one of the gentlewomen of the Queen's Majesty's
" Privie Chamber" ; it is recorded " in the year of
" Christ 1091 Robert Sitsylt came with Robert
" Fitzhamon to the conquest of the countrie of
" Glamorgan, and after wedded a ladie by whom
" he had Halterennes (Allt-yr-ynys) and other lands
" in Hereford and Gloucestershire."

Robert Sitsylt settled at Allt-yr-ynys and
founded the Sitsylt Family, one of which, David
Sitsylt (son of Richard Sitsylt), migrated into
Lincolnshire early in the 16th century, and became
the grandfather of Sir William Cecil, Lord Burghley, the great statesman of Queen Elizabeth's reign,
and through him the ancestor of the present
Marquess of Salisbury and Marquess of Exeter.
Dr. Powell gives the full pedigree of the Sitsylt
Family down to Richard Sitsylt, with the following note :—" These Petegrees and descents I
" gathered faithfullie out of sundrie antient re-
" cords and evidences   *   *   *   which
" remaine at this present in the custody of The
" Right Honble. Sir William Cecil, Knight of the
" Most Noble Order of the Garter, Lord Burghley
" and Lord High Treasurer of England, who is
" lineallie descended from the said Richard Sitsylt,
" Father to David Cecil, grand-father to the said
" Sir William Cecil, now Lord Burghley, and at
" this time William Sitsylt or Cecil, Esquire,
" Cosen Germane to the said Lord Burghley,

"removed by one degree onelie, is possessed of
"the foresaid House of Halterennes in Ewyas
"Land as the Heire male of the House of Sitsylt
"and is descended from Philip Cecil, elder brother
"to the said David."

In the Record Office, London, is deposited a
MS. Book of 3 Vols. which not only contains the
Sitsylt Pedigree as given by Dr. Powell, but also
states that the lady whom Robert Sitsylt married,
and from whom he received Allt-yr-ynys, was a
daughter of Sir John Gwyn, "Lord of Allt-yr-ynys
in Ewyas Land and Gwynston." It was deposited
in the Record Office by the Earl of Cawdor, and is
called the "Book of Golden Grove," from Lord
Cawdor's seat, Golden Grove in Carmarthenshire.

The name Sitsylt has undergone various alter-
ations; Sitsylt or Sissillt, Seycil or Seisel, and
ultimately Cecil.

In a survey of Allt-yr-ynys House and grounds
made in 1647, the situation of the "antient Capital
House" is accurately described as being "on the
"stream called 'Nant Cravell,' which runneth
"close unto the Wall of the House on the west
"side, and into the river Monow on the south side,
"within a few yards of the Gate-House; into
"which river Monow cometh the river Hundy also,
"so that all three rivers meet close by the Manor
"House on the south side thereof, being a pleasant

ALLT-YR-YNYS HOUSE.

" clear water full of troutes, were there any order
" to preserve them from the annoyance of the
" Otter and ill demeaninge persons."

The Gate-house has disappeared, but the old
house still retains some trace of its better days.
In the early part of the 17th century both Allt-yr-
ynys and Tre-wyn passed into the possession of
the De-la-Hay Family, and so remained until the
middle of the 18th century. The present owner of
both Estates is Mr. Philip Barneby, who resides at
Tre-wyn.

        *   *   *   *   *   *

Much might be written of other places around
the Black Mountain Range ; of Longtown with
its ancient Castle, the seat of the Lords of Ewyas
Lacy. Of Craswall Abbey, which lies some six
miles above Longtown, and is said to have been
an adjunct or cell of the Abbey of Grandmont in
Normandy, from whence its Monks came. It was
founded by the Lords of Ewyas Lacy and, for its
maintenance, the Abbey of Grandmont was endowed by them with the whole of the Parish of
Craswall. This and similar alien Priories, founded in England by the Norman Barons, were con-
fiscated to the Crown in the reign of Edw. IV.
Some interesting portions of the ruins remain,
but the site is not easy of access.

Of Hay with its Castle and Manor.

Of Talgarth, with the Porthaml branch of the ancient Family of Vaughan, now represented by the Earl of Ashburnham, whose late father speaking at the National Eisteddfod of Wales, held at Brecon in 1899, said " It was a matter of " great pride to him to feel that he stood there as " the representative of the Family of the Vaughans " of Porthaml and as a descendant of Sir David " Gam."

Of Cwm-du, with its remains of British and Roman Camps, and with its more recent memories of the Reverend Thomas Price—the celebrated "Carnhuanawc" who did so much for Welsh art and literature—Prose writer, Bard, Harpist, Orator and a Pioneer of the Welsh Renaissance. He was the principal supporter of the late Lady Llanover in founding The Literary Society of Cymreigyddion at Abergavenny in 1833 and also in founding the Welsh Manuscripts Society. He was made Vicar of Cwmdu and perpetual Curate of Tretower in 1825 and was buried in 1848 in the " beautiful earth of the parochial graveyard " of Cwmdu, as he had wished and directed.

Of Tretower where stood, before the coming of the Normans, the Castle of " Genillin " or "Cenhillyn," Lord of Ystradyw and Prince of Powis, during whose reign the Font in Partrishow Church was made, his name being engraven on the rim ; and where now stands the rare rectangular Norman Keep of the Castle subsequently erected. Where also stands the 14th century Manor House, " Tretower Court " (now a Farmhouse,) formerly the residence of the Tretower branch of the Vaughan Family, the first of whom was the youngest son of the famous Sir Roger Vaughan of Bredwardine. Other members of the Family were, Thomas Vaughan, who in the reign of Henry VI. was attainted for his attachment to the House of York; Sir Roger Vaughan, who, fighting in the same cause, was killed in the great battle of Danesmore, near Banbury; and Sir Thomas Vaughan, Chamberlain to the young Edward V. who, with the Lords Grey and Rivers, was beheaded at Pontefact by Richard III. The house afterwards became the residence of a branch of the Parry Family, of which mention has already been made when writing of the Vale of Grwyne-fechan—These several places however are somewhat outside the scope of this work, and the writer hopes that sufficient information has been given to bring into prominence the many attractions of the hills and vales of the Black Mountain District.

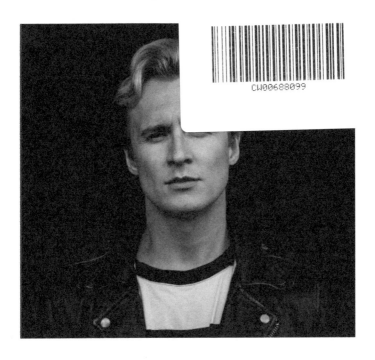

About the Author

Anton Brisinger was born and raised in Los Angeles, California, and graduated from Exeter University. This is his first novel.

We Might Take Some Getting Used To

Anton Brisinger

We Might Take Some Getting Used To

Olympia Publishers
London

www.olympiapublishers.com
OLYMPIA PAPERBACK EDITION

A CIP catalogue record for this title is available from the British Library.

ISBN: 978-1-80074-140-9

First Published in 2022

Olympia Publishers
Tallis House
2 Tallis Street
London
EC4Y 0AB

Printed in Great Britain

Dedication

To my mother, father, Emma, Alex and Miko.

Part One

I

"You goddamn millennials," my dad hissed. "You're all so fucking entitled."

I watched his hands tighten around the steering wheel as he checked the rearview mirror before merging onto Malibu Canyon. I could tell he was mad since he was pushing eighty in a forty-five, which was ironic, because he'd just spent the last twenty minutes scolding me for my own *'disdain for authority,'* as he called it. I immediately started praying that he'd get pulled over.

"Do you have any idea how much this is costing me?"

"No."

"*No,* you don't. You have *no* idea. You don't know how much *time* and *effort* I'm forced to put into this...into *you,* " he paused. "Would you *like* to know how much this is costing me?"

"Okay," I said, sinking deeper into the car seat.

"Three fifty an hour. That's three hundred and fifty dollars an *hour*. But you know something? I don't even know why I bother."

"So why *do* you?"

"Shut *up*," he snapped. "I just..." he exhaled slowly, really dramatizing his irritation. "Do you know how frustrating—how *embarrassing*—it is, to have to leave work early to pick up your fourteen-year-old son from the principal's office... *again*?" My dad never picked me up from school—I always took the bus—

11

so, whenever he did, you knew I was in trouble.

"I don't even get why it was such a big deal."

"You don't get why it was such a big…your essay was titled '*I fucking hate it when people tell me what to do.*' What the hell did you expect? Did you think you were gonna get an A?"

"*What*? We were supposed to write about ourselves, so I did. I was literally just *following* directions. "

"You're just like your mother. Such a goddamn smart ass. You knew *exactly* what was gonna happen if you turned in something like that."

"That teacher hates…"

"…The teacher *hates* you?" he interrupted, shaking his head. "He, and every other teacher you've ever had, right? They all *hate* you?"

"I'm *serious,* " I pleaded. "He *does*."

"You ever think that if *every* teacher you've ever had hates you, then maybe they're not the problem, but *you* are?"

"Well, you said I have ADHD. Doesn't that explain it?"

"Well," he began, as if catching himself. "That's what the medications for."

"I don't like it," I said shamefully, as if it was somehow my responsibility to make sure the pills worked.

"Yeah, well I don't like paying three fifty an hour for an entitled little brat who ditches class and doesn't do his homework, but the world isn't perfect."

"They make it hard to sleep."

"Well, you'll just have to count sheep until you can."

"Mom doesn't even think I *have* ADHD," I said resentfully.

"*Right,*" he let out a loud, sardonic laugh. "*Mom* thinks. And remind me again what medical school *she* attended?"

"It's not like *you* went to medical school."

"No, you're right. I *didn't*. But I *did* do my homework, something *neither* of you seemed to find very important. But if I ever need medical advice from a failed actress, I'll be sure to call her."

"You don't have to be an asshole," I muttered under my breath.

"*I'm* an asshole?" he scoffed. "Maybe they're right. Maybe boarding school is the only thing that'll work."

I sneered, and I could feel him glancing over at me with a sudden relapse of sympathy, followed by a guilty sigh.

"How was school?"

Out of every generic question he could've asked, he picked *that* one. Parents always ask that ridiculous question. It's like we were an old married couple who hadn't had sex in years, and we didn't have anything else to talk about and, despite knowing the answer, he'd ask the question anyway because that was the level of intimacy our relationship had succumbed to.

"Fine," I said vacantly. I heard him continue talking, but it all faded out as I could only focus on the speedometer crawling up to ninety.

"*...need to stop being so defiant and follow the rules because if you don't...*"

Kids learn more from how you act than what you preach. Grownups don't seem to realize that.

We pulled up to a generically suburban house enclosed by a white picket fence with Benzes and Beamers lined up and down the street and, just like last week, my dad gave me the rundown of how, and *why*, this was *important* for me. I swear, whether it was my long hair or my bad grades, I was always on trial for something.

He pulled the keys out of the ignition, a long, middle-aged sigh escaping his mouth before he turned to me with that officious, parental glare.

"So, do you wanna tell me why we're here?"

"Okay," I said, with an indiscreet eye roll.

"Why are we here?"

"Because I'm a screw up and I need to change my attitude."

I could tell he was struggling not to murder me by the way he flared his nostrils.

"*Alexander.*"

That's when you knew it was on: when they said my full name, instead of just *Alex.*

"Yes."

"Why-are-we-here?"

"Jeez, *I*-don't-know. I really don't see the point of me even being here in the first place. This place sucks and that creepy ass lady…"

"*Hey!* Cut it out! You *know* why we're here, don't try to put this on me. If you were participating and doing what you were *supposed* to, we wouldn't even be having this conversation. But you're *not*. You're disruptive. You're lazy. You don't do your homework…Jesus, Alex, you don't even go to *class!*" He closed his eyes and massaged the bridge of his nose between the tips of his fingers while incredulously shaking his head. "I just…" he sighed again. "I just don't understand how you can so *shamelessly* come to school without having done your homework. It's as if you really don't give a shit what the teachers going to say when you turn up empty handed. It's actually fascinating, because that thought didn't even *dare* to enter my mind when I was your age. I was *terrified* of the teacher, let alone my *parents*! What goes through your head at night when you get home and know you have homework, but so *carelessly* decide not to do it? *Seriously*. I'm not trying to be funny, Alexander. I really want to know."

"Well, I don't know," I said, avoiding eye contact. "I do my homework in *some* classes. I have an A in art."

My dad had flunked art, and that was the only class he ever flunked, but it's the only class I've ever done well in. It's ironic too, because my mom once told me that that was my dad's true passion when he was younger, but he just wasn't good at it. He became an investment banker instead, which sounds like the most boring job in the world, but at least he had two BMW's and a big house in Malibu to show for it. If I ever brought up anything art related, he'd get defensive, but now that I think about it, you know who *also* took a different path after he failed art school? Hitler.

As soon as we started walking towards the house, I started getting nauseous, which unfortunately happens constantly. I hadn't eaten all day besides a couple of Oreos at lunch, so I thought I might've just been getting hungry, but either way I felt like I was about to puke at any second.

"Dad, I'm nauseous."

"Oh, *stop,*" he said indifferently and kept walking.

"I'm serious. I'm really, really nauseous."

"Did you have lunch?" he asked, as he continued his authoritative march across the front lawn towards her house.

"*Sort* of," I paused. "Not really. I forgot."

"Well, it's not my fault your diet consists of half a bag of Doritos every thirty-six hours."

Finally, I couldn't bear the pain anymore and I completely keeled over, struggling to keep my insides from becoming my outsides.

15

"*Dad*," I called out in agony. "I'm serious. I think I'm gonna throw up." I knew he wasn't going to believe me, but I swear, I felt awful. My dad let out a frustrating groan and ran over and grabbed me, his cupped hand digging into my armpit.

"Ow! Let go!" I said, shaking myself free.

"Cut the bullshit, Alex!" he said through his teeth, dragging me towards the door like a captured animal. "You're not getting out of this."

When we finally reached the door, he said quietly, "We'll ask her if she has some crackers or something. She's... *old*. She probably has some."

My dad may be good with numbers and money and whatnot, but he didn't know a goddamn thing about health. I swear, he knows just as much as any unenthusiastic elementary school teacher, nevertheless a *nurse*. The only advice they have for you if you're feeling sick is, *'Put a wet paper towel on it.'*

This lady's house smelled *and* looked like somewhere no kids had been in for centuries, and you could really tell, because she had one of those ancient wooden play structures—the one you find in the pediatrician's office—covered in dust and cobwebs.

It was pretty obvious that she didn't know the first thing about kids due to how awkwardly she greeted me every time.

"Hello, hello Alexander. And how are we doing today?" she said in this condescending goo-goo gaga voice, as she tried to rough up my hair like we were best buds who had known each other for years.

"Fine."

"Robert," she said, addressing my dad with an exaggerated smile.

"Hi, Rachel, good to see you again," my dad replied with a

thin-lipped, fatherly nod.

"So, Alexander…" she had these bronzed teeth that alluded to a lifetime of coffee drinking, and her bony shoulders were draped in this ratty old cardigan that smelled like old people and disinfectant. "…it's been a few weeks now. How's the medication making you feel?"

"Fine."

"And how are your hands?"

"What?"

"Your hands," she repeated coldly, reaching for them. "Let's see your hands."

They always asked me this. I had to show them my hands to make sure my knuckles weren't bruised or scabbed, or that the nails weren't completely chewed off, or something. She inspected them and nodded approvingly.

"Oh, *good*. They're almost fully healed now," she continued, surprisingly pleased.

"Yeah, I guess."

"And as for the medication, have you noticed any progress in school yet?"

"Not really."

"Oh, that's quite all right. It'll come. There's nothing *wrong* with you," followed by a confident chuckle.

"I know," I said quietly.

"Sorry?"

"I said I know there's nothing wrong with me."

She let out a loud snort followed by a nervous laugh, the same one parents do when you embarrass them in public. She glanced at my dad, and then back at me, and started waving her finger an inch away from my nose, pouting her lips and talking in that forged goo-goo gaga voice again.

"Well, that's very good, Alexander. We wouldn't want you to think that, now, would we?"

She took us into this dark, secluded room in the back of her house where she didn't have anything except for this chunky TV from the '90s.

"And no more lying, right?" she called back to me with a chuckle, and I instantly felt my dad's eyes burning into the back of my neck and, as I walked through the dark corridor, the face of every teacher, parent, counsellor, school principal or security guard flashed before me with that familiar, disapproving glare. Last time I was here, we spent the whole time talking about my constant lying. She told me that it was dangerous and that it could get me into a lot of trouble, even more trouble than the one I found myself in regularly, but, I swear, I'm not a liar, I'm just always so bored with the real world, so I prefer to make up my own.

"So," she began enthusiastically. "Do you like video games, Alex?"

"They're okay."

I wasn't lying. I've always hated video games because of how badly I suck at them. I've tried playing *Call of Duty* a couple times, but those are some of the dullest experiences I've ever had. All you do is die, and if you ever play online, you have a bunch of prepubescent kids from, like, *Arkansas,* or some other redneck state, calling you a nigger and telling you they fucked your mom so, I don't know about you, but that's not my idea of a good time.

"Well, we've got a great game planned for you today. Kind of like a video game, except it requires just a *little* bit more concentration," she said, the pitch of her voice getting higher at the end.

"Okay," I said.

Then she went into this cupboard behind that prehistoric TV set and pulled out these gigantic headphones. They looked like those that the retarded kids wear, or the guys who guide the airplanes out over the runway with those neon glow-sticks. They were huge.

"So, first what I'm going to do is tell you a little bit about the game, okay? And then I'm going to ask you to put these on, and when we've gone over the instructions, your dad and I are going to leave the room. Sound good?" She finished, slowly explaining herself as if *I* was retarded.

"Okay."

"Great," her enthusiasm skyrocketed. "So, here's what's going to happen: you're going to see a white dot on the screen, okay? Now, when that white dot appears, you're going to hear a loud cowbell in the headphones..." she said, followed by her own miserable sound effect: "*ding!* ...just about a half second after the dot appears. Sometimes, the cowbell will ring directly after; sometimes, it'll come a second, or two, after. What I want you to do is, I want you to clap your hands when you see the dot, *not* when you hear the noise. Got it?"

No, but I nodded anyway.

Then she set up this webcam looking thing on top of the TV.

"This thing here will record your reaction time, which will allow us to see how well you did. Okay?" she continued, beaming with assurance.

I really wasn't sure how to react, so I just nodded to get it over with.

"Great," she said, and patted me on the head again.

She came over and strapped those gigantic headphones around my head and fastened it so tightly I thought it might slice my head in half.

"Now, your father and I are going to leave the room, and we'll be back in about ninety minutes."

"An hour and a *half?*" I gasped, but all she did was chuckle, like I was in on the joke, or something.

"Oh, don't worry. It'll be over before you know it. You're going to have fun, I promise."

Fun my ass. Before she slithered out of the room she killed the lights, abandoning me in the dark. My dad didn't say anything either, he just followed her out the door. She hadn't told me when it was going to start, so I just kind of stood there with these ridiculous headphones on my head like an idiot, waiting for something to happen.

Then, out of nowhere, this big white flash exploded on the screen, instantly blinding me, and then it vanished just as quickly as it had appeared. I forgot I had to clap, but right as I was about to, that fucking cowbell thundered through my ears so loudly I thought I was going to fall over. I was about two seconds into this stupid game and only a step away from becoming the next Helen Keller.

I tried to clap on time for the next flash, but the sound of the cowbell became so apprehensive that I started wincing, bracing myself for it before it even came.

Eventually, I lost track of time, but suddenly the darkness shattered as the lights switched back on, and I felt the headphones being removed from my head.

"Hmm," she said, inspecting the monitor on top of the TV. "Well," she began, with underlying concern. "It's definitely a problem that can be fixed, so don't worry! Let me see here," she walked over to a nearby table and opened up a spiral notebook. "Why don't I fit you in on Wednesday and…" she flipped through a few pages. "Well, let's see, what would you prefer? I can do one hour on Thursday and Friday, or three hours on Saturday."

"I can drop him off on Saturday," my dad answered without hesitation.

"Great," she said proudly. "So, Monday, Wednesday, and Saturday. Sound good?"

"Great. Thanks again," my dad said. "See you Wednesday."

On the car ride home my ears were still ringing, and as I looked out the window, everything I saw just looked white and blurry. I asked my dad if there were any potential side effects I had to worry about, but he just kind of looked at me funny, like he didn't understand the question but, after several months I finally began to concede that, although results may vary, there are no side effects in hell.

II

The following Saturday, after therapy, I met up with Ocean and Beau at the beach. You'd recognize the name of Ocean's dad from all of the 'thank you' speeches at the Oscars; and Beau's dad is a music producer, responsible for the success of pretty much every single artist in your parents' record collection. Since it was now early September, any trace of obnoxious tourism had almost completely vanished, the only ones left at the beach being other locals, with the occasional homeless guy pissing in the sand, and asking for a dollar.

"I can't believe that fits you," Ocean snickered, as I struggled to slide into the battered wetsuit that he brought for me. "You're so fuckin' skinny, dude."

"Shut up," I said.

"At least you don't have man boobs like Norbit, over here."

"I don't have *man* boobs," Beau said irritably.

"What do you call *those* things?" Ocean said, slapping Beau's left tit.

"Cut it out!" Beau snapped, and quickly zipped up his wetsuit to his chin.

"So," Ocean began. "Why've you been such a gimp lately?"

"What do you mean?" I asked, caught off guard.

"Hasn't he been a complete fag lately?" he said, turning to Beau for reinforcement.

"Yeah, kinda. Remember the other day you—"

"—spent the whole lunch in the library. *Yeah.* What the fuck was that?"

"*What?* I had a test."

"A *test?* On what, ass eating? I bet you got an A." Ocean and Beau snickered.

"Yeah, your dad was my tutor," I said. "He's the expert."

"Wouldn't surprise me," Ocean snorted. "He probably is."

A long pause.

"*Well?*" Ocean demanded.

"There's nothing *wrong,*" I insisted.

"Dude, you're such a liar."

"You *have* been pretty weird lately," Beau added.

"I dunno what you're talking about," I paused. Finally, "I started ta   king Adderall a few weeks ago, but it's not a big deal," I said furtively.

"*Adderall?*" Ocean gasped. "Duuude, that shit makes you retarded."

"I'm al*ready* retarded," I said. "Thanks to hanging out with you two all day."

They both snickered.

"It's not that bad," I then said quietly.

"That's what *you* think. But you dunno what it's been like having to hang out with you lately."

"You shouldn't take that, man," Beau said.

"Dude, I saw a movie about that stuff. It's so gnarly. Some guy was on it for months and once he started sleepwalking and he jumped off a cliff. And you get really skinny and gross like Christian Bale in that one movie when he's, like… super skinny and gross, you know that one? And I read a study about it one time. Like, nine out of ten users turn gay before the age of twenty."

"Yeah, I think I read that too," Beau chimed in.

23

"You guys *read* that?" I mocked. "You guys don't even know *how* to read."

"I *read*," Ocean said defensively.

"Really?" I said, tilting my head. "What's the last book you read?"

"Shut up," Ocean said, kicking sand at me.

"It's true, man," Beau said. "Like, Zach McKee, and me, were at the same camp last summer, and he had been on it since he was, like, ten, and he hadn't gotten a boner since up until like a month ago when he accidentally clicked on gay porn on the computer and then he realized he was gay," Beau added proudly.

"*See?*" Ocean threw his hands up. "First your *dick's* not gonna work, and then you're gonna turn *gay*? It's over, dude," Ocean continued. "And besides, you're *already* skinny enough."

"Isn't Zach kind'a balding too?" Beau asked.

"He *is!* I bet that's 'cause of the Adderall," he chuckled quietly. "Told you, dude. First no boners, then you turn gay, and then you start balding."

"*What*? That's the stupidest thing I've ever heard," I said defiantly. "That's not true."

"Well, it's what I read," Beau retorted.

"Yeah, dude. Can't fight science. Go talk to Zach McKee about it next time you see him at school. Ask him to take off that ugly-ass hat that he wears literally *every-single-day*. Bet you he won't do it. Probably 'cause he looks like a gay Bruce Willis now, who can't get a boner."

"That's retarded. That's not gonna happen."

"Just don't try to blow me or ask us to go wig shopping with you in a few years, man." They both laughed.

"You still texting Rachel?" I quickly asked Beau, deliberately switching the focus from me to him.

"I dunno," Beau said bashfully, blushing. "Sort of...I guess."

"Still?" Ocean asked.

"It just feels like we have, like, a...genuine connection."

"Genuine connection?" Ocean mocked. "I think you should genuinely connect my balls to your mouth."

"Fuck you," Beau growled. "What about Lucy Stewart then, huh?"

I noticed Ocean instantly getting uncomfortable.

"What about her," he said defensively.

There was a long pause.

"She's fine, I guess." Ocean quickly zipped up his wetsuit in silence.

"Aren't you guys' parents working together?" I asked.

"Yeah, I think so," he paused. "Her dad's kind of a fag, though. Apparently, he just sits in his trailer all day."

"Who told you that?"

"My dad."

"I didn't know he was back in town," Beau said.

"He's not," Ocean said coldly, before getting up and heading towards the water.

The freezing water instantly severed all the warmth from my feet, sending a shock through my entire body. As soon as I began to paddle out, I felt my whole body go completely stiff. I couldn't move my arms and I kept swallowing seawater; it felt like I'd never even been in the ocean before, or like I even knew how to fucking swim. I started thinking about the last three hours, being stuck in that asylum, and suddenly I didn't want to be in the water any more.

I quickly swam back to shore, and dragged my board back

to the dunes and laid flat on my back, my wetsuit rolled down to my waist, and stared up at the sky. I ran my fingers through my coarse, wet hair and licked the salt crystals off my lips. Even for September, it was overwhelmingly hot, and I felt myself staring at the heat waves dancing across the sand, which seemed to calm me down a bit.

Beau and Ocean came up like an hour after I did, which was nice, because it gave me some time to embrace the warm solitude by myself. My hair was almost completely dry, but as soon as they got out, they started flapping their wet hair in my face, getting me wet again.

"What the fuck! Knock it *off*," I groaned. "I literally *just* got dry."

"Pussy," Ocean snorted.

"Why'd you get out so early?" Beau asked.

"I just wasn't feeling it. I had a really long day."

"*Long day?*" Ocean mimicked. "And what've *you* done today?"

"Nothing," I lied. "I just...didn't get a lot of sleep."

"Yeah, no shit," Ocean snickered. "You look like a zombie."

Ocean brushed his hair behind his ears, laid down next to me and burped proudly.

Beau was still standing, shaking the water out of his ears, and I could tell he was insecure about the comment Ocean had made earlier, since he was refusing to unzip his wetsuit in front of us. Beau had always been the skinniest one out of the three of us, but his parents had gotten a divorce in June, and after the summer he'd gained a lot of weight. Most of the time I tried to pretend like I hadn't noticed, but it was hard not to, especially when I'd catch him stuffing his face with Oreos in the bathroom in between classes. Some people said they heard him throwing up sometimes, but I never asked him about it.

"What day is it today?" Ocean asked abruptly.

"Saturday," Beau answered. "Why?"

"*Dude.* That means that taco truck is here."

"I'm kinda over tacos," Beau moaned. "That's all we ever eat."

"You're so picky," Ocean sighed.

"Says you, mister I-don't-eat-mustard," Beau snickered.

I laughed, and Ocean blushed.

"Shut up," Ocean groaned. "What do you want then?"

"I dunno," Beau said bashfully. "Pizza?"

"Dude, D'amores sucks, I'm not eating there."

"Yeah," I agreed. "The crust is too thin."

"We don't have to go there. Why don't we go to McDonald's?"

"What?" Ocean said, baffled. "McDonald's doesn't have pizza."

"Yes it does," Beau protested.

"Dude," Ocean scoffed. "Are you fucking retarded? They sell burgers, not pizza, you dummy."

"Yeah," I giggled. "They don't have pizza."

"Yes they do!"

"Dude," Ocean snapped. "McDonald's?! Are you insane?! They don't have fucking pizza!"

I was laughing at this point.

Finally...

"Are you sure?" Beau asked.

"*Yeah.* Now come on, titties. Quit whining and just eat your stupid taco. I'm fuckin' starving."

I saw Beau's face sting from embarrassment, but he stayed quiet.

27

We dragged our boards across the entire beach, which took forever, but finally we saw that little taco truck waiting by the café just like Ocean had promised. I didn't have any money, but I found this wet five in one of the zippers that Ocean must've crammed in there, ages ago.

As we were propped up against the back of the van waiting for our food, Ocean suddenly hit my arm and pointed towards a guy approaching us who I finally realized was Mark Wahlberg, wearing shorts and a tank top.

"Hey, man," Ocean called, as Mark was ordering. "Big fan. I love the Bourne movies. "

Mark turned and tilted his head, suspiciously glaring at Ocean. His food was finished almost instantly—way before ours—and when he grabbed it, he turned back to us, and said, "Get a fucking haircut."

When he was far enough away, Ocean whispered, "I could so kick his ass."

"I like Boogie Nights," I said.

"You just fast forward to the last scene, you fag," he snickered.

"I knew you were gonna say that," I said, and rolled my eyes.

We sat in the parking lot eating silently, and I could feel the sun burning my shoulders and my scalp, so I stood up and walked over towards one of the bungalows and sat down in the shade.

"Dude, where are you going?" Ocean asked.

"I'm getting burnt. I need some shade."

"Pussy."

"Dude, are you really trying to prove yourself to the sun?" I scoffed. "It's the fucking *sun.* "

"The suns a bitch," he snickered, and flexed both of his bony little arms.

"Yeah, the suns a bitch until you wake up tomorrow looking like Mr. Krabs, you loser," I replied.

The two of them laughed.

Ocean looked up and brought his hand up to shield his eyes, weighing up what I'd just told him. Then he looked down at Beau, also noticeably concerned, and then both of them walked over and sat down next to me defeatedly.

"Shut up," Ocean said as he sat down, before I even had a chance to say anything, but I just smirked at him victoriously.

Suddenly, "Sucks we don't have any weed," Ocean said.

"Since when have *you* smoked weed?" I asked, raising my eyebrows.

"*I've* smoked weed," he said defensively.

"Haven't *you*?" Beau inserted.

"Uh, yeah," I lied. "*Obviously.*"

"Maybe we can get some later," Ocean said, stretching his arms out.

"Do you still have the bong?" Beau asked.

"Nah, my mom found it and made me smash it. Fuckin' dick."

When we finished eating, Ocean nervously interjected, "So how's that, like, boarding school thing looking?"

That kind of caught me off guard, but as soon as Ocean said it, Beau timidly poked his head up too, as if it'd been a question they'd both been waiting to ask.

"I dunno, why?"

"No reason," Ocean dismissed. "Just wondering."

I was so tired I didn't notice the shakiness in his voice, but then he quickly yelped out again, "So you're not going?"

"We haven't really talked about it for a while. Because, like, every time my parents and me all meet up to talk about it, they just start arguing about alimony, so we never really get a chance."

"Oh," Beau said quietly.

"But so, like," Ocean stuttered. "If you *do* go, when would that be, do you think?"

"They said next year, but they talk a lot of shit, so I dunno."

I felt like such a dick, giving them these thoughtless, half-assed answers, but I really couldn't help it. All I could think about was that awful room with that blinding white light and those uncomfortable headphones and that piercing cowbell noise that lingered in my ears long after I'd left.

What happened then, you'll never believe it: our science teacher, Mr. Humphrey, showed up in his big, white paedo-mobile. We immediately realized why he had shown up at the beach at this hour, too. Every year he assigned a project for all the eighth graders, where you had to go down to the beach and collect all this oceanic data that wasn't interesting to anybody else in the entire world except for him, and, like, two other nerdy scientists. We'd have to calculate the PH level of the water—whatever the fuck that means—and then write down how many seagulls, pelicans, etc. we saw. Then, some poor soul would be forced to walk out into the ocean, as the rest of the class watched, and fill up a giant bucket with seawater, and spend the rest of the day in sandy, wet jeans. We'd then be forced to drag this giant bucket of water all the way back up to campus, and for the rest of the week we'd sit with a microscope and try to find plankton. Now for the real kicker: this was ninety percent of our grade, and if you got anything less than a C on it, you failed eighth grade science. Why this was even allowed, or who on earth would find this to be remotely useful for the future, is still a mystery to me.

As you probably could've guessed, I got an F. Not because I didn't at least *attempt* to do the work, but because I always called seagulls, *seagulls*, and not by their scientific name: *Larus Occidentalis* (bet you've never heard *that* name before). It's not that I couldn't remember it either but, really, I just refused. Fail me if you want, but the rest of the world calls them seagulls except for you, and those two other nerd scientists who have nothing better to do than jerk off to Animal Planet. Sounds pretty ridiculous, right? Well, not for Mr. Humphrey it didn't. He just absolutely *loved* the name of those goddamn Larus Occidentalis' more than he'd ever loved anything else in his life.

So, there he was, Mr. Humphrey, taking data for next week, and getting a hard-on at the thought of all the plankton he was about to catch. He always wore the same thing: a waterproof vest, a visor, and those cargo pants that have so many pockets it makes you wonder who *really* needs to carry all that cargo. We watched him gather his gear and make his way towards the water and, without a word, Ocean quickly pulled out his wax comb from his swim trunks and separated it, revealing a skinny metal rod.

"Dude, we *have* to," he grinned mischievously.

We left our boards by the fence and scurried over and hunched down by Mr. Humphrey's van.

"What're you gonna do?" I asked Ocean.

"Watch."

Ocean started stabbing the back tire with the metal rod, but it just wouldn't puncture. He kept stabbing and stabbing and stabbing, until finally, a giant *POP!* and the whole tire deflated instantly, the weight of the car dropping to one side. We all started giggling and high-fived each other, but then a thick shadow suddenly towered over us, and when we turned we were met by a fat little man with a badge that said 'B*each Patrol*' staring down at us.

"Aw, *fuck*. Seriously?" Ocean protested, not so much embarrassed as he was irritated. The officer grabbed us by the hair and escorted us to his little golf cart. Thankfully, Mr. Humphrey was far away and the officer probably assumed that we were just doing it to a random car, because if Humphrey would've found out, I swear, he, *or* my parents, would've castrated me.

It wasn't my first time inside one of those places, but the inside of those wannabe police stations always looked exactly the same. There's a few American flags stabbed into the walls; some irrelevant certificates; a plaque dedicated to the local little league team that one of the "officers" coaches on weekends; a moldy, prehistoric   coffee machine; a couple of those '90s computers the size of a minivan; and the eerie linoleum stench of artificial government.

We were still in our wetsuits, which *sucked,* but at least they gave us towels to wrap ourselves in. Keep in mind, that we were only fourteen and it's not like we set someone's house on fire, so the guy had really just taken us in to get picked up by our parents, praying we'd be so shaken up that we never wound up there again. Nevertheless, I was shitting myself, but not because of the cop, but because I knew how pissed my dad was going to be when he showed up.

"Dude, it's gonna be *fiiiine,*" Ocean said, although it carried minimal reassurance.

"My dad's gonna kill me," I kept repeating, burying my head in my hands.

"Just tell him *I* did it," he said. "And besides, you'd never

32

have the balls to slice somebody's tires. And he's smart enough to know that." Ocean and Beau began giggling, and I didn't have anything to retort so I just mocked their laugh and made a stupid face.

The cop came walking towards us, more like wobbled, grinning victoriously, his fat, little fingers clutching a Styrofoam cup of coffee.

"So, I just got off the phone with your parents, and one of them is coming to pick you up."

"Whose?" Beau asked.

"*Some*one's," he said, praying the ambiguity would strike fear in all of us, something he'd clearly been salivating over.

I hung my head in defeat, certain that it was going to be *my* dad. Ocean tried to console me with a pat on the back, but I could tell he was trying to hide his smile.

"So. Now that I have your attention, I thought we'd discuss what you boys did today."

None of us said anything.

"Well? Any of you have anything you'd like to say?"

Silence.

"What did we learn today?" he asked again, his irritation building.

"That—" I started.

"—that we should always stay in school," Ocean interrupted. The cop raised his eyebrows with surprising approval and began to nod, awaiting the next words. "Because otherwise, if we don't, we'll become a fat beach cop like you." The cop's face lit up with anger, but Ocean just continued. "I bet you tried to get into the police academy or something, huh? But they probably found you stealing string cheese and jerkin' off in the janitor's closet, or maybe it just took you way too long to run a mile, and now you spend your time busting little kids having fun on the beach, before goin' home and fingering yourself to re-runs of *Cops* every night."

The cop sprung from his seat, but just then my dad burst through the door and pretty much saved Ocean's life. I wasn't relieved to see him, but I bet Beau and Ocean were.

"There you guys are! What the hell happened?!" my dad shouted. His tie was loosened, he was sweaty, and his shirt and hair were all disheveled.

Ocean quickly stood up and valiantly stuck his hand out towards my dad. "Mister Lexington! What a pleasant surprise. You came a little early though, we were just teaching the kind officer over here how to count to ten."

Beau and I couldn't contain our laughter, especially after seeing the cop's reaction, but my dad ran over and grabbed us, pulling us towards the exit.

"Well, *jeez*, I know it probably sounds a bit elementary, but they only teach you how to count to five in the beach cop academy, so go easy on the guy," Ocean continued. "Well, thanks for showing us the ropes, officer, and thank you for doing your best at keeping us safe. It's a hard job, but with you in command I think everybody in Malibu can feel a little bit safer at night, and I'm definitely gonna consider a career with a lifetime guarantee of no pussy when I grow up."

"Ocean!" my dad finally snapped. "Shut-your-*mouth*!" His face was so close to his that they were basically touching. That shut him up. My dad mouthed an apology to the cop, before violently dragging us out of the building and stuffing us all in his car.

My dad dropped off Beau and Ocean at each of their houses, then

34

we headed back home. I always hated going to my dad's house because he had just married this twenty-something-year-old gold digger who had bigger horns than the devil himself but, naturally, as any story about evil stepmothers can tell you, he didn't notice a thing. Most of my friend's dads fucked around with younger girls—by *most,* I mean pretty much all of them—but they'd always toss them aside after a few months when they'd been used up and served their purpose; my dad was the only one dumb enough to marry one. Everyone told him not to marry her, even his old, rich friends, but my dad's always been possessed by some misplaced sense of rebellion that always makes him do the *exact* opposite of what everybody says. Now that I think about it, that's probably where my own defiance stems from and, ironically, that's the thing he always scolds me for. Ain't *that* a trip?

My dad and I walked inside and, as expected, shrink-wrapped in a Juicy sweatsuit with two watermelons bursting through the seams was Esmeralda, standing in the kitchen yapping into her phone; trying to look preoccupied. She claims she's Guatemalan, and proudly states it at least once every half hour, although she's raised in Woodland Hills, and speaks worse Spanish than I do. That's where my dad found her, at some racquetball club, where she was working as an assistant to the receptionist. She had a piercing in her belly button, and the first time she came over for dinner she was wearing a shirt that said, *100% real...real expensive.*

About a week after they met, she started bringing her clothes over, and within a month she had moved in. At night I could hear her moaning from their bedroom, and the louder the moans, the more submissive my dad was when she was around. Once,

Esmeralda slapped me in front of him because I said her breath stank, but he didn't even budge. I was so shocked it almost felt like he hadn't even seen it. I brought it up with him afterwards but all he said was, *"She's from a different culture."* Talk about pussy power.

Esmeralda was making something that smelled terrible.

"Babe, it smells delicious," my dad exclaimed, and went over and smacked her on the butt. She grabbed him by the back of the neck and they began making out so loudly I could actually hear the saliva being exchanged between the two of them.

I watched her pour her miserable excuse for a meal—which I can only assume was breathing a few minutes ago—into a bowl, and my dad accepted it with such gratitude you'd swear he'd just been freed from the camps. When she finally noticed me, she recycled her performance of artificial affection that I was more than initiated to, at this point, followed by, "Oh *hi*, Alex. So good to see you. I'm so sorry, I had no idea you were coming so there's nothing for you to eat," she smiled sourly, with just enough contempt to let me know how she really felt about me.

"It's fine, I'm not hungry," I said, before heading off towards my room.

"*Alex*," she called after me.

"What?"

"Come here for a sec."

"What is it?" I said, standing still.

"*Aaalex*," she hummed, and signaled for me with her finger. I sighed and walked over.

"*What?*"

"We're having a bit of a get-together tomorrow, so it'd really mean a lot if you cleaned up a bit."

"Clean up?" I looked around the room. "*Where?*"

"Well, your *room* would be a good place to start."

"Why, is everyone gonna hang out in *my* room?"

"*Alex,*" she began, clenching her jaw. "Don't you think cleaning up a bit around here is the *least* you could do after what happened to you today? You know your daddy and I had plans tonight, but we had to cancel them because *someone* got arrested."

"I wasn't *arrested,* he was barely even a security guard."

"Well, that's not what it sounded like to me. But your daddy drove *all* the way out to pick you up, so I think you should be very happy that you're not grounded right now, don't you?"

Then my dad looked up from his eating, and interjected like a proud child in a classroom, "Yeah. *Exactly. I could* ground you."

"*See.* So, I think you should— "

"—Esmeralda, you're not my mom."

She smiled contemptuously. "Well, if you had a mom who *cared,* then maybe I wouldn't have to act like one."

I sighed. "Whatever."

"Alex," she called again, right as I'd turned around.

"*Yes?*" I asked, my irritation evident.

"Why don't you do everyone a favor and clean up that attitude. And then, when you're done, you can clean up a bit around the kitchen, too."

"*Yeah.* Cut the fucking attitude, Alex," my dad mimicked.

"Yes *sir!*" I said, and clicked my heels together followed by a Nazi salute. "And maybe when I'm finished, Esmeralda can point out America on a map," I muttered as I walked away, but I don't think they heard.

That night in bed I heard her moaning again, even though their room was on the other side of the house, but I'm sure my dad loved it because it made him feel like a man, and she was smart enough to realize that, so I bet she turned it up to eleven, every chance she got.

I wondered if my dad knew why she was with him in the first place, because I can assure you of one thing: it wasn't because of his fucking personality. But then again, maybe he *did* know, and he just didn't care. Maybe that was part of the little game adults play when they get older, preying on each other's weaknesses to get what they want. Looking back, when it comes to finding out how pathetic and simple adults really are, I wish I'd just taken the blue pill from the very start to save myself the headache.

* * *

My days after that were pretty much exactly like the ones I just told you about. Ocean and I got into a pretty big fight and didn't speak any more, and Beau got home-schooled for a while, and the following months before I left for England were pretty awkward. I spent most of my weekends alone in my room (Esmeralda and my dad would come home drunk most weekends and I'd listen to them fuck in their bedroom; sometimes even in the kitchen) while my friends were out at parties and stuff and smoking weed, and although I often thought about going, I never did.

I still did that correctional therapy a couple of times a week, but my anxiety got so bad that I was prescribed valium, and then my dad had to get me a *second* therapist because of how fidgety I was all the time: *"Instead of complaining, why don't you show some goddamn gratitude after all the things I'm paying for. You think any fucking kid has the luxury of having* two *therapists?"*

Eventually, I was forced to move in with my dad and Esmeralda full time because of what happened with my mom, but I don't really want to get into it.

They finally sent me to boarding school when I turned sixteen, which was actually intended as punishment but, I swear, I'd never been so relieved before in my life. I remember, years later, a lot of the kids I grew up with would complain about moving away to college and how much they'd miss their parents and their dog and their backyard and their siblings or whatever, when in reality they just were moving from Los Angeles to, like, Santa Barbara, or something, which is barely even a two-hour drive away. I'd see them write Facebook statuses saying, "Can't believe I won't be home for Labor Day weekend! Gonna miss my dad's barbecue!" Those are the same type of kids who will spend one semester abroad in Spain, and refer to every sandwich for the rest of their life as "Not as good as the sandwich I had when I was living in Ibiza," deliberately pronouncing it with a lisp. Christ, they really make me want to kill myself.

My parents and I used to go on vacation when I was younger before they got divorced so I was pretty used to long plane rides and stuff, but now, for the first time, I was flying completely alone. To be honest, I was pretty nervous at first—I thought I'd have a problem not finding the gate, or something, and maybe go to the wrong terminal—but I swear, as soon as I walked through security, I don't think I'd ever felt so free in my life. Getting to do everything at my own pace and not having to abide by anyone's rules except my own, was paradise. A lot of people hate flying alone because they say it gets boring and lonely, but for me, not having anybody breathing in your ear complaining about the airplane food for twelve hours sounds like the best thing in the world. If I could, I'd fly alone for the rest of my life.

A week before I left, Esmeralda started filling my room up with her stuff, slowly removing my posters, and paintings I'd done as a kid, replacing them with her own stuff, like her degree from University of Phoenix, an online 'school,' which doesn't even require you to know how to read, in order to get accepted. And, although they weren't even married yet, if I was ever in the room when the phone rang, she'd look at me and proudly answer with, "This is Esmeralda Lexington."

Although we fought in the beginning, eventually it just wasn't worth it anymore because I always lost in the end, and afterwards my dad would force me to apologize, and make me ask her if she *needed any help around the house*. I'm sure you're wondering why a kid from L.A. would be sent to boarding school in England when there's plenty of them in the U.S., but it was Esmeralda's suggestion, and I guess my dad thought that it was a pretty good idea.

"Don't you think it'd be better for him to get as far away as possible?" I heard her say once.

My flight to England was at one p.m. on a Saturday, but I went to the airport the night before and slept in the empty terminal. That probably sounds really petty or dramatic, but whatever.

The next morning, I woke up to the sound of airplane engines howling across the runway, and, suddenly, I realized I wasn't nauseous anymore.

Part Two

III

You'll never realize what a clean-freak you are, or aren't, until you're forced to live together with other people. I always assumed that I was a slob—according to my parents, I was—but when you're shipped off to a different country and crammed together in a single room with some random kid you've never met before, you finally start to grasp just how gross most people can be.

Much like the next teenage boy, I'm victim to a couple of jackets piled up on a chair in the corner of my room, along with a few socks and t-shirts scattered here and there, and this, I was told, was the epitome of filth—and then I met Curtis Frye, my first-year roommate.

"Have you ever had sex?" was the first thing he ever asked me, after having remained silent for the entire first month of living together.

After the first week, I couldn't walk around our room barefoot any more, unless I was fine with having a bunch of muffin crumbs, boogers, fingernails, or jerk-off hankies stuck to the soles of my feet. In the mornings, when I'd wake up, over by his side of the room, there'd always be a fresh set of three or four hardened tissues, like a childish attempt at origami, surrounding his bed.

"What are those from?" I'd ask.

"Uh," he'd pause, and absently glance down at them. "I had to blow my nose."

If he ever ran out of tissues, I'd find hard, crusty socks scattered around the room instead.

Sometimes, when I'd be sitting perched up against the wall in my bed watching a movie on my computer, he'd silently come over just to see what I was watching, and I'd be able to see right down into his scalp, an ocean of crusty, dandruff flakes enjoying a rent-free picnic in the caverns of his hair-bed. All the dorms had mixed showers, and sometimes I'd watch him, as furtively as possible, walk in and out, without any soap, shampoo, conditioner, *nothing*. If we were ever in there together, I'd even ask if he wanted to borrow some shampoo, or something, praying that he'd get the hint, but he'd meekly hold out his hand in rejection, as if he had some soap related childhood trauma that he just didn't want to revisit again. He'd never stay in there for more than a minute and, when he'd leave, I'd listen to his puffy little feet waddling out of the bathroom, wondering to myself what the inside of his house looked like.

There was another guy, Emil Tessmar, who lived down the hall from us—about six-four, a hundred and thirty pounds, with a large skin-tag on his cheek—who'd make fun of Curtis for having a small dick, and, although I despised living with him, I'd feel a strange sense of responsibility in defending him, simply because we lived together, like a younger sibling; someone I hadn't chosen, but was now obligated to protect.

Curtis never said anything about Emil's comments, he never said anything about *any*thing, but, sometimes, before he'd shower, I'd catch him tugging on his dick to make it hang lower, just in case Emil, or anyone else, happened to catch him.

Our bathrooms had large windows leading out to the trees, and one time Emil entered when Curtis and I were in the shower and, standing right in front of the half-open window, preparing his first, sardonic remark against Curtis, I charged forward, pushing him out of the window and shutting the latch behind him, forcing him to run around the entire dorm in the middle of winter, completely naked, crying, and banging on the front door for over five minutes until somebody finally let him in. Emil never said anything after that.

Curtis never said thank you, he never even brought it up, but after that day, he slowly started picking up after himself until, finally, our room started looking slightly more habitable again. For the rest of the year, he mostly kept to himself, but I'd always know when he was coming up the stairs with those precarious little footsteps of his, as if he still wasn't sure of where he was going.

Right before spring break, I came up to my room after class and noticed that Curtis' side of the room was completely empty, with nothing left but the bed and drawers that had been there to begin with. I didn't understand what had happened, but as I looked around the room, on our shared desk by the window, I found a handwritten note that said: Hope there's no hard feelings. Thanks for everything. It took most people in our dorm well over two weeks to even notice he was gone, but I never saw him again after that.

When you're forced to live so intimately in a big dormitory with a bunch of other boys, you find out so much more about how different, and truly strange, some people really are.

At a public school, after eight hours, everybody goes home, and you don't see them until the next day. So, if some kid's a complete weirdo, you'll only really get a brief glimpse of it, because you only see the persona of that kid in a classroom, or at lunch, a few hours each day. But, when you're crammed together in a big house with all these weirdos, you really find out what makes them tick and what daily rituals they have and how they shower and how they brush their teeth and how dirty they are and what their hobbies are and what kind of music they like and all those meticulous little details people shield from the outside world, the details that turn someone from being simply just another person, to a Curtis Frye or an Alexander Lexington.

In fact, looking back, I don't think I knew *any*one until I came to Durnford. That was the name of the school, by the way: *Durnford Hill College.*

* * *

In second year, I finally got my own room. It was on the top floor of our dormitory, and it had a little window that looked out over this big, grassy field where we'd play soccer, or *football*, as the rest of the world calls it.

During the winter, if it got cold enough, there'd be a thin sheet of snow, or sometimes ice, covering the entire field, and at night you could see all the windows of all the other dormitories flickering in the darkness. I'm not one to usually say corny stuff like this, but I swear, it looked like a fairytale.

My buddy Patrick and I, (Patrick *Valancourt*)—he was from a rich, surprisingly liberal political family in London, and his dad had gone to Oxford and looked exactly like Peter Finch in *Network*)—had bought this rope ladder online, and we'd throw it out of the window at night and shimmy down and go hang out and drink with our friends from the other dormitories out by the lake or in the woods, or something. If you want me to be honest, I even started smoking when I was there. I'll admit, I felt like such a sellout when I started, but I couldn't help it; everyone I met smoked. But here's the thing: I smoked for a few months, until one weekend we had taken the train into London to go to this party and my friend Archie asked me if I wanted to join him for a fag. It was fucking freezing—all the Belgravia windows were all covered in frost—and when Archie was stepping out onto the balcony, I watched him muscle his way into his duffel parka, tie his winter boots, which took close to ten minutes per foot, put on his gloves and his scarf and stick on this giant winter hat, and I swear, after seeing all that preparation just to do something that's not even that fun to begin with, I realized that I had to stop smoking. I *did* join him outside, but I didn't smoke. Instead, I just watched his trembling hands struggle to light this meager little lighter he had, while his lips turned bluer by the second, shivering like a maniac: *"I don't know why I'm shaking so much, I'm not even that cold."*

Durnford had these old groundskeepers who'd patrol all night to make sure kids weren't running around—they were annoying as hell, because if they caught you, it meant your ass— but, I swear, it made sneaking out all the more exhilarating. I was always pretty hesitant to sneak out most of the time, because honestly, I just couldn't be bothered to go out into the freezing darkness, but whenever we did it was usually worth it. I had been getting with this blonde chick named Sabrina for a little bit, but every single time we were about to have sex, she'd always stop me at the last second, saying that she was getting with this older boy, who was heir to the throne, or some shit, and she didn't want to *lose* him because of his royal status. She'd always insist that she wasn't *'that kind of girl'*, even though we'd make out for hours at least a few times a week. She said the only thing she considered cheating was literally being inside a person or having someone inside you, everything else was just *'carelessness.'* I swear, the prettier a girl is, the more delusional they are since their beauty is such a VIP pass through life, letting them get away with pretty much anything they want. Nobody will ever tell them that though, because they're just so nice to look at, and every guy's a sucker who'll desperately wait in line for something so little as a handshake.

That night we were supposed to go drinking with a couple of our friends down by the lake, and apparently some of the new fresher girls were joining, who we hadn't really had a chance to meet yet.

"You seen that new French bird, mate?" Patrick asked, checking his hair in the mirror.

"Who?" I asked.

"You know, the one with the dark hair that Archie's been tryin' to pull for weeks now. Has a peculiar name though, can't remember it for the life of me."

"I don't think so."

"Ah, you'll probably see her tonight. Seriously fit, mate."

Archie wasn't that handsome to be honest, but he had this unapologetic confidence that I guess girls just radiated towards; it was quite impressive to watch. Whenever he was dancing—by dancing, I mean fist-pumping and head-banging to techno—he would just grab any girl and throw her around long enough until she got dizzy and nearly passed out, and then he'd make his move. So, hearing that Archie had been trying to get with this girl for a while must've meant that she was pretty damn cute, although something about girls who were immediately hailed as the next Helen of Troy slightly turned me off from them. I guess I just never wanted to be like a horde of suckers drooling over them, knowing that they'd never get a shot, but still talking about how hot they were, and what they'd do for a chance with them. It was like the girls weren't even people anymore, but rather some dish at a Michelin star restaurant. With that said, give most of these girls some makeup remover and they'll quickly drop from 'Gordon Ramsay' level cuisine, to three a.m. 'cheesy chips' at your local kebab shop. Patrick opened my window and habitually threw out the rope ladder. Since we both lived on the top floor, which was basically like an attic, we called ourselves the attic wolves. Pretty lame, I know, but whatever, it was fun.

So, being the attic wolves that we were, Patrick had printed out these hoodies for the two of us with a wolf on them and *Attic Wolves* stitched underneath. I swear, I had never been so excited over a stupid hoodie before in my life. So, as usual, when we snuck out together, we were both wearing our hoodies as we shimmied down the ladder.

To get to Archie's dormitory we had to cross that giant grass field I was telling you about, but when it got cold at night, the layer of snow would turn to a thin layer of ice, and I swear, every step we took was like crossing a minefield.

The ice cracking beneath our feet echoed throughout the entire woods and gave me a mini heart attack each time because I kept thinking one of the groundskeepers would hear us. I'm really paranoid like that, you know. Never been sure why, but I'm definitely the most paranoid person I've ever met. Whenever I leave a place and lock the door, I have to go back at *least* ten times to make sure I've locked it. If I'm alone I even have to film a video of my hand physically locking the door, and then I'll watch it several times throughout the day to reassure myself that the door is actually locked. I always feel terrible for whoever I'm with because I always make us late, and even if we're *not* late, I'm sure it's just frustrating as hell having to watch some whacko like me anxiously run back and forth from the door a hundred times to see if I locked it, or not. One of my therapists once told me I should learn to meditate, but thus far I've been too stubborn to try.

So, when you get past that icy minefield, there's this long, downward hill that leads to the dormitories at the bottom of the hill. Three girl dorms—Deerfield, Holland, and Marlborough—and one boy dorm—Nelson house—which, of course, Archie had the luck of living in; sandwiched in between like a million girls.

Patrick and I got down outside Archie's window and knocked on it quietly. Patrick, naturally more used to English weather than myself, came prepared wearing a parka over his hoodie, complete with mittens and a hat. I was wearing jeans, Vans, and a grey hoodie; thinking ahead has never been one of my strengths. Patrick kept knocking and knocking, but Archie never opened up his damn window.

"Do you think he's even in there?" I asked.

"If he's legged it without us, mate, I swear," Patrick said irritably.

Finally, Patrick's phone rang. Archie told him that he had already made his way down to the lake and was waiting there with all the girls, *"What is taking you two so bloody long?!"* I heard his voice call on the other end. I told Patrick to give me the phone so I could yell at him for telling us to come to his room when he wasn't even there, but he hung up before I had the chance. Archie possesses an extremely annoying habit of being the kind of guy who, if you ever call him on the weekend, would answer for about five seconds and shout in rapid fire along the lines of, "Mate, I'm at this crazy party! So many birds! I'm hammered!" and then hang up, and be completely unreachable for the rest of the night. Then when you see him on Monday, he'll describe the weekend like it was an after party at Charlie Sheen's house, and you missed out on the most insane night in history.

I tried not to get too bothered by it because I knew that Archie owed me twenty pounds which he had promised to pay back in alcohol that very night. I hadn't been drunk in a while, and although I've never been a huge fan of drinking, I was actually really looking forward to it.

We eventually got down to the water, and even though we were about a mile away, we could make out a bunch of tiny little silhouettes gathered around the boat docks. I started to get really anxious about meeting all these new 'hot' girls that Archie had told us about. I think that's the worst thing there is for me: meeting new people that you *know* you have to make a good impression on. Whether it's a potential boss, a teacher, somebody's parents, or just a couple of girls that Archie dragged along hoping to sleep with. Suddenly, I got so nauseous that my body started to feel weak and shaky, and all I wanted to do was just puke my lungs out. I started biting at my nails again, trying to stabilize my anxiety.

"Mister Lexington and Mister Valancourt! Pleasure to see you both," Archie shouted bombastically as he saw us approaching. He had a big, drunken smile stretched across his face, both arms wrapped around two different girls, with a beer tightly clutched in each hand. "And, sorry, but uhm..." he pompously checked his Rolex. "...What time do you call this?" He started laughing and addressed one of the girls in his grasp, "You see, Tilly—"

"It's *Tiffany*," she corrected, mildly offended.

"Yes, yes—*Tiffy*, what*ever*—you see, Mister Lexington over there is the sort of bloke who would be tardy for his own funeral. Expecting this man to show up at any time other than his own is an act of sheer implausibility—isn't that right, Alex?"

Before I could answer, Patrick kicked Archie in the leg.

"You shouldn't speak when you're so battered, mate, people might catch on to your retardation."

"Ow!" Archie yelped theatrically. "Patrick Valancourt engaging in violence and verbal abuse? Just wait till I have a word with your father, young man! What will the parliament say about this?!"

Patrick kicked him again and grabbed a beer and handed me one and we both sat down next to Archie who continued laughing at himself.

Although I tend to talk quite a lot, in these situations I get pretty quiet, at least in the beginning, so I just joined everyone by dangling my feet off the ledge and looked down into the water below us. The moon illuminated the thin sheets of ice floating around the lake like water lilies, and the night wind distorted everyone's features reflecting off the water. I looked at the dark face, slightly resembling my own, staring back at me from beneath my feet, but all I wanted to know was if he felt as nauseous as I did.

I silently cracked open the beer, but the first sip slid down my stomach like a firecracker, so I just made a loud slurping sound to give the impression I was drinking. I always hated it, too, because this nausea mainly comes around when I'm at parties, and that's when you're always supposed to show off how much beer you can chug, at least if you're friends with a bunch of alcoholics like I am. Instead, I was always the one who needed about an hour just to finish his first beer. It always embarrassed the hell out of me.

"Bah! My manners betray me. Ladies, I regret to inform you that these two are unfortunately the best I could do for tonight. If you know anything about anything you'll recognize the four-eyed gentleman as Patrick Valancourt—I'm sure you've seen his father in the paper—and the quiet lad sitting beside him is some Yank joining us all the way from Los Angel*eez*: mistuh Alex-*awn*-durr Lexington."

I cordially raised my beer and nodded my head, but most of the girls just giggled anyway. I couldn't even tell if any of them were as hot as Patrick or Archie had claimed because of how dark it was. Naturally, Archie didn't share any of the girls' names, but as the night went on, I almost forgot that they even had names. You probably could've called them whatever you wanted to, because when you're a teenager, girls who are even just a year younger than you will giggle at literally anything you say. I never knew if it was because they were being fake, or just nervous because they were around 'older kids'. Either way—and I'm ashamed to admit it—the drunker I got, the more it rubbed my ego.

Archie lit a cigarette, "So, where you lot from?"

"I'm half German," one of them squeaked.

"Whereabouts?"

"Dresden."

"Dresden?" Archie exclaimed. "Didn't we bomb the shit out of you?! Well, you certainly made it out alright," he laughed proudly, and I saw the girl's face sour.

After a few bottles of liquid courage, I recycled the same song and dance I recited to every new person I met in England, which was to blabber about Los Angeles. I don't think people understand this, but being from America in Europe, nonetheless *Los Angeles*, is literally like being famous, or saying that you went to Harvard, or something. You can go completely unnoticed the entire night, but as soon as you tell them where you come from you have an unshakeable spotlight on you for the rest of the night. It's honestly quite baffling because, at the end of the day, it's just a stupid place on a map. So, when I told the girls about it, as expected, I suddenly became the most interesting person on the planet. I told them that I surfed and that I lived on the beach and that I've had dinner with Brad Pitt and that Jennifer Lawrence pays me to walk her dog and a bunch of other bullshit that almost makes me cringe just thinking about it, but it didn't matter, because they were all eating out of my hand. I could tell Archie was getting annoyed because his position as the alpha had suddenly evaporated, as he had now become the Robin to my Batman, and as the girls' laughter escalated, his sneer stretched further and further.

"So, do you know, like, *loads* of famous people?" one of them asked.

"I mean, you know, not *loads*, but a few," I said modestly. "You guys ever heard of Leonardo DiCaprio?"

"*Leo*?!" another one shrieked.

"Yeah, he's actually my neighbor," I lied. "In return for surf lessons, he takes me to all his movie premiers."

"Are you kidding?!"

"He's a super chill guy. Totally down to earth."

"That's mental!"

"I am literally obsessed with him."

I thought they were going to faint but, for the life of me, I couldn't figure out why. I never understood the fun in listening to someone *else* talk about meeting someone, especially if that someone isn't anything more than a simple movie star, but I guess it's the feeling of being so close to something so unattainable, that makes it all the more exhilarating. Like being physically handicapped and listening to someone describe climbing Mt. Everest: since you know you'll never get there, maybe the fantasy is good enough.

After my fifth or sixth beer I was pretty drunk. At this point, Archie was noticeably agitated over the shift of focus, so he did what all desperate guys do when their spotlight starts to dim: he started making a complete ass out of himself, in hopes of regaining some attention. Not saying I blame him for it, but, as a guy, it's pretty embarrassing to witness, and I always wonder if other people find it as pitiful as I do. That's the thing about Archie: he's always had it easy with the ladies, but he prefers little to no competition when he's trying to get some, because if any competition *does* arise, he goes into panic mode. Archie isn't a funny guy as much as he's fun to laugh at, but he never seemed to be able to differentiate the two. Now he was standing on all fours, and running into these poor little girls, headfirst, making these awful pig grunts, desperately praying that at least *one* of them would laugh. Some of the girls giggled awkwardly, but I could tell that most of them were pretty turned off by the whole thing. He went on like this, getting louder and more abrasive by the minute until, finally, the anvil of beer in his stomach eventually got the best of him, as he finally rolled over like a defeated dog, submissively cracking open another one in silence.

It must've been around three or four in the morning when we started making our way back up towards campus. As fun as it was to mess around with those girls, when the time came to make a move, I just really wasn't interested any more. It's weird, but I usually never am. As soon as I know somebody's interested, I get completely turned off. It's a shame, too, because I've probably missed out on some eventful nights that could've been a lot more fun had I made a move but, to be honest, I always felt like a one-night stand was nothing more than a glorified wank. Plus, after every one of the few one night stands I've had, I get so disgusted with myself that I can barely look at myself in the mirror afterwards. Apparently, that's called *post coital angst*, or at least that's what my therapist said.

Archie had his arm around one of the girls, and was swaying back and forth with every step, clinging on to her for dear life. I could hear him whispering to her, "You're gonna have to help me into bed." I prayed the girl had some brains, and didn't fall for Archie's recycled pickup lines.

"How we feelin'?" Patrick asked, with a smirk. His glasses were all fogged up so you could barely see his eyes.

"Battered, mate!" I replied in my best British accent. "I think you should get a refund on those windshields, though. I don't think they installed the anti-fog screen when you bought them." I laughed, but as I turned, I noticed the little horde of girls following closely behind us.

"*Alex*," one of the girls with way too much foundation called out.

"Yeah?" I asked, turning around.

"You reckon you could teach *me* how to surf some time?" All of her friends started giggling like hyenas. I wasn't sure if she was kidding, or not.

"Sure. I'll get my board and we can hop on right now."

Again, they started giggling.

At the fork that led to all of the different dorms we said goodbye to Archie, and his potential shag, a bit further away from campus, but as Patrick and I walked off alone, we realized the little group of girls were still following us. That's the thing about girls that I'll never understand: the less interest you show in them, the more interested they get. I'm sure that's pretty standard knowledge at this point, but I still can't understand why. I don't think Patrick and I said more than a word to any of the girls on the way home and, *still,* they insisted on asking us a million questions and asking what the inside of either of our rooms looked like.

"What home are you guys in?" one of them asked, with a shiny mouthful of metal. She would've been pretty cute if it wasn't for those braces, but when she opened her mouth, it looked like she was eleven years old.

"Highland Hill," I said. All the dormitory names were followed by '*house*,' but Highland Hill was the only one that had '*hill*' instead of '*house*', because it was the oldest dormitory on campus, from the 1700s, or something crazy like that. Because it was the oldest, it was also the most sought after and the most expensive dorm to live in, which only enhanced your status to all the little Surrey girls who rode horses and played tennis, and who were now following us.

"*Oh,*" she began, excited. "Highland Hill? Somebody said that's where all the fit boys lived. I guess they weren't lying," followed by more giggles.

At this point, I almost felt like a parent trying to put an annoying child to bed.

"Listen," I said to her. "Why are you trying so hard?"

Her lewd, hopeful expression quickly vanished.

"I'm not trying *hard*," she scoffed.

"Look, you're all really cute, but—"

"—*Cute*? Am I a fucking puppy?"

"Uh—"

"Fuck off then, *twat.*"

"Sorry, *what*?"

"Fuck *off*," she repeated, louder. "And by the way, you're not even fit," and then she quickly stormed off, her friends tailing

57

closely behind.

I turned around to Patrick and threw my hands up in the air.

"What the hell was that?"

Patrick began laughing and shook his head.

"Mate, I don't blame 'em," he snickered. "They were throwing themselves at you and you were being a cunt. What'd you expect?"

I guess I wasn't really expecting much when I said it, but I suppose he was right.

"Probably for the best though, considering those braces, eh?" Patrick chuckled, as we climbed back up the rope ladder. "Wouldn't want your knob anywhere near that meat grinder."

IV

Did I tell you about the uniforms? They were preppy as hell, and really screamed *'heir to the throne'*, something you'd expect from a school like Durnford Hill. A lot of the kids thought they looked real smart; the girls looked *great*. They had these short, dark brown skirts that they always rolled up way too high, despite school rules, and they'd wear those tight black leggings under tall black boots, and it just made you thank God for giving you such good eyesight. I don't know what it is, but nothing gets me as excited as high socks or leggings. The boys had basically the same thing, and some of the guys really liked them; I thought they were shit. We had these diarrhea colored trousers, as the Brits call them, with a gray blazer bearing our school insignia on the left chest, along with this horrible red and yellow tie which didn't so much scream expensive boarding school as it did McDonald's employee. We'd have to wear this uncomfortable uniform every single day, and if we ran home and took it off before dinner, we'd get penalized. I don't think I ever told anybody this, but out of the three years I spent at Durnford Hill, I think I washed my uniform twice, I'm not kidding. Back in middle school, I think I washed my P.E. uniform around two times my entire three years, as well. The prefects would inspect our shoes before we left the dorm every morning to make sure they were polished, but I'd usually just run them under the faucet before I left so they looked shiny for a few seconds, and that'd usually suffice for their inspection. When it didn't, I'd always have to *'see them after dinner'*—a recurring phrase often heard around campus—but I didn't care.

Every Monday morning the entire school assembled in the auditorium, and the headmaster went over the things we should be focusing on, and how to improve ourselves and all that crap that nobody actually listens to, especially when it's that early, and the only thing on your mind is making sure your morning wood goes unnoticed. It reminded me of every speech the president gives, just recycling the same old catch phrases like, "My fellow Americans/students (insert dramatic pause) we have come so, so far, but we still have so much left to do." Like, give me a fucking break already, pal, nobody cares. Go kiss a baby on the forehead, give some shallow promise that you're going to clean up our air, and then fuck off.

After the headmaster finished his weekly recital of bullshit, they'd force us to watch some lobotomizing slideshow of the sixth graders' most recent trip to some ski resort somewhere in Europe. The pain didn't stem from the fact that it was so fucking boring, even though it was, but more so in seeing how they'd dictatorially line up every mortified little sixth grader—that was the youngest grade on campus—in front of the entire school, stick a microphone in their face, and then force them to describe a small portion of their trip in front of the entire school, while everyone else was dozing off in the audience. These poor kids would basically stick the entire microphone in their mouth, so all you could make out were sounds of inconsistent vowels, occasionally hearing something like, "And then for breakfast I had porridge. The next day, I had porridge again. Then, on the third day, we didn't have any more porridge, so instead I had Weetabix." Talk about depressing. These little performances would go on for hours, with every kid mumbling incoherently about god knows what, and within the first ten minutes I swear the entire school was completely asleep, most of the teachers included. If we were really bored, Patrick and I would make loud snoring noises from the audience, but we'd always get caught by some disgruntled old teacher who'd drag us outside and shout at us, but somehow that always made it funnier.

Anyway, it was a Monday early in December, and Patrick and I had plotted this great plan as to how we were going to avoid every assembly on Monday mornings. The way our routines at the dorms worked were as follows. We had these old people living in each of the dormitories who were like a stand-in parent—our *guardians,* if you will. Basically, their only job was to check that all the kids were in bed on time, make sure they were doing their homework, and check that they weren't smoking cigarettes out the window, or lighting firecrackers in the toilet, or something. Lucky for us, we pretty much had the coolest dorm parent in the entire school. She was this old Russian lady named Vera who had this gnarly Russian accent, and she was so deaf she could never hear a damn thing, which was awesome because Patrick and I lived directly above her, and she never once came up to check on us, no matter how boisterous we got. That Sabrina girl I was telling you about, her dorm had probably the worst lady you could ever imagine. Her name was Martha, and she had this wispy blonde hair, and bags under her eyes that made her entire face droop like a saggy pair of tits you'd find in National Geographic. Every night we'd have to be back in our own dorms by 10.30p.m., and God forbid I ever stayed over until 10.31, because if I did, she sent the gestapo after me. She'd call up Vera and chew her out for not having better control over her reckless and unsophisticated boys. One time Patrick had borrowed his parents' car and drove up to school because he needed this special mattress to help with his neck pain, but Martha saw him in his car and called the headmaster and had him suspended for two days because students aren't allowed to drive on school property. He tried to explain why, but Martha was so militant that she convinced the faculty to stay firm with their decision in suspending him.

So, back to what I was saying, every morning you had to be down at breakfast by 7.30a.m. at the latest. If you weren't, Vera would come up and check on you to make sure that you were at least awake and getting dressed. So, what Patrick and I did was, we'd put our alarms at about 7.29a.m., and then quickly get up out of bed and put on our uniform trousers. We'd stay in that position, strictly pants on and nothing else, until Vera came up and opened our door to check on us, where we'd then say, "Good morning Vera! Was just getting ready, coming down in a minute!" She'd give us a proud, approving smile, and then go back downstairs. Then all we did was take off our pants, lock the door, and go back to bed until the assembly was over. Eventually we'd go to class, but our tactics gave us about an extra ninety minutes of sleep—brilliant, *mate*. The best thing about being the only two living in the attic was that it was quiet up there, a total contrast from the first or second floor where you wouldn't be able to fall back asleep to save your life, because there'd always be some asshole blasting house music at six in the morning or singing in the shower.

Since I'd always sleep through breakfast on Mondays, and I'd pretty much sleep up until a minute before school started on regular days anyway, I'd only have time to grab a banana or an apple or something before school. It probably wasn't the smartest tactic since I'd get these terrible hunger headaches, and then my hunger would turn into nausea, which would turn into migraines, and then I'd have to check in early after school, slowly feeding myself little pieces of toast or apple sauce or *some*thing until my body eventually stopped shaking.

Patrick and I didn't have any classes together, so we wouldn't really see each other during the day except for maybe at lunch sometimes. Archie was in a few of my classes, and then a couple of other guys who lived in Bulworth house had some classes with me too. They always stuck together though, so I was always unsure whether they were just scared of being alone, or whether they just genuinely liked each other *that* much. There were three of them to be exact: Arthur Wallace, Eliot Harvey, and William 'Billy' Chambers, but most people called him Chilly. Arthur and Eliot were at least 6'3, and Chilly was probably like 5'6, but still, Chilly was by far the toughest, most intimidating guy in our entire grade. He started playing rugby a week after he learned to walk, and had a neck like a California redwood, so he weighed close to two hundred pounds, most of that weight concentrated around his thighs. Ironically enough, Arthur and Eliot had never even been in a fight in their entire lives, whereas Chilly found himself in one almost every single weekend—probably an allusion to his severe case of Napoleonitus—but he *never* tried to prove himself around us, only when people were being rude, and actually deserved a crack in the teeth. He had this thick red hair that he shaved down to the skin; this really made him stick out like a soccer hooligan since every other kid had much longer hair that they'd slick back behind their ears with about a pound of hair goop. If you looked up *'posh twat'* in an encyclopedia you'd find a photo of Arthur and Eliot but, to be honest, I think they quite relished the stereotype. Although they weren't related, if you didn't know this beforehand, I swear you'd think they were twins by the way they stuck together. Every morning they'd both read the finance section during breakfast; both proud members of the clay shooting society; avid tennis and polo players; an affinity for political discussions with old, bald intellectuals and, whenever possible, look for an excuse to completely obliterate any and all liberals, or, *'rampant lefties,'* as they referred to them. Chilly came from the exact same background as they did and although he should've taken the same interest, he took the more aggressive route in rugby, probably a testament to his stocky build and being vertically challenged. So the three of them really moved together as one single organism: Chilly the brawn; Arthur and Eliot the brains. Where, or how, I fit into this three-man-unit I couldn't tell you, but somehow, we all got along.

So, Chilly, Arthur and Eliot were sitting next to each other as usual, and signaled for me to come over. Although you could never get any of them to shut up most of the time, they were really disciplined when confined within the school walls. Ironically enough, they'd always be the ones telling *me* to zip it, because they were trying to pay attention and take notes, or something. However, whenever we were out and about, I'd literally have to take a number and get in line if I wanted to get my voice heard.

I daydream a lot and hardly ever pay attention to the teacher, but I really can't help it, because thus far in my entire school career I've never found anything the teacher says to be even remotely interesting.

So, as usual, there I was, first period on a Monday in December, and I was already falling behind due to my constant daydreaming. So, as I was dozing off thinking about how bicycle tires are made, or something, the door opened, and some new girl walked into class who I had never seen before. Now I'm not going to bore you with any of that "she was the most beautiful girl I had ever laid eyes on," bullshit, but I will tell you she did make me sit up in my seat to get a better view. She wasn't like traditionally pretty though, if you know what I mean? By traditionally pretty I mean, like, the Kate Uptons and the Scarlett Johanssons and all those boring, generic blonde girls with big tits who guys named Kyle have as a screensaver on their iPhone. She was more unique looking, but in a really appealing way. She had these pale blue eyes, dirty blonde hair that she had tied in a ponytail, and she entered the room totally indifferent to what the world thought of her. I became so fixated, that I didn't even notice that it had begun to snow outside. Everybody started cheering, but I just couldn't stop staring at her.

I swear, some people in this world are so mesmerizing that you'd feel lucky just knowing that once in your life you had the privilege of getting to look at them, even for just a few seconds.

V

Remember when I told you that my parents forced me to take Adderall because of what that doctor said all those years ago? Well, they never took me off of it, but I'm not kidding when I say that I think I stopped taking that stuff after the first week. I don't know if you've ever tried drugs, or anything, but if you've ever taken really bad ecstasy, just know that the come down I got from Adderall felt like *that,* times a hundred. But here's the funny part: since my grades had improved so drastically at Durnford, my dad was wholly convinced that it was a testament to the Adderall, and nothing else, never once considering that maybe the teachers at my old school were just awful, and at Durnford they actually cared about their students, but whatever.

Since my GPA was substantially higher than it had ever been, my dad kept sending over more and more Adderall, but all I did was sell it for about ten pounds a pill. Total rip off, I know, but most of the kids I sold them to didn't even really know what it was, and really just wanted to live out some rebellious fantasy since they were now living away from home, hoping their newfound capacity for mayhem would leave all the other kids impressed. And, besides, most of these kids were loaded anyway, so I didn't feel too bad about ripping them off. There was one super weird dude who lived in Bulworth house named Donald Ostreicher who had several classes with me—he'd been kicked out of Eton and Harrow, and Durnford Hill wasn't going to accept him but his family paid some outrageous amount of money to rebuild the school library, so finally the school submitted, and accepted him—and he came from a really well-respected family, but he was the black sheep of the bunch which always made me feel bad for him. He never went to class, so all he'd do was roll joints and smoke them alone on his windowsill all day.

So this dude, *Oz*, would buy an entire bottle of Adderall at a time, and, just to demonstrate his disdain for authority, he'd line up his books in front of him in class, crush up these tiny little pills, and snort them right there in the middle of class. I asked why he insisted on snorting them, but he claimed that it, '*enhanced the high.*' He was the kind of kid who would bring his pet tarantula for show-and-tell, and then be surprised when none of the kids showed up to his birthday party. Total fucking weirdo. One day, not too long after she first started in our class, I was staring at that girl I told you about; she was sitting completely alone, so finally I got the nerve to go up and ask her what her name was. The teacher had left the room for a second, so everyone was just kind of talking amongst themselves pretending to discuss the fall of the Third Reich, or photosynthesis, or whatever the hell it was that we were learning at the time. She was sitting secluded in the corner and her hair was tied up in this little bun sealed with a white ribbon that really made her stick out from the typical 'Surrey girls' that made up eighty percent of the school demographic.

"Hey," I said tentatively. She was buried in some book, so I kind of raised my voice a little bit and asked again.

"Hey!" I repeated, immediately aware of how much louder I had said it. She jumped, and I instantly saw our potential relationship crumble before me.

"Sorry, sorry, sorry! I just—fuck, uhm—you didn't hear me

the first time, but I didn't think it was going to come off so loud. I didn't mean to scare you."

"Oh, you're American," she said, giggling, politely putting her book down.

"Oh, you're...not British?" I replied, noticing her accent.

"Ah, so your hearing *isn't* terrible," she smirked. Then I just kind of stood there, smiling, like an idiot; like when Bambi grows up and sees Faline for the first time.

"But then again...maybe it is?" she said, quietly.

"I'm...Alexander. But—*well*—most people just call me Alex."

"Hello Alexander, the American. I'm Bardot."

"Bardot? That's a cool name."

"You think so?"

"Well... I mean... *I've* never met anyone with that name."

Then, wouldn't you believe it, fucking *Oz* comes up and started tapping me on the shoulder.

"Alex," he says.

"Gimme a sec, Oz," I replied dismissively, but the guy wouldn't stop poking me.

"Aaaaaleeeex," he continued in sing-song, his fingers anxiously hammering into my skin.

"Okay, okay. What is it, man?" I said irritably, turning my whole body around.

"Do you have anything on you?"

Bardot immediately turned suspicious, and I held out my finger signaling that I needed a minute, quickly shooing Oz away from her so she wouldn't hear.

"Jesus, dude, are you retarded? You can't just ask if I '*have anything*' in the middle of class. What's'a matter with you?"

"I just need some more Addies, mate."

68

"*More*? *Dude,* I gave you an entire bottle like a week ago. That's like a ninety-day supply. What happened, did you pour milk over them and eat them with a spoon?"

"*No,*" he said, clearly unamused.

"Well, then what the hell happened to them? That was a *big* bottle, man."

"Well, basically, I gave some to my friend and then he asked for some more, so I gave him some more and—"

"—*Oz*. Listen. I can't give you a whole bottle at a time for a much cheaper price than I give everybody else, especially if you're gonna give half of them away to some guy I don't even know and then come ask me for more for the *same* discounted price that—"

"—*Mate*, just gimme a couple more. Please, mate. Just like...ten...maybe twenty more."

"*Twenty*? No way, man. If you need them this badly, you're addicted. This isn't good for you."

"But, mate, I'll *pay*! I'll pay twice the price of what I usually pay!"

"That's not the point, dude. The point is, I'm not gonna be the culprit behind your first stint in rehab. So, I'm sorry, dude. Pharmacy's closed."

Then, like a man possessed, Oz stood up from his chair and got right in my face and flared his teeth like a rabid dog.

"Oz, sit down, man."

"I *need* them, Alex," he continued sternly.

"I said *sit-down*, Ozzy," I said, and put my hand on his shoulder, but he slapped it away.

Nobody had really noticed what was going on since everybody was so focused on their own chitchat, and nobody noticed that he began raising his fists towards me. He started gnashing his teeth, and his left eye even began to twitch—he looked completely insane.

"Oz. For the *last* time—sit *down*."

Then, what do you know, he swung at me. Hit me right in the mouth, too, but he was so strung out and so fidgety that there wasn't much force behind the blow. It barely grazed my lips, but still, getting punched in the face is pretty high up on the list of things that don't feel too great.

Before I could even react, Chilly appeared behind him, put Oz in a full nelson and slammed his head against the desk, his nose exploding on impact, blood squirting horizontally across the laminated surface.

"You finished, mate?!" Chilly shouted at him. For Oz's sake, I prayed he was.

"Chilly, he's good. Thanks," I said, fingering the inside of my lip.

"How's your face, mate?" he asked.

"I'll be fine. Thanks."

Oz seemed barely conscious, and the blood leaking from his nose began to slowly pool around his face. Chilly and I grabbed him and sat him up straight.

"You okay?" I asked.

Oz didn't say much, but at this point the entire classroom was in complete shock, and I could feel, what felt like, hundreds of eyes judgmentally staring at me.

"It's okay, it's okay. He's fine. We're just gonna take him to the nurse," Chilly said reassuringly, holding out his hands trying to neutralize the scene. I avoided eye contact with Bardot as I left the classroom, praying this hadn't completely ruined any chance I had with her.

Chilly left as soon as we arrived at the nurse, awkwardly leaving Oz and I alone.

"Sorry, mate," he suddenly whispered, his tone soaked in guilt.

"It's fine. Really."

"Nah, mate. It's not. I don't know what got into me. It's just I—I *need* those pills," he said desperately.

And for the first time since I had been selling Adderall, I began to realize the true side effects of those apathetic little demons. Oz was a weird kid, no question about it, but never in a million years did I ever think he'd sucker punch me right in the mouth, and in the middle of a *classroom,* nonetheless. His pupils were still dilated, and after looking at his mouth I realized his teeth must've been grinding for weeks. I put my hand on the back of his neck, and even though he had just gotten his face kicked in, it was much sweatier than it should've been. His foot was anxiously hammering against the floor, his whole body vibrating. I took a step back, stared at him, and suddenly I felt extremely guilty.

"I'm out, Oz. I'm completely dry."

"What?" He gasped, his tone mirroring that of a man who'd just witnessed the murder of his own family.

"I don't have any more, Oz, and unfortunately I don't think I'm gonna be getting any more anytime soon."

"But you have to!" He shouted, grabbing my shirt with both hands, forcefully pulling me towards him.

"Oz, please let go of my shirt."

"What? Oh. Oh, shit—sorry, sorry. I di—I didn't mean to— "

He let go, and apologetically tried to straighten out the creases he'd formed.

"It's okay. Just…you know. Try to get a grip on yourself."

"I know, I know. You're right, mate. You're right. I know. I just—what am I supposed to do?"

Thankfully, the nurse came in at that exact moment, or I would've given some surely terrible advice.

"Hello boys, what seems to be the—oh!" She gasped, catching a glimpse of Ozzy's nose. "And what on earth has happened to you, dear? Snowball fight gone awry?"

Oz looked at me, and I managed to bury the bottom half of my face in my scarf so she wouldn't notice my bruised lip.

"I slipped on the ice," he stuttered, "…and fell into a wall."

"Ouch. Let's have a closer look, then."

The nurse began poking around in Ozzy's face, and I saw it as my only window to leave.

"Oz—miss—I gotta go."

"Go? Well, all right, but don't you need a slip for class?" she asked.

"No, no. I'll be fine, don't worry."

"Well, don't forget to sign out when you leave—"

Her voice trailed after me as I booked it out of there, found the nearest bathroom, and puked in one of the stalls

I didn't even bother going to class for the rest of the day, I just went back to my room instead, because, usually, if I've puked once, that means there's a chance it'll come again, and the last place I want to be when that happens is stuck inside a classroom. I started thinking about my dad and how, if I had been taking the Adderall instead of selling it, it would've been me in the nurse, instead of Oz, and he clearly just didn't care, as long as my grades were better.

As soon as I got into my room, I shut the door behind me

and jumped face first onto my bed. I laid there for a few minutes, struggling to breathe through the sheets and seeing how long I could last without having to come up for air. After a minute or so I sat up and found the remaining Adderall pills I had stashed up in this Advil bottle I kept locked in a drawer. I realized how self-absorbed I was, not wanting to take the pills myself because of how shitty they made *me* feel, but I had a guilt-free conscience making a profit at somebody else's mental and physical expense. Christ, as soon as I wrapped my head around that, I just wanted to throw myself out of the window. I figured Oz probably wouldn't snitch on me, because then *he'd* get in just as much trouble as *I* would, but *still,* that didn't make me feel any better.

"Alex?" a robotic voice called out.

Without even turning around I instantly realized who it was. Fergus was this obnoxious, yet completely harmless weirdo who had moved around the world like crazy when he was growing up, so he was mediocre in about four languages, but not perfect in any one of them. I always felt sorry for him when I could tell he was struggling to express himself but, naturally, he was the most proficient in English. A lot of the guys in the home often got annoyed over his undoubtedly autistic tendencies, but he was a nice kid, and I didn't mind him too much, only sometimes.

"Hey Fergus," I said absently, sitting up in my bed.

"Hello, Alex. I was wondering what you were doing," Fergus said, as he mechanically waltzed through the door and sat down in my chair, each arm at a perfect ninety-degree angle, with both palms placed flat atop his thighs.

"A bit tired. What've you been up to?"

"I—I was thinking: have you ever seen *Spider-Man 3*?"

"Yeah, why?"

"Me too."

73

"Cool. Why, you wanna watch it or something?"

"Watch what?"

"*Spider-Man 3.*"

"What about it?"

I began to rub the bridge of my nose, and sighed.

"Fergus, you just asked me if I've seen *Spider-Man 3*. Now I'm asking why you brought it up, if you didn't even wanna watch the movie in the first place"

"Oh. No, I just wanted to know if you'd seen it."

I'd really love to know what the hell went on in that brain of his.

"Okay, Fergus," I said, shaking my head.

He did brighten my mood though, quite a lot actually. I had felt so damn shitty before he came in, I seriously think I might've thrown myself out of the window had he waited just another minute or so.

"Well, Alex, unfortunately I can't stick around and chat forever," Fergus said as he abruptly stood up and made his way to the door, avoiding eye contact, as usual.

But right as Fergus reached for the door handle, our prefects, Klaus and Giles, kicked open the door, slamming Fergus in the nose, sending him tumbling backwards into my room. Klaus was this half-German weasel with an overbite that made it look like he was sucking on his bottom lip at all times, and Giles had worse teeth than Austin Powers, but had long, thick hair that he was convinced made him look like a young Mick Jagger, which couldn't have been further from the truth. In my first week at Durnford I had been sent to town to buy cigarettes for Klaus and when they didn't have the brand he requested, he locked me in the freezing cellar for three hours, making sure I didn't have a jacket with me, or anything else, to keep warm. When he finally

74

let me out, he made me learn, and then recite, the entirety of *Childe Harold's Pilgrimage* by Lord Byron in front of all the seniors in my dorm, and for every word I got wrong I had to drink a glass of mustard, raw eggs, and spoiled milk. If I felt like I was going to puke, they made me puke in the pitcher from where I was drinking, and then drink everything all together—it took four hours before I could get it all down. Every morning at breakfast, Fergus would have to recite all the current events from The Wall Street Journal and butter Giles' toast, and if he stumbled over anything—which he often did—he would be asked to *'see them after dinner.'*

"Well, well, well," Giles began humming maliciously. "Fancy finding you up here, Fergie. But, my, how strange, because, if my memory serves me right, earlier today, after breakfast, you were instructed to be in your room this evening in order for us to correct your inability to remember current events. But now I find myself at a loss, because this morning you clearly complied, and yet, *now* you've shown a com*plete* disregard for a very simple set of instructions, as I find you in Alex's room as opposed to your own. Would you please care to explain yourself?" Giles continued, slithering around my room with his hands clasped behind his back.

"B-b-but you said it was after dinner, and w-we haven't eaten yet," Fergus stuttered, sweat rapidly beading across his forehead.

Suddenly, Giles snapped and quickly spun around, with his greasy hair falling in front of his face. "Are you talking back to your *prefect?*"

"No, no, of course not I just—"

"—Hey, marmite breath," I barked. Giles and Klaus both turned to me. "Leave him alone."

Giles' demeanor completely shifted, a wry grin stretching across his face.

"Ah, Alexander," he snorted. "You pathetic little turd."

"Listen, if I throw a Rolex down the stairs, will you two just fuck off," I said, straightening myself up.

"Judging by those trainers, I doubt a Rolex is in your price range," Klaus snickered.

Giles laughed and began clicking his tongue, waving his bony little finger at me. "Poor old Alexander," he hummed. "Still intoxicated with delusions of adequacy," followed by a long sigh. "How much punishment must you endure before the rules of this institution finally cement themselves in that thick skull of yours? I know you think you're such a bloody rogue, but, trust me when I tell you, that you are nothing more than a repugnant little pest."

"Do you have any hobbies besides jerking off to a thesaurus all day?"

"Allow me to translate," Klaus growled. "You're a cunt."

"Well, you are what you eat," I said. "But, if my breath stinks, it's only because Giles' mom doesn't shower too often and..."

Giles lunged forward and pounced on me, fists flying down from above, striking my arms repeatedly; shocks of pain coursing through my entire body. He must've continued for close to a minute until, finally, panting, he sat up and got off of me.

"*Man*," I chuckled. "It's clearly not just the women who like being on top in your family," I said as I sat up. Without turning his head, Giles swung his arm around and cracked me across the cheek with the back of his hand, his signet ring slicing my lip, which almost knocked me over.

"You little American cunt, shut up!" he shouted. "Shut up, shut up, shut up!" Finally, I did, as I was distracted by the taste of blood pooling inside my lower lip, but when my eyes came back into focus, I saw Fergus on all fours, oinking like a pig, with Klaus straddling his back, laughing and spanking him.

"On we go, piggy, on we go," he kept repeating, as Fergus struggled to move below him. Giles and Klaus were both in hysterics, and suddenly I felt my body begin to shake. I stood up and, as if in slow motion, my body lifted off the ground with my hands stretched out in front of me and I felt them clasp around Giles' throat, the two of us tumbling to the floor, his head hitting the corner of my bookshelf. Then everything went quiet.

Klaus yelped in terror before throwing himself to Giles' side, and then he turned back to me and cried, "Look what you've done! You foolish cunt! You could've killed him!" He began shaking Giles' limp body, his voice trembling, "Giles! Giles!" Then he turned back to me, "The headmaster will hear about this, a-a-and you'll be expelled!" he squealed, but my body was still shaking, and then I stood up and began moving towards him.

"Klaus," I said, as I felt my clenched fists begin to vibrate. I almost needed to stabilize myself because my whole body was shaking so much. "If you don't leave my room right now, I'm going to hurt you," I said, inching closer. Klaus began to sniffle, as he continued shaking Giles.

"Do you have any idea what you've done," he whimpered under his breath. "Do you have any idea the trouble you've just made for yourself, you arrogant fool. You have no idea the world of pain you've just brought down upon your thick head."

I kneeled down and leaned my face right next to his. I felt his breathing grow heavy.

"You don't know pain, Klaus," I whispered. "You think you do, but you don't. But I can tell you something," I thought I was going to be sick. "*I do*," my fingers tightened around his wrist.

"And if you two don't get out of my room right now, I promise I'm gonna share it with you."

Suddenly, Giles let out a loud groan, and a gasp of relief escaped Klaus' mouth as he immediately began to hoist Giles up to his feet, throwing his arm over his shoulder. Giles let out another loud, clumsy groan and his eyes slowly opened, and I saw him glance around my room in total confusion. Before he left, Klaus said he was going to tell Vera about this, but I rolled up my sleeves and showed him the countless bruises on my arms, and that immediately shut him up.

I sat down on my bed and tried to slow down my breathing, noticing that my entire body was red and covered in goosebumps.

Fergus was sitting in my chair staring into his lap, his hands shamefully pressed in between his thighs.

"Are you okay?" I asked.

Fergus nodded.

I stood up and put the fallen books back on my shelf, before turning back to Ferus.

"Do you wanna watch *Spider-Man 3*, later?"

He looked up at me and nodded again, his nervous eyes saying thank you as best as he could.

Fergus quickly stood up and ran out of my room, and I sat there idly for a few minutes, staring into nothing, before Patrick walked in, carrying his school books under his arm.

"You alright, Walter Mitty?"

"Huh?" I asked, still dazed.

"You're just staring into space," he chuckled.

"Oh," I said, shaking out of it. "Nothing. Just…Giles and Klaus."

"Ah," he grimaced. "Ugly bastards." He paused. "You wanna watch the footy later? Or, sorry, soccer," he mocked, in his best American accent.

"I said I'd watch a movie with Fergus"

As great as Patrick was, he couldn't stand Fergus, so I knew he wouldn't want to join us. We had a pretty decent sized TV in this games room we had on the second floor, but we also had this massive old pool table that was always being occupied so paying attention to the TV was impossible whenever that was going on.

Fergus would always make about a pound of popcorn, and the smell would stink up the entire dorm. Vera would always ask him to keep the windows open when he was making it, but I swear that kid had the memory of a squirrel with Alzheimer's, so he never did.

Patrick grinned and rolled his eyes, "Good luck."

Fergus was one of those guys who was kind of like a dog: he would always make mistakes and always do and say clumsy things, but no matter how hard you tried to discipline him, it just never worked. All you could do with a guy like Fergus was to just accept his flaws, and love him for the childish dog that he was. Once, on a night back in my first year, we had all been drinking out in the woods with a couple of girls from some of the other dorms. Everybody was pretty drunk, but Fergus had been pounding more shots than anyone, and by the end of the evening he was knocking on the gates of death. We managed to carry him back to his room quietly enough so that Vera, or any of the night guards, didn't hear, but the next morning his roommate came running out of their room screaming. Immediately we all freaked out because we thought Fergus had choked on his vomit and died in his sleep, or something, but, really, he had just thrown up and shit himself, and was now obliviously snoring in a big pool of shit and vomit. The smell of that room for the next few weeks

was something for the record books, I swear. His roommate—
some wormy kid who was always computer gaming, and smelled
like sunscreen even in the middle of winter—had to sleep on this
thin, prison-like mattress in *my* room until the stench finally
disappeared. That story always cracks me up every time I think
about it. Good old Fergus: shitting his pants and making popcorn,
without a care in the world.

After dinner I asked Fergus if he had any popcorn and he said no
so I said I was going to walk into town and asked if he wanted to
come along but he said he had to finish some very important
errands in his room before '*the sun sets*'—even though it was
already well after dark—so I grabbed my coat and decided to
walk down by myself. The little town by my school wasn't so
much a town as it was a village, but I actually really liked it; a
complete contrast to the chaos of Los Angeles. Old brick
buildings and army barracks; symmetrical houses, each with an
identical chimney sprouting from the roof; little old ladies
walking their dogs that looked to be the same age as them, and at
the end of the so-called 'high-street', there was an eroded little
pub where old alcoholics would drink their sorrows away and
watch soccer and miserably complain about the parliament to
anyone who could be bothered to listen. After dinner you'd
always run into other kids heading into town too, most of them
usually doing the same thing I was doing—buying snacks for a
movie night back at their dorm—but you hardly ever ran into
anyone worth talking to, as it was always some weird kid you
barely knew, who'd try and hijack you into conversation about
some boring topic that you really had no interest in: '*Do you
watch How I Met Your Mother?*' No.

I was standing in one of the aisles of the modest corner shop with blinding, fluorescent lights shining down from above, and when I turned around, I saw Bardot, also completely alone, standing at the end of the aisle.

"Bardot?" I called out. Her hair was poking out from beneath a thick, wool hat with a ball of white fluff on top.

"Hello, Alexander," she said, clearly surprised to see me too. "Movie night?" she asked, eyeing the bag of popcorn kernels in my hand.

"Oh, uh—" I stuttered. "Yeah, sort of."

"Anything good?"

"Uhm," I lightly shook my head. "Not really. This guy I live with—he's nice, but kinda weird—wanted to watch *Spiderman 3,* so I'm getting us some popcorn."

"Oh," she smiled. "How ro*mantic.*"

"Yup. Nothing screams romance like two guys watching Spiderman together." She laughed. "What are *you* getting?" I asked.

"What I'm *getting* is a bit of a cold. So, I'm buying some ginger," she said, holding up a large ginger root in her hand.

"Why don't you get some LemSip, or cough syrup?"

She laughed and shook her head disapprovingly.

"You Americans...you think pills and potions solve everything."

"I didn't mean it like *that,* but it *does* help," I said, almost defensively.

"Well, *Doctor Lexington,* I guess I'll just have to suffer."

"Hey, wait...how'd you know my last name?"

Bardot grinned, and walked off towards the check-out counter. I quickly followed her.

"Seriously," I said, catching up. "How'd you know that?"

As she was handing the clerk her money, she craned her head over her shoulder, "When you left class after your little fight today, I walked over to your desk and saw your paper, and you'd written your name."

"Oh," I mumbled. She began to leave, so I quickly paid for the popcorn and left, the cold air biting into my cheeks as I stepped outside.

"Uhm," I awkwardly began, after I'd caught up to her. "I hope you don't think I'm some lunatic after that."

She smirked. "Well, I think *every*one thinks you're a lunatic after today."

I hung my head in embarrassment, "Yeah, that makes sense."

"May I ask why he hit you?"

"Uhm," I began, no clue what the hell I was going to say. "Basically," her eyes caught mine, awaiting an answer. "I don't know, really," I said, fumbling the words. "Basically, so, I borrowed a PlayStation controller from Oz a few weeks ago and I haven't given it back and he really wanted it back, but now Patrick—the guy who lives next door to me—brought it back to London and so he got super pissed and hit me," I said, instantly realizing how pathetic that lie sounded.

"So," she paused. "When he found out you'd lent his controller to someone else, he decided to punch you?" she asked, clearly unconvinced.

"Well, okay, no, not entirely, I— "

"—*Alex*," she interrupted.

"Yes?" I asked, our eyes meeting.

"If it's something you don't want to tell me, you don't have to. I'm just some girl you barely know."

"Well...I don't know you yet," I blurted. She blushed and

quickly turned from me, and I saw her smile discreetly as she tried to bury her face into her scarf.

We reached the school entrance at the bottom of the hill, and she turned and asked which dorm I lived in.

"I live all the way at the top in Highland," I said. "What about you?"

"I'm in Deerfield," she replied. Deerfield house was in the complete opposite direction, and then I felt sad because I suddenly realized that our conversation was now going to end.

"Oh," I said, my tone dropping. "I guess that means goodbye."

"For now," she smiled. "Stay out of trouble and give Spiderman a kiss from me."

"I'll try. I hope you feel better."

"So do I. Good night, Alexander."

"Good night, Bardot."

She lingered for a second, smiling, before turning around and heading towards Deerfield, her blonde hair reflecting off of the street lamps before the night eventually swallowed her.

Stepping foot inside Highland was like walking into a wall of hot air, so I quickly unbuttoned my parka and took off my hat, and Vera peaked her head out of her office as I walked past.

"Sasha! You go to town? You not get cigarettes?" she asked in her thick Russian accent.

"I don't smoke," I said. "You know that."

"Ah, yes, yes," she said proudly. "Only boy at Durnford who do not smoke! So, what you get?"

I held up the bag. "Popcorn."

"Ah, yes." Then, suddenly, "Your smile! It is *big!* What is happened?" she said, inspecting my face.

"What? It is?" I blushed. "No, it's *not*."

"Sasha..." she began, shaking her head. "I work at school *many* years. I take care of many boys and I am mother to three sons, all many years older than you. You tink I do not know? I *know*. I know when smile is more big than normal," she paused. "And there is only one reason when boy have big smile, and tonight you have big, *big* smile," she said, triumphantly tilting her head to the side. "So...who she is?"

"Well," I surrendered. "I don't know, really. I just met her today."

"*Ahhh*," she began in singsong. "So, what her name is?"

"Bardot."

"She is *French*?" she looked suddenly disappointed.

"I actually don't know...I haven't asked, but I don't think so."

"She is *pretty*?"

"Yeah," I paused, an image of Bardot in her furry hat staring back at me.

"*Yeah*," she said, trying to mimic my American accent. "You are good boy, Sasha..." she paused, "...But if you make *popcorn*, you tell Fergus to *keep-window-open*! It always is smell *too* much! Everybody go crazy!"

"Okay, don't worry," I laughed, and then I headed upstairs to my room to drop off my coat.

As I was about to leave my room I remembered the Adderall, so I unlocked my drawer and took the Advil bottle with me and walked over to the bathroom and poured the rest of the pills down the toilet. I thought about Oz, and although it was relieving to know that nobody else would become victim to these pills like him, I swear, it felt like I was flushing pure money down the toilet when I saw each one of those blue little pills swirl down the drain. I had already made a pretty decent amount of cash that I had saved, but still, I won't lie and say that it didn't sting knowing that that would be the end of that income.

When I got to Fergus' room, he was sitting comfortably in these *Doctor Who* pyjama bottoms that he always minced around in, eating popcorn out of what wasn't so much a bowl as it was a bucket, even though he had said earlier that he didn't have any, but I couldn't get mad at him. He had already started the movie, naturally, but I didn't mind, because I just liked looking at him eating his popcorn and watching a movie *that* bad with so much enthusiasm. In a strange way, it was comforting to know that all the things that mattered to me would probably never be of much importance to Fergus, and the only things that mattered to him were if you were kind and wanted to watch a movie together every once in a while. You know, after I sat down, I even leaned over and hugged him. Real long and hard, too, but I don't think he noticed.

VI

Christmas was coming up, and I was anxiously wrapping my head around the fact that I was going to have to go home to California for the first time in nearly two years. You may be wondering why I hadn't gone home earlier, or something, but honestly it was my choice. My dad and Esmeralda had a kid or two, I think, and I hadn't really spoken to my mom for the last six months, so God knows what she was getting up to. The last two summers I had spent with Patrick and his family in London, or at their summer house in Wiltshire. As for what I did during the winter, Chilly's parents had both died in a car crash about five years ago so he spent holidays and stuff with his cousins, who he despised, so instead he and I spent Christmas together in his old house that he used to live in with his family when they were still alive. His aunt had tried to sell it but he managed to keep it for himself, but since it was just him in that big, old house, he asked me to spend Christmas with him. We wouldn't really do much, we'd just sit in his living room and watch movies and order Dominos. But sometimes, at night, he'd ask to sleep in my bed, saying that it was too hard to sleep in his room because it smelled like his mom; but in the mornings, if I ever asked him about her, he'd always switch the subject and ask if I wanted to go shooting.

My dad had called me up a few days earlier and told me that it was time I came back to L.A. and that he missed me, a comment which really took me by surprise, but as soon as I heard Esmeralda yapping in the background my whole body began to ache, and any traces of optimistic nostalgia instantly vanished. I also had this huge project coming up that I hadn't even started, and it was only about four days until I had to leave, and I get really stressed in those kinds of situations because I don't know what to pack and I don't know what to expect when I arrive, and all that crap was really messing with my head.

Remember how I told you my window overlooked that big grassy field? Well, despite the angst I was feeling, I had bought these Christmas candles from a little shop in town that I had put up in my windowsill so that when I opened my window, the light illuminated the snow falling from the sky. I'm not usually one for all that '*Sur La Tablé*' bullshit, but I have to admit I was pretty chuffed with the way my investment had turned out. They had this really nice scent too, and oddly enough it reminded me of my mom. The last few years before I left for England, I didn't see her much, and now I hadn't even spoken to her in over six months, but the smell reminded me of a time before my parents' divorce, when we'd celebrate Christmas together and my mom would always set up these candles on the windowsill of this crumby little apartment we used to live in, on Venice Boulevard down in west Los Angeles. It's weird, but the best memories I have of my parents being together are all from when we had almost no money, and they were struggling just to pay rent for this one-bedroom apartment with tiles falling off in the bathroom, and crackheads screaming outside my window during all hours of the night. Then one day my dad finally made it big, and overnight we went from oatmeal for dinner, to two BMW's and a house with a pool, in Malibu. I was so used to sleeping on a floor mattress in my parent's bedroom until I was like ten years old, so even when we moved and I got my own room and a king-sized bed with a plasma screen glued to the wall, I still insisted on sleeping on the floor in my parent's bedroom. I didn't even have a mattress any more, I slept straight on the hardwood floor and they'd ask me what the hell was wrong with me, but I didn't care.

Anyway, I was sitting there looking out the window thinking about my mom, when I heard a knock on the door.

"Come in!" I yelled.

"Alexander?"

Without looking, I recognized the voice instantly.

"*Bardot?*" I asked, confused, turning around in my chair. "What're *you* doing here?"

She laughed, "Should I leave?"

"No, no! Please...stay," I blurted. "I just...I wasn't expecting you. You didn't...I mean...*well*...I feel kinda bad cos it's messy and...*wait*...who told you where I live?"

"Well, *you* did," she laughed.

"I did?"

"The other night you said you lived in Highland."

"*Oh*... yeah, maybe I did."

She sat down on the little couch I had and crossed her legs and brushed her hair behind her ears with both hands. Her hair just barely draped over her shoulders, and she had these dark, black nails that kind of contradicted her otherwise fairly preppy demeanor. I couldn't tell you why, but I'm the biggest sucker for black nail polish.

She began glancing around my room observantly, "You know, it's actually not as messy as I expected it to be."

"You thought it was gonna be messy?"

"A little bit," she shrugged with a giggle. "...but that's a good thing. It means you're not boring."

"Well, *that's* a relief to hear."

We sat in silence for a while, and I watched her observe all the stuff in my room, wondering what she was thinking about when she saw everything. I had never had a girl in my room before because it always felt way too personal letting someone enter my own fortress of solitude, a place where I'd immediately be judged on where I placed things, how I organized stuff, what books I read, what I had on my shelves, and I always felt like I had to entertain, like I had to make sure whoever was inside wasn't bored, or else they'd judge me even more, like walking into a museum after having paid the expensive entry fee, only to be disappointed by what you find inside.

"So...what've you been up to today?" I asked abruptly, not being able to stand the silence anymore.

She jerked her head, as if I'd interrupted a dream. "Oh, nothing really. Just packing. Almost finished with that Freud project. How's it going for you?"

"Yeah, I'm almost done with that too, I just have like, another page or so, to write," I lied. I had pretty much forgotten that it was even *on* Freud until she told me right then and there. I think she could tell though, because as soon as I said it she raised her eyebrows at me.

"That's good. Will you be spending Christmas with William again this year?"

"With *Will*—oh, *Chilly,* " I laughed. "No, I'm not. But, *wait,* how'd you know that?"

"He told me," she smirked.

"He *told* you? How'd you guys get on that subject?"

"I saw him today at lunch and we spoke for a bit. I asked what he usually does for the holidays, and he told me, but he wasn't sure what your plans were yet. He said he hadn't spoken to you."

"*Oh*. Oh, yeah. No, I uh…I gotta go home. Back to uhm…to California."

"You don't seem too excited."

"What? No, no. I am," but even *I* could hear the dishonesty in my tone. "I just haven't been back in a while, so it's gonna be kinda weird I guess."

"You don't like California?"

"No, no. I do. I dunno why I sounded so…I dunno, so *miserable*, when I said it."

"Hmm," she said.

"What?"

"You made the same face when you told me why that boy hit you. But at least *now* I know everything *else* you've told me is true," she smiled. I tried to hide my embarrassment, but she just laughed, "It's okay, Alexander. Just like I told you; you don't have to tell me everything."

"Well, it's not that I'm *hiding* something. It's just…I dunno. I guess it's because I haven't been back in so long, and I'm a bit nervous about going back to a place where I don't have the best memories from."

"Is that why you came here?"

"Yeah, I guess so."

"Well," she paused, "I'm happy you did."

I tried to conceal my smile. "So, what about you, where're you going?"

"Back to Sweden."

"Ah, so *that's* where you're from. I thought you might be French because of the name, but you don't *sound* very French… *plus* you're not an asshole."

She laughed, "Well, I'm delighted to hear that. But you're

right, the name *is* French. My mother was driving when her water broke, and Brigitte Bardot was playing when it happened, so that's where she got it from."

"Do you like Brigitte Bardot?"

"Do *you*?" she asked, taken aback.

"Why, do I seem like I wouldn't?"

"Well," she said, pointing to the posters on my wall. "I don't know who *they* are, but they look a bit angrier than Brigitte Bardot."

"That's presumptive," I said. "They're actually a Brigitte Bardot cover band."

"Really?" she asked, surprised.

"Nope, but at least now I know how gullible you are."

"Oh, shut up," she stuck her tongue out at me.

"So…" I began, after she had resumed her scanning of my room. "Are you fully Swedish then?"

"Well, I'm a bit of a mutt, really," she said, seesawing her head from side to side. "I don't really know my father, but my mom is Swedish, and I've grown up with her."

"Oh," I said. "I'm sorry to— "

"—Alex*ander*," she interrupted. "Don't be. I have had a wonderful life, so the only one missing out is him," she said proudly.

"That's a positive way to see things."

"The world is already filled with so much negativity, so what's the point of complaining and making it worse?"

"I'm kind of embarrassed now," I said, blushing.

"Why?"

"I feel like I can be pretty negative."

"Don't worry," she said, smirking. "Boys are always a bit

slower, but you'll learn."

Then she said something that I didn't hear.

"What?" I asked.

"How long is your *flight*?"

"Oh, uh, like…eleven hours I think."

"Oh, wow. That's a long time. I've never been on a plane for that long before."

"Yeah, it can get pretty boring, but I usually stay up all night before, so then I can just sleep the entire flight."

"Ah, that's very smart!" she said. I thought about asking her something, but I stopped myself because I didn't want to ruin it—it was just nice feeling her presence in my room.

"So, what're you wearing to the dance?" she asked suddenly.

"The dance?"

I totally forgot—the *dance*.

Every year, the juniors and seniors get this big Cinderella ball dance, and as soon as it's announced it's the only thing anybody talks about right up until it happens. I remember Patrick brushing it by me a few times, but now that I had been stressing over going back to L.A. and this stupid project I had completely forgot.

"Yes, the *ball*," Bardot said, raising her eyebrows.

"Oh, I'm not sure yet. Probably just my tuxedo, I guess. What about you?"

"I've been looking at dresses online, but I haven't decided what to get yet. I've found a few pretty ones but I'm not sure if I'd look good in them."

"I'm sure you'd look good in anything," I said. She blushed and started looking around my room again.

"How long are you away for?"

"In California?" She nodded. "Not that long. Like, two weeks."

"I've never been before."

"To California?"

"To America," she replied, with a bashful smile.

"*Really? Never?*"

She shrugged, "Nope."

"Well...the only thing you're *really* missing out on is *In N Out*, everything else is propaganda."

"What's that?"

"It's a hamburger chain. They're really good."

"Like McDonald's?" she said, her face souring.

"*No. Much* better than McDonald's. They only have them in California, they're the best burgers you'll ever eat in your life, I promise."

"Hm..." she tilted her head and looked at me. "So, you live in the most famous city in the entire world, but the only good thing about it is hamburgers?"

"Well, *no.* We have other stuff."

"Like what?"

"Like...good weather and...the beach."

She laughed. "Well since I *have been to a beach before*, I guess I better go just to try this in and..." she scrunched her eyebrows, and looked to me for an answer.

"*Out,*" I added.

"In and *out.*"

Then she grabbed the framed photo of Beau, Ocean and I, and pointed to my long hair. "And who told you *this* was a good idea?"

"Shut up, I was cool."

"*Cool?* No comment," she smirked. "Are you excited to see your parents?" she asked, putting it down.

"Sort of, I guess."

"Sort of?" she turned to me with a look of concern.

"Well," I hesitated. "My mom's dead."

She gasped. "Oh… Alex," she said tenderly.

"It's okay, it's not a big deal. But now it's just me and my dad," I said as vaguely as possible.

"When did she die?"

"A while ago. She was sick, and there was nothing we could do."

"My mom's sick too."

"Really?"

"I'm not sure what the name is in English, but it's something to do with your liver," she paused. "She used to drink a lot after my father left."

"Does she still drink?"

"She says she doesn't, but sometimes I'll find half empty bottles around the house. She says they're not hers, but there's nobody else living there," she shook her head. "So, I don't know who else they would belong to," she paused, and rolled her eyes. "She's the kind of person who will pretend to fall down the stairs, and then tell people she's in too much pain to even walk."

"My mom would do that too," I chuckled.

"Really?"

"When I was a kid, she said she got some weird illness and didn't leave her bed for months. So many doctors came over to check on her and they all said there was nothing wrong with her, but she'd just scream at them to get out, and tell them they didn't know what it was like being a mother."

We both started laughing.

"Once my mom burnt her tongue from a coffee at McDonald's, and she made me help her research how to sue them, because she saw it in a movie and thought they'd have to give her a million dollars," Bardot said, in between giggling. "Her friends finally got her to stop trying, saying that stuff like that only works in America."

"It probably would've," I laughed. "America's pretty gnarly. You can sue anyone for anything."

"*Gnarly?*" she tilted her head.

"Gnarly...it means uh, well," I paused. "It's a very Malibu word. It just means like...I dunno, *intense*, I guess? Like, *those waves were gnarly,* or, if a test really sucked, you could say, *that test was gnarly.*"

Bardot smiled at me and exhaled through her nose.

"*Gnarly,*" she repeated. "That's fun to say."

"One step closer to being a true Malibu local."

"I guess I just need to get a head scarf like you had in that photo."

"Yeah...except we call them *bandanas.*"

Bardot mockingly rolled her eyes and tried to imitate my American accent, "*Bandanas.*"

She turned away from me and began flipping through a book off of my shelf.

"But the thing about my mother," she began again. "Is that many people think she is exaggerating to make it seem worse than it is."

"Why would she do that?"

"Well, in Sweden you get money from the state if you are sick or handicapped. So, many people think she is abusing the system."

"What do *you* think?"

She took a deep breath, looking guilty over whatever it was she was thinking.

"All I know is that I try to be honest, and I'm not sure she can say the same," she paused. "Are you honest?"

"Well," I swallowed. "I think so."

"Good," she smiled. "Honesty is all we have."

Then, just as we were staring at each other, the fucking dinner bell echoed throughout the entire house. Bardot jumped, and pulled out her phone to check the time.

"Oh my god, it's already dinner! They go crazy if we're late!"

Without another word, she grabbed her coat and bolted out my room so quickly that I didn't even have a chance to say goodbye. When she left, I looked around and almost felt like I had woken up from a dream, or something. The anxiety housed inside me at all times had suddenly disappeared and, for once, I felt calm. I heard her footsteps slapping against the ground outside, and I rushed over to my window so that I could see her running back to her dorm. The dinner bell rang again, but all I did was write a note and taped it to the front of my door, saying I was sick and shouldn't be disturbed. Vera was always super cautious about that kind of stuff, and if you had one of those notes on your door you could literally stay locked in there for a week, and nobody would check on you out of fear of getting sick since everybody lived so intimately in one big building. After I taped the note to my door, I went and laid down on my bed and wished how the dinner bell hadn't rung so that I could've had just one more minute alone with Bardot talking about nothing.

* * *

The next day after class our home had a soccer match against Bulworth house in the pouring rain. There were always at least two guys in every dorm who were convinced they were the next Ronaldo, and took those games so damn seriously it made you want to throw up. If anyone even made the slightest foul they would scream at the ref and have a complete meltdown unless a point was deducted from the other team. During my first year I loved going down to the games to support my dorm because showing any school spirit was a foreign concept back home in Malibu, so I loved screaming and shouting and wearing our home colors and showing my enthusiasm. But now, nearly two years later, I couldn't stand the games, especially soccer, since it was outside, and England isn't exactly known for its Caribbean climate.

I could never keep track of all the kids and what dorms they lived in, but that day I instantly realized it was Bulworth House when I saw all the kids walking onto the field. Aside from Chilly, Arthur and Eliot, everyone in Bulworth straight up sucked. They had this half-English, half-Russian, truffle face named Norman Samson who was probably the worst kid you'd ever meet in your life. I think he had more Armani clothes than Armani himself, and he wore these pointy Gucci sneakers with Velcro that he pampered with such delicateness you'd think he'd given birth to the shoes himself.

Norman was out on the field, and any opportunity he got, he'd rip his shirt off and run around jumping and throwing himself into his teammates; it really made you gag. Norman worked out a lot, but only his upper body, so he looked like one of those swollen guys you see down at Muscle Beach in Venice, who are so bulky that they have to answer their phone with the opposite hand, because they've gotten so big that they can't even touch their own shoulders because of how stiff they are. Poor guy.

It was really pouring down, and Patrick and I were standing in these school raincoats that we were forced to wear at all the games, shivering like crazy.

"Mate, when's this over?" Patrick asked.

"I dunno, when someone wins?"

"Ah," he sighed, rolling his eyes. "Splendid."

I was looking down at the field, trying to forge an interest, when suddenly I saw Oz snag the ball and start dribbling it down the field. Although it had only been less than a week since our stint at the nurse, he already looked much better. He even scored a goal. Oz was jumping and laughing, and I don't think I'd ever seen him look that genuinely happy before.

Patrick started nudging me, "Mate, isn't that Ozzy?"

"Yeah!" I said, equally surprised.

"Didn't he dust you up a few days ago?"

I nodded, "Yeah! But it's okay, I deserved it," I said, realizing how enthusiastic I sounded.

Patrick just laughed, and for the first time since my first year there, I got really eager to watch the rest of the game. I even rooted for Oz who was on the opposite team, but I didn't cheer out loud since I didn't want Klaus or Giles to hear me.

After the game, I ran up to Oz and congratulated him on how well he played. He looked pretty shocked to see me, almost scared even, but I told him it was fine and there were no hard feelings.

"Mate, genuinely," he said shamefully, looking down. "I'm so sorry about hitting you."

He apologized over and over for hitting me, but I told him

that it was my fault, and that I was almost bummed he hadn't hit me harder. After a minute or two of convincing, he finally caved, and hugged me, which came as a surprise, but I hugged him back. He told me he had realized how shitty those pills made him feel now that he didn't have any left, and how he had begun playing soccer again every day after school and felt like this giant weight had been lifted off his shoulders. We stood there, alone in the rain for at least fifteen minutes, just laughing and talking shit, until we both began trembling and realized that we should probably get back to our dorms before one of us got hypothermia.

"I'll see you in class, mate," he called over his shoulder, as I watched him run off towards Bulworth.

* * *

A few days later, the same day of the ball, I was sitting in my room packing the last of my bags since I was leaving the next day. I looked at the photo that Bardot had been inspecting a few days prior, the black and white photo of Ocean, Beau and myself at the beach next to our surfboards and felt a sudden rush of melancholy. It's probably the only photo I've ever liked of myself, and I've kept it next to my bed ever since I got it framed. Ocean and Beau didn't have Facebook, so I hadn't really spoken to either of them at all since I came out to England. Ocean had texted me once on my English number asking when I was coming home, but after I texted him back, he never replied. I started to get really anxious thinking about having to see him again after all this time, and I really had no idea how he and Beau and everyone from back home was doing.

So, as I was throwing stuff into my suitcase, Klaus, Giles and Antoni Castellanos—this Greek midget who was prefect at

Bulworth—barged in through my door.

"Evenin' Alex," Giles hissed.

"Evenin' girls," I said. "Ah, Giles, so good to see you. Come to take another nap on the floor?" Giles snorted as he locked the door, the three of them slowly surrounding me.

"If you really want your prostates examined, can't you just do it yourselves? I would, but I just have so much packing to do, so I'm afraid I'm a bit short on time," I continued, as I resumed my packing. Klaus quickly snatched the back of my neck, his uncut nails digging into my throat, and slammed my forehead into the ground with a thud.

"Position!" he shouted. I tried to push my head back, but Giles kneed me in the ribs, completely knocking the wind out of me.

"Now, now Alex," Giles said, regaining his breath, brushing his hair back. "You have been a notoriously naughty boy as of late, and that is something that we simply cannot dismiss without proper correction," Giles continued, as he squatted down and craned his head right next to mine while Klaus kept my head firmly cemented to the floor. Giles let out a long, disapproving sigh. "Seeing as you, time and time again, refuse to obey the rules implemented by this institution, you have found yourself in a rather prickly situation. We have, as prefect and vice prefect, concluded that the only solution to your disdain for authority, your insubordination, as well as your misplaced sense of rebellion, will be as follows…"

Castellanos walked over to my bed and stripped one of my pillows and threw the case to Klaus who placed it over my head and tightly duct-taped it around my neck. I felt my hands and feet getting tied, and then I felt a shock of pain course through my entire midsection, and I started coughing.

"You're not so tough *now,* are you?" Giles howled.

"I can't hear you," I wheezed.

"What?" Giles said.

"I said I can't hear you. You've tied the pillowcase too tight. I can't hear anything you're saying."

"Well, take the bleeding thing off then, you imbecile," I heard Giles say to one of the others.

I felt fingers dig into the duct tape around my neck, struggling to rip it off. Finally, they managed, and everything came into focus, and I saw Giles an inch away from my face.

"There. *Now* can you hear—"

And then I spat him right in the face.

"Ugh!" He yelped. I started laughing and he wiped off the phlegm from his nose, turned back around and slapped me. I fell backwards and hit my head against the floor, and, after that, they didn't say anything. All I felt was my entire body going through a woodchipper. I wish I could tell you that I fought back, but it was three on one, so I didn't amount to much. Finally, the hitting stopped, and I heard them laughing as they got up, and I slowly opened my eyes and waited for them to refocus.

"What was it you said again, Alex? Something about *knowing pain,* and how you were going to *share it* with us?" Klaus said, with a sardonic laugh.

"Well, it appears it's been shared with *you* now, you thick-headed shit-sack," Giles said proudly.

I rolled over on my back, my hands still tied behind me, struggling to breathe.

"I'm gonna get you," I said, coughing.

"Oh, is that so?" Giles smirked.

"I'm gonna get you, man," I wheezed. *"That's* a promise."

"Oh, is it, *man?"* Giles mocked. "Is that a promise, *maaan?*

Scary! Isn't he, boys?" Giles said, and the three of them laughed. Giles kneeled down and placed his head next to mine. "You know something, Alex? I *do* admire the way you try. Pathetic, albeit rather valiant. Like a persistent little mutt, you are." He patted me on the head, stood back up, and let out a big sigh. "Now, hurry up untying yourself, and go serve me my dinner, you, measly little toad," he said, and gave me one last kick in the stomach.

The three of them walked out my room and slammed the door behind them. I laid there on the floor for a while, trying to regain my breath, and I could already feel the bruising start to form on my ribs and all I could think about was how sore I'd be on that exhausting flight all the way back to L.A.

As soon as I sat up and managed to untie my hands, Vera burst through my door, panting.

"Sasha!" she cried, trying to catch her breath. "You are in charge of dinner tonight!"

"I am?" I asked, confused. I really had no idea.

"*Da!* You must get down to kitchen and begin preparations! It is Christmas dinner tonight, you know this!"

"Shit," I muttered. "Okay. I'll be down in a sec," I said reassuringly. She smiled, relieved, and quickly booked it back down the stairs. I stood up and tried to shake my body loose from all the pain I was in, but it stuck to me like stink on shit.

The entire hallway was completely fogged up before I entered the kitchen, so I figured whoever had kitchen duty with me tonight had already started. I opened the door and was hit with a clammy burst of hot air; it felt like entering a sauna. I noticed the faucet screaming, and standing over by the refrigerator filling up pitchers with water was this ginger dude on the second floor named Edmond. He was a smart kid, but he was someone who, despite having lived under the same roof as him for almost two years, I still knew almost nothing about.

"Alex! Mate, I really need your help. If you could fill up the sauce bowls that'd be great, and then—" he got cut off by the sound of a bunch of pots and pans clanging together in the sink, but I felt like helping for once, so I obeyed his orders, and did what I could. It was a bitch trying to breathe, thanks to that beating I'd just endured, so moving at an even remotely quick pace, while trying to carry bulky containers of food, was harder than it should've been.

"Christ, Alex, I'm not asking much… but if you could, you know…speed things up a bit," Edmond begged.

"Sorry, man. But I just got my shit kicked in by Giles and the Third Reich," I said, and lifted up my shirt. It had only been about ten minutes, but you could already see the bruises starting to blossom across my pale torso like a Rorschach test. I showed him my arms too, which were all yellow, purple and gross.

"Shit! They did that just now?"

I nodded, wincing, and delicately pulled my shirt back down.

"Ah, shit, mate. That looks horrendous. If you need to sit down, and just relax, it's okay. I didn't know about that. Sorry for being snotty," he said. He was very considerate, Edmond. Looking back, I wish I'd spent more time with him.

"Dude, it's fine," I said with a laugh. "I don't need to sit down, I just wanted to show why I'm moving so slow."

"All right, mate. Well, like I said: if you need a break, just give us a shout."

"Actually, there is something that you could help me with."

Edmond paused, and his eyebrows suddenly crept up his forehead. "Sure, mate. Anything."

"If you could go watch the door for just a few seconds,

there's something I need to do."

Edmond didn't even hesitate, he just nodded, and walked over to the kitchen door and stood watch. We were serving some miserable excuse for a steak dinner with mashed potatoes topped with brown sauce that looked, and tasted, like wallpaper paste, but the seniors drank it like water. I walked into the corner, zipped down my fly, and began pulling myself off, aiming my dick into the bowl.

"Mate, you're *mad*!" Edmond gasped, cupping his mouth in shock.

"Shh, I can't focus when you're talking," I said, and continued tugging. I didn't even have to think about anything sexual, because as perverted as this sounds, the thought of what I was about to do was stimulating enough. Finally, it started to build, and then my legs began tensing up. Suddenly, I felt the primal clench of my jaw, and then it shot out of me and splashed into the bowl below. My butt cheeks clenched together, and I could feel my toes curling inside my shoes—it felt good.

"Yummy," I said to myself, and placed the bowl back on the counter. I began stirring it around and held up the spoon, and watched as drops of silvery, brown goop slowly parachuted back into the bowl with a small splash.

"Boys!" Vera shouted, as she opened the kitchen door, "You must bring out food now! Everybody waiting!"

"Cheers, Vera. We'll be out in a second," Edmond hollered, giggling, and then glanced back at me. "You absolute madman. How're you gonna pull this off, mate?"

"Don't worry."

Edmond and I loaded up the meal carts with all the food and began rolling them out to our dining room. Since it was supposed to be a 'formal' dinner, everybody was lined up outside the dining room dressed for the occasion: blazers, ties, ugly Christmas sweaters that weren't actually intended to be ugly, slacks, and loafers. Vera was doing some last-minute touch ups to the placemats and silverware when we came in and started laying out the separate trays on each table. By the time we finished setting everything it was getting so rowdy outside it sounded like they were about to kick the door down.

Patrick and I usually sat next to each other during dinner, and I'd always insist that Fergus sit at our table, too.

I couldn't help but overhear the urgency in the conversation between the two guys at the table next to us, Arthur Seaton and Georgie Phipps, both proud members of the debating society, and aggressively conservative, the former having asked me, on our first day of school, '*Where do you summer?*'

"How was Windsor?" Georgie asked.

"Ah, mate. Glorious," Arthur boasted. "Wall to wall with cunt."

"Any birds we know?"

"Gave Safa Jacobs a shag."

"*Safa Jacobs*?!" Georgie asked. "Mate, she is *mingin'*!"

"Oh, *fuck* off," Arthur Protested. "She's serviceable."

"Maybe like…*seven* pints in," he snickered through a mouthful of potatoes.

"Yeah, yeah. Only thing though, mate," he lowered his voice to a nervous whisper. "Actually, been rather anxious about this. Problem is, mate, she's half bloody *Paki*…and," his voice got even quieter, "I didn't wear a johnnie."

"You gave her the cream custard?" Georgie asked, highly amused.

"Can you stop taking the piss? I'm actually quite nervous.

105

You reckon she'd get herself pregnant?"

"Mate, you are *such* a bloody retard," Georgie began to laugh. "I take it you didn't inquire if she was on the pill before you dipped it in."

"Well, *I* don't fucking *know*, mate. You know what those bloody ragheads are like, with all their religious bullshit. It's probably against their religion or something. Like eating pork or taking a bloody shower."

"Ah, mate, you'll have a hairy little mini-Arthur, running around in a turban, calling your old man granddad," Georgie chuckled, his flabby chin slowly dissolving into his neck as he did. "Bet he'll be thrilled about that, mate."

"Mate, can you fuck off? If she finds out about my dad, and she's not on the pill, I'm *finished.* If I pollute the bloodline, he'll cut me off completely. I can kiss the trust good*bye!*" Arthur shouted so loud the whole room nearly went quiet. I turned to Patrick and shook my head.

"That boy Seaton is the bloody antichrist, mate," Patrick muttered under his breath. "If that girl *does* end up getting pregnant, I'm sure his dad'll have her murdered like they did Diana."

Everybody at our table was talking about their plans for break and if they were taking any vacations with their families ("You'll be in Bad-Gastein too, then?"), and what they had wished for Christmas ("I reckon the Submariner would be the best long-term investment") and all that. Fergus had brought a notepad to dinner and was just rewriting the number two in a blue marker over and over again and hadn't touched his food or spoken to anybody the whole night. I thought it was pretty weird, but it was Fergus, and I had stopped asking questions a long time ago.

Then, just as planned, I heard Klaus shout out to me, "Alexander! Why is there no sauce at our table? It feels like I'm chewing on a brick!" I tried my best to look as unassumingly apologetic as possible, as I briskly walked over with my head low, and my hands clasped together at my waist.

"No sauce? Klaus, I am so, *so* sorry. Let me go get that for you immediately," I said theatrically, and hurried out to the kitchen. Sitting just where I'd left it, I whisked the sauce up with a fork so that it didn't look so separated, and then brought it back out to Klaus and placed it in front of him.

Klaus quickly flung his hands up in the air, "No, you mongoloid. *Pour* it!" he snapped and kicked me in the shin.

"Of course, of course. So sorry," I winced, and began pouring, submerging everything on his plate.

"*Garçon*, some for me too," Giles added, as he, too, discreetly kicked me in the shin under the table. After I poured his, I went back and sat down at my own table next to Patrick and Edmond and, after I watched Giles, Klaus, and the rest of the table put that first bite into their mouth, I told Patrick what I had done and I swear he started gagging so hard I thought he was going to puke all over the table. It's a funny thing, too, because although this happened so long ago, I don't think that feeling of personal triumph will ever be topped. A couple of sadistic brats like those two, who got off on beating younger kids, will probably have a nice future working for their dad's company in Switzerland, or something, and they'll approach everybody else in life with the same dismissive arrogance they developed during their years at boarding school, yet no matter how much success they achieve in the future, they'll go through life completely oblivious to the fact that some kid spoon fed them his own jizz for Christmas.

* * *

Patrick and I were getting ready in my room—for the ball, that is—and I, for the life of me, couldn't figure out how to tie this stupid-ass bowtie. I must've watched forty different videos on YouTube on how to do it, but every dude explaining it went from step 1 to 'completely finished' in about 3.5 seconds, making it damn near impossible to follow anything he was doing because it was too fucking fast. Patrick ended up having to help me, and when I looked in the mirror afterwards, I was actually quite impressed. He grew up in Knightsbridge, though, so what can you expect? I'm sure he learned how to tie a bowtie before he even learned how to wipe his own ass.

My nausea started creeping up on me again, as I began to realize my journey to L.A. was just a few hours away, but the abrupt sound of Patrick chanting interrupted my depressing reverie, and I turned around to see him holding a pretentious looking whiskey bottle above his head. He kicked the cap off and began pouring it down his throat. He finally set the bottle down and let out a long, gratifying sigh.

"Mate, what's wrong?" he asked suddenly, wiping his mouth with his expensive coat sleeve.

"What," I said, surprised.

"Mate, you look like you're about to top yourself. What is it?"

"*What*? No, I don't..." I paused. "*Do* I?"

"You're sitting completely deflated like some depressed orangutan. What's'a mattuh?" he stuttered, noticeably a bit drunk.

"I swear, dude, I'm fine," I replied, my tone hinting at my

desire to change the subject. He just raised his eyebrows at me, and continued chugging away. Even though I didn't want to talk about it, it always brightened my mood knowing that a guy like Patrick genuinely cared for me and wanted to know how I was doing. Not many people can say that about themselves. Most people ask how you're doing, just to segue back to themselves and talk about their *own* problems, instead of actually caring about what you have to say.

Fergus came waltzing into my room in this three-piece suit that was surprisingly tailored and well fitted for a guy as aesthetically inept as Fergus.

"Fergus, you look great, dude," I said, and patted him on the back. The sight of him immediately brightened my mood and I felt myself getting enthusiastic about the evening.

"I know," he said, as he straightened out his lapels and sat down. "This suit was very expensive."

"Fergus, ol' chap," Patrick began, slurring every word. "Gonna pull some birds tonight, mate?"

"I don't like the girls at this school. I think they're ugly and rude."

"Every girl is *ugly* and *rude*?" Patrick gasped. "Every single one?"

"Yes, which is why I'm saving myself."

"For who?" I asked.

"Kate Beckinsale." Patrick and I started laughing, but Fergus didn't even blink. "I know exactly where she lives, and I've looked up her hobbies and common interests on IMDB, and I have concluded that we would become great friends were we ever to meet, which we will, one day. After our friendship grows, I don't see any reason as to why I would not be able to make love to her. I am handsome by traditional standards, and this suit was very expensive, which is why I'm going to wear it when I meet her. She'll be very impressed, especially when I tell her everything I know about the *Underworld* franchise, and I also think I'd make a far better husband than Michael Sheen, who has a weird nose and looks like a ferret," he said robotically.

I loved his enthusiasm, even though it was a bit creepy, and I pitied Kate Beckinsale, or any other girl, Fergus fell in love with.

"Well, I think you're handsome as hell Fergie, and Kate would be lucky to have you," I said, as I rubbed his head.

"Thank you," he answered, and adjusted his glasses.

"Hey, tell Patrick that joke about the glasses you told me a few days ago," I said, with an encouraging pat on the shoulder. Patrick immediately put his bottle down and eagerly honed in on Fergus.

"Oh. *Right*. Well, the joke goes like this: I like my women how I like my glasses—sitting on my face," Fergus said, with a completely straight face, and Patrick laughed so hard that whiskey squirted from his mouth and hosed down half of my wall.

Archie had been texting Patrick and I all night—*"lads! Debrief!"*—but we told him we'd just meet him outside the entrance to make it easier. Chilly and the gang were almost always down in town at this pizza place called *Marty's*. I swear, Chilly must've spent close to five thousand pounds at that place by the time we graduated because he ate there so often. He even made a joke to the owner that he should get a pizza named after him and, believe it or not, the guy actually agreed to it. Funny thing though: Chilly is the pickiest guy I've ever met, and the only thing he ever ordered was cheese pizza, so they just renamed it *Chilly's Cheese*, with cheese pizza written next to it in parenthesis so nobody got confused thinking it was anything else. Now that I think about it, Chilly actually sent me a photo of him alone at Marty's a couple of months ago smiling next to *Chilly's Cheese* on the menu. Chilly was great, because he was really easily amused, and the second I got that picture I knew that he didn't care one bit that he mobbed it all the way out to Durnford Hill, completely alone, just so he could get his signature pizza one last time, something I was certain made his entire year. I really admire—if not *envy*—people who are that easily amused. Honestly, I wish I loved *anything* as much as Chilly loved his stupid cheese pizza.

We left Highland and were walking down the hill towards the auditorium and Patrick, the drunken idiot, was holding onto me for dear life. His whiskey breath was moistening my neck, as he struggled to put one foot in front of the other. Fergus was walking absurdly erect next to us in complete silence and was instead just making odd, little hand gestures and speaking to himself. If you want to know the truth, Fergus is probably the only guy I've ever met who's more in his own head than I am.

"All right, all right stand up straight, dumbass, or the teachers'll know," I said, hoisting Patrick up straight.

"Yeah, yeah I'm good, mate, I'm good," but he really wasn't; he looked like a deer on ice-skates.

We stood freezing outside the auditorium for at least ten minutes, until, finally, the headmaster popped up from behind a podium and regurgitated the same little speech he cited before our last Christmas break exactly a year ago, and probably since the first day he started working at Durnford.

"My fellow students," he began, and cleared his throat. "What a tremendous first term it has been. What a term indeed.

We have soared to insurmountable heights, and been confronted with—and de*feated*—certain challenges to which I thought I would eternally be a stranger…and yet…! I do feel that this may be the greatest year I have ever had the privilege of teaching at Durnford Hill College…" God, what a script. It's like he thinks this speech will have an impact on our Christmas break when, really, all we wanted to do was get wasted and throw up on the dance floor next to whatever teacher we hated most. "I do not have much more to say, other than I wish you all the happiest of holidays, and I want to thank you all for this wonderful year and I look forward to the year we have in store. Happy Christmas," he finished, his final syllables trailing off into the wind.

I think like four kids, teachers exempt, clapped for him. But whatever. I was excited to go inside, praying I didn't have frostbite already. Patrick and I started towards the stairs until I heard someone shout, "Alexander!"

I turned around and saw Bardot, standing in this long, red dress with a fur coat and that furry winter hat that she always wore.

"*Bardot,*" I stuttered, taken aback by the sight of her. "Hey, uhm…You coming in?"

"No, I-I can't…I'm sorry," she said, looking down at her feet. She looked really sad too when she said it, but she was all dressed up so I didn't understand why. I heard everyone piling in behind me, and then the big auditorium door slammed shut, leaving the two of us alone.

"What? Why not, y-you're all dressed up and stuff. You going to some *other* party?"

"No," she laughed. "I'm going to Sweden. My flight is tonight."

"What!" I gasped. "What do you mean? Wh-why're you

going to*day*? You're…you're gonna miss the dance," I said, and then all of a sudden I wasn't excited to go in any more. I felt all the joy completely drain out of me. Bardot started moving closer to me, until we were just a few inches away from each other. I recognized her smell, and, as it slowly moved in through my nostrils, suddenly, in that moment, I felt very warm.

"I know, I'm sorry," she said despairingly. "My mother booked the tickets because she thought the ball was yesterday, and now there's nothing I can do."

"So're you gonna fly in that dress?" I asked.

"No," she said, looking down at her feet. "I put it on because I wanted to show you how I'd look tonight." She looked back up at me and smiled, and I felt so stupid because a million things were racing in my head, but I didn't know what to say, so all I did was try and smile back.

"Do I look pretty?" she asked, with a bashful glint in her eye. I'm not religious, but if I was, I'd tell you that she looked like what God saw on that first Sunday morning when he stepped out on his front porch and looked out over the universe he had created.

"Yeah, Bardot. You look…you look really pretty."

A cab suddenly pulled up to the corner, and a compact, frigid man stepped out. "Oy, you *Bardot*?" he shouted, mistakenly pronouncing the T at the end of her name.

"Yes, I'm coming," Bardot called out, her tone sad and empty. "Just…give me one minute, please." She turned back to me, "I'm sorry, Alexander. I have to go."

"Wait!" I said, and grabbed her by the wrist.

"Yes?" she asked tenderly.

"I, uhm…" I hesitated. "*Fuck*," I panicked, and let go of her wrist. "Sorry, I just…I'm not good at this because I dunno what's happening right now."

"What do you mean?"

"I don't... I don't know what it is that you're doing to me," I stuttered. "I don't know why I'm feeling like this."

She smiled, and we looked at each other and, finally, I felt my mouth open and I heard some noises coming out and all I could do was pray that they weren't terrible but she smiled and swung her arms around me and I could feel her hair brushing against the side of my cheek and she gripped me so tightly that I prayed she would never have to let me go.

"I'm gonna miss you, too, Alexander," she whispered in my ear. "Merry Christmas."

I wish I could tell you that I kissed her, but I didn't. I copped out because I'm a pussy. She walked back over to the cab and I watched her climb inside and drive away, and I stood there, shaking, asking myself why on earth I was feeling the way I was feeling. I had been getting with that Sabrina chick for months and felt nothing, but all Bardot did was look at me and I just melted. I must've stood there for a good five minutes just staring down the road, trying to savor the trail of perfume she left behind her. I completely forgot there was a huge party with all my friends going on only a few feet behind me. Shit, I even forgot I was *cold*. Only after a while did I hear this odd, rattling noise and notice that it was my own teeth chattering. I took one last look down the road, and then I went inside to go find my friends and drink to forget about how I'd regret not kissing her for, what I was sure would be, the rest of my life.

When I got inside, I finally stopped shaking, but standing in the back of a dark, sweaty room with deafening house-music made it nearly impossible to find anyone. After scanning the room, I finally saw Patrick desperately trying to get the attention of some girl, who looked to be several grades below us, over by the DJ booth (and by DJ I mean that one guy who made an Avicii remix and now thinks he's a legitimate DJ, and bombards everyone on Facebook with his awful SoundCloud links). At first, I didn't approach him because I didn't want to cock-block, but after observing the state he was in and how south his attempts were headed, I walked over anyway to save him from further embarrassment. I tapped him on the shoulder, and he turned around with a vacant gaze, each of his eyes pointing in a different direction: "*Aaaye*, you aw-right, mate?"

"How you doin', buddy?" I asked.

"Battered, mate. Abso*lut*ely *cunted*."

"Where's everybody else?"

"They should be over—wait!" Patrick interrupted himself, instantly sobering up, "I almost forgot, you cheeky sod! Bardot! Did you neck her?!"

I hung my head in defeat, as I answered, "No."

"What on earth—why *not*?! You've been blabbering on about her for bloody weeks!"

"I know, I know, I know. I just, I dunno, I couldn't do it," I said.

Patrick grabbed my shoulder with his left hand, and although at first it seemed like he was trying to console me, I realized that he just needed some stabilization.

"Don' worry, mate. You'll get 'er next time. Less'go find the rest of the lads," he slurred.

Patrick and I started moving into the crowd, and after that I don't remember anything.

* * *

The next morning, after my cab dropped me off at the airport, I don't think I stopped running until I literally got to the gate of my flight. I was still wearing my tuxedo, by the way, which didn't look so much smart and handsome as it looked ridiculous. When I got to the gate and finally got a chance to sit down, I noticed I had dried puke and mud on my shoes from the previous night, and then when I started to think about it I nearly threw up again. I had lost my bowtie and my handkerchief, which really pissed me off, and I was now sitting in this dirty-ass tuxedo that now resembled more of a grayish/brown than it did black, and I didn't even want to imagine the state my hair was in.

I heard the flight attendant start to pile in passengers over the intercom, but I swear, if she hadn't said anything I would've passed out had I gotten the chance to sit there and relax just a few seconds more. My throat was dry and chalky and I had a throbbing headache, and before it was my turn to board I quickly ran over to the bathroom across the corridor and puked in the sink.

When I finally got on the plane and got to my seat, I noticed that I was sandwiched in between these two, fat, American kids wearing matching Union Jack sweaters, each covered in Cheetos and licking their orange fingers with each new bite.

I asked if it was possible for one of them to move to the middle, so I get either the aisle or the window seat, but they just looked at me like I was some insane door-to-door salesman trying to sell them herpes. I told them I was going to throw up if I didn't get an aisle seat and that I get claustrophobic and plane sick, but they didn't budge. I thought about having a fit, or fabricating some story about how I have a medical condition that requires me to sit in an aisle seat—something my mom always did when she wanted her way—but I was so tired and hungover that I just really couldn't be bothered any more. Although I was starving, knowing how picky I am, I knew I wouldn't be able to force myself to eat any of the airplane food; the thought of this only made me hungrier and even more upset. When I finally stuffed my bag into the overhead compartment, and managed to squeeze myself in between those gelatinous Cheeto twins, I felt all the back sweat that had accumulated over my sprint through the airport, slither down into my underwear and moistly press against my back, and my shirt collar was clenched so tightly around my neck that I thought I might pass out. I burped a few times, and the taste of expired alcohol burst up and out of my throat and taunted my taste buds as if it were purposely trying to torture me even more. The smell of Cheetos next to me wasn't exactly helping either, and all I wanted to do was sleep, but I knew I wouldn't be able to because sleeping on a plane is about as easy as dragging a catholic to an abortion clinic.

Suddenly, a flight attendant came over and sneered, "Sir, *please* fasten your seatbelt as we're preparing for take-off. You were the *last* passenger to board."

Christ. I feel like throughout my entire life I'm always nauseous, tired or late.

Part Three

VII

I woke up from the sudden jolt of the wheels hitting the runway. It took me a second to open my eyes, but I could hear the pilot proudly describing the weather, as he welcomed everybody to, "*sunny Los Angeles, California.*" The Cheeto twins on either side of me were already complaining about how they had to take another flight back home to Arizona, and oddly enough, a part of me almost wanted to join them. I recalled my dad saying he was going to pick me up, and although I had been dreading it, I was surprisingly excited to see him now that I had reminded myself of it. I figured we could stop at In-N-Out, and maybe go see a movie, or something.

As I slowly descended the escalator to the arrivals section, I began to notice all the funny looks I was getting because of my dusty, wrinkled tuxedo, but I was still so worn out, that I couldn't have cared less. Christmas decorations were strategically placed around the terminal; snowmen, clad with surfboards and sunglasses, which shamelessly catered to the global perception of California and its aggressively *chill* reputation.

After I got my suitcase, I walked up, and out the ramp at Tom Bradley expecting to go find my dad. I saw everybody run up and hug and kiss their children, husbands, wives, girlfriends, boyfriends, parents, whatever; people of all ages and races so happy to see one another. I paced around anxiously for a bit thinking that maybe he'd gone to the wrong terminal, but after about thirty minutes of looking around I felt so lonely and miserable I wondered why I had even come here in the first place. I sat down on a bench, until I noticed a short, bald man in an unfitted black suit holding a sign reading, *Mr. Alexander Lexington,* in very elementary handwriting.

"I'm Alexander Lexington," I said, puzzled, as I approached the man.

"Oh, great, wasn't sure who I was looking for," he replied, limply shaking my hand.

"Did my dad send you?"

"Uhm…" the man pulled out his phone. *"Robert Lexington."*

"Yeah," I sighed. "That's him."

We shared a moment of awkward silence, as the man eyed me up and down.

"Is that everything?"

"Yeah."

"Okay. Car's this way."

We approached one of those slim, black Lincolns—the ones that always look so governmental—and he insistently took my suitcase and struggled to hurl it in the trunk before opening the door for me.

The interior was clean, a nice change from the Cheeto atmosphere on the plane, but I was so uncomfortable in my sweaty tuxedo that it was hard to relax. The driver pulled out of the parking garage and made his way onto Sepulveda Boulevard and I rolled down the window and tried to absorb everything. Contrary to what you've heard about the summer, an L.A. winter brings a different assortment of weather. The weather feels dated, almost, as if recycled from the past, like staring at an old black and white photograph. Although you can see the sun prying its way through the clouds, followed by an unavoidable wave of naive European tourists wearing sunscreen and jean-shorts, you can't help but feel inexplicably cold and dry, no matter how visually promising the weather may seem.

The smell of the ocean made me tired, so I rested my head against the half-opened windowsill and fell asleep to the calming sensation of wind blowing through my hair.

"Wake up, kid," I heard, followed by a stiff nudge to my shoulder. "We're here, pal. Wake up," I heard again. I finally opened my eyes and saw the driver, assertively standing outside my door, my suitcase planted next to him.

"Where are we?" I asked, rubbing my eyes.

"Home."

I couldn't believe it—*home*. My first time back in nearly two years, and oddly enough I was excited to see my old room, so I pulled myself together and climbed out of the car, shaking the needles out of my feet as I struggled to stand up. But, as my eyes continued regaining focus, I began to realize that this was *not* home. At least not mine.

"Where are we?"

"Home," he repeated irritably.

"This is *not* my home," I said, pointing at the house. "Seriously, where are we?"

"Uhh..." he started, as he pulled out his phone, "...Woodland Hills," he said, stuffing his phone back into his pocket.

"*Woodland hi*—The fucking *valley*?" I said, gasping.

He nodded indifferently. An image flashed before me of every kid I'd ever met from the valley: guys named CJ, AJ, TJ, Cody or Kyle, who all drank monster energy, and had gage earrings; and girls named Stephanie, Tiffany, Amber or Allie who say 'legit' every other word and wear more makeup than all the members from KISS combined. I swear, at that moment I thought about asking the driver to take me right back to the airport so I could get on another plane and go back to the only home I had left, but I didn't. All I did was stand there, baffled, and glared at the symmetrical houses with basketball hoops in the driveway and minivans sprinkled up and down the street.

"Well," the driver said, interrupting my nightmare. "Take care."

"How am I gonna get in?"

"That wasn't in my job description," he said, and climbed in and drove off.

When I reached the house, I knocked several times until a short, Mexican maid—sweating mildly with a mop in her hand—opened up, before quickly running off again. I walked in through the front door and was instantly reminded of that therapist's house from all those years ago, an image of that blinding light flashing before my eyes, followed by the loud cowbell ringing in my ears. Lined up against the wall by the entrance were several pairs of tiny baby shoes, all in different colors, and I began to wonder how many kids the old man had pumped out by now. As I walked further into the living room, I noticed there wasn't one piece of furniture that I recognized, as everything was new and tacky, and then, above the TV, there was a giant photograph of Esmeralda in a white gown, victoriously carrying two newborn infants with a smile that didn't so much scream 'proud mother,' as it did 'smug lottery winner.'

I looked into each room as I passed, but each was clearly occupied by either one of the kids, or Esmeralda herself. I continued down the hallway, which was lined with more photos of my dad, Esmeralda, and their new kids, and then I finally found a room at the end that had nothing but a big, unmade bed, with folded sheets and a single pillow, lying on top of the mattress. I was so tired at that point I didn't even care about making the bed. I took off my tuxedo, which I had been wearing for over twenty-four hours, threw it on the floor, laid down on the mattress and passed out almost instantly.

* * *

I woke up to the sound of a violent shriek echoing throughout the entire house. I was so disoriented I almost expected to see the inside of my dorm room back at Durnford, but slowly realized that I wasn't at school anymore and that I was back in L.A. The shrieking continued in short bursts, and I tried to drown it out by humming something and covering my head with a pillow, but it didn't work. Finally, I got up, opened my suitcase and put on jeans and a t-shirt.

I didn't know where anything was, but I followed the screams into the living room which brought me face to face with, who I later discovered to be, my little brother. I'd never experienced the feeling of going to the hospital and seeing your newborn, tadpole of a sibling curled up and breastfeeding from your mom—the knowledge slowly budding inside you that this tiny individual would now be entitled to all the affection that you had—so when I saw this little kid, who looked nothing like me, I didn't know what to say, and neither did he, because the second he laid his eyes on me he started screaming again. Then, in our most primal first encounter, Esmeralda's mom marched through the door with an undeserving sense of entitlement, a trait I'd become accustomed to since our first meeting. When Esmeralda and my dad started dating, he'd drag me to her mother's house after school for dinner, but she never had enough chairs, so he'd pull up a sofa cushion and I'd have to sit on that, the table surface barely parallel to my eyes, and everyone thought it was so funny, especially Esmeralda: *"He's so cute! It's like we have a little dog at the table!"*

She walked in with a couple of grocery bags and tailing closely behind her—which I'm sure she loved—were two Mexican maids carrying another child, and more groceries. *She,* herself, was a maid, but now, thanks to my dad's credit card, she could afford them in spades.

"Hola?" she said, as she looked at me, puzzled, picking up the screaming infant.

"It's me, Alex," I said.

"Alejandro?" she asked again.

"Sure," I said, rolling my eyes.

"Ah," she said callously, and continued towards the kitchen. Then I heard another voice in English and although I knew whose it was, I hardly recognized her upon seeing her peroxide dyed hair.

"*Mom*! These fucking Mexicans don't understand an*y*thing!" she shouted in the doorway, still unaware that I was there. "I-need-you-to-put-this-in-the-kitchen. Do-you-*e'speak*-English?" she snapped at one of the maids who was struggling with four grocery bags. Then she turned, and nearly stumbled at the sight of me. "*Alex?*" she exclaimed. "What're *you* doing here?"

"It's…Christmas break."

"*Oh*," she said, frowning with disappointment. "How long are you gonna be here?"

"Like, two weeks."

"Hmm," she paused and scratched her head. "Are you gonna

be at the house a lot?" She paused. "Like, are you gonna celebrate Christmas here?"

"Has my dad not said anything?"

"*No.*"

"He didn't say I was coming?"

"*No,* Alex," she sighed again. "Your dad *didn't say you were coming.* But listen," she began, heading towards the kitchen, snapping her fingers at the maids as she walked. "We got a lot of plans for the holidays, okay? Santa's coming in a few days and we're having a photo shoot with the kids, so I'd really appreciate it if you found some place else to stay those days just because we need the house to be... *clean.*"

I didn't respond, I just watched her boss the maids around the house, snapping at them whenever they put something in the wrong place.

"*Well?*" she asked, turning back towards me.

"Sure," I said.

"But, like," she sighed. "Okay, so, my family's coming for Christmas, so if you're gonna be here could you maybe not—"

But I slammed the door on her before she could finish, and left.

My phone was dead, and I had no fucking clue where I was, but I'd exchanged my Adderall money at the airport before I left, and the pound was much higher than the dollar, so at least I had a pretty handsome chunk of change in my pocket.

I walked down my street for several blocks until I came to another street, which I then walked down for another few blocks, until I finally came to a sign that said Ventura Blvd. I don't know if you've ever been to L.A., but even if you haven't, I'm sure you know that it's a pretty big city, and that doesn't even include the valley, which is where I was now.

What exists within the confinements of Los Angeles is, like, Hollywood, Beverly Hills, Bel Air, Westwood; and then you have all the areas by the water like, Venice, Santa Monica, and Malibu, although Malibu and Santa Monica aren't technically part of Los Angeles. The valley is a whole other story though, and although I've lived here basically my entire life, I don't think I've spent more than a few hours in the valley. During the summer it gets hotter than Vegas, and during the winter it gets so cold you wouldn't think you were in California any more. Why the Kardashians decided to move here and make it 'cool,' is beyond me, and the fact that the local kids are pretty much the worst kids you'd ever meet in your life doesn't exactly aid the valley's reputation either.

Although I'm not too familiar with the valley, I *do* know that Ventura Boulevard is about the only redeeming sliver of hope that this city has. This street has literally anything you could ever imagine, and that's what makes it so eerie, because you always wonder how the hell these places stay in business. Places like: 'Bubba's Vacuum Cleaner Bags', 'Russian Pharmaceuticals', or 'Ethiopian Bookstore', all of which had signs that hadn't been replaced in decades. Since I didn't have a phone on me, I felt completely off the grid, but after about a mile, or so, of walking it was actually pretty relieving. It's nice knowing that no matter what, nobody can contact you, and no matter what obligations, or prior engagements, you may have, they won't matter until you get home because there's nothing you can do about it now anyway. Suddenly you start forgetting about everyone and everything else, and for once in my life I wasn't thinking about anything, only the ancient, desolate road that I was walking on, and all the weird shops on either side that I was passing.

I passed everything from Krav Maga dojos, to bowling

alleys, to Medical Marijuana dispensaries, to Tarot readers, to XXX bookstores. After a while I even began to like it, the weirdness of it all. Because on the other side of the mountain—Hollywood, Beverly Hills, Santa Monica—everything is so pristine and refurbished, but over here, on Ventura, it was almost like nobody gave a shit about any of that. They just kind of let people open up whatever shops they wanted, and then just left it like that, no matter how much they began to deteriorate.

Trash was blowing up and down the street, and my only company for the last hour had been the flickering, neon lights of every store bleeding into the night sky, reflecting off of the gasoline rainbows pooling down the gutters.

As I was walking, my back really started to hurt, probably because I had been sandwiched between those orange marshmallows for ten hours. Since Ventura has the most obscure shops you could ever imagine, it didn't take long to find a massage parlor that looked remotely presentable.

I walked in through the door and a little bell jingled upon entry, and the second it did, about a hundred little Thai women appeared out of thin air and ecstatically greeted me like I was the president.

"Hallo, hallo sah! Velcum, velcum! Yu need massage?" one of them asked, sensually stroking my back.

"Yeah, but just for my lower back, it's killing me," I answered, as more Thai women began rubbing my shoulders, before escorting me to the back. "I only need, like, a quick massage on my back. I don't really need a full body massage. Is that cool?"

"Yas, yas. This okay, this okay! Very coo, very coo! Come, come. We take care of yu! Yu feel betta, much betta!"

Their alarming eagerness left me slightly reluctant to follow because the anxiety in me started to wonder if they were going to cut me up into small pieces and feed me to the parrots, or something.

"Here! For yu, handsome! Great room, great room! Massage, very good, good price!" said, what looked to be, the owner of the place. She was probably sixty years old with a waxy complexion, and she was followed by the rest of the other women who were maybe just a few years younger than her. One of the others escorted me into a room with beads hanging from the doorframe, which worryingly reminded me of *Taxi Driver*, and the rest of the women disappeared back into the shadows, leaving the two of us alone.

"Please, sah, clothes off," she said, her hands clasped together at her waist, as she slightly bowed her head, her eyes staying on me.

"No, no. *Listen,*" I began, exaggerating the clarity of my voice. "I don't want a *full body*. I just need you to take care of my *lower back,*" I said, pointing at it. "That is *all* I need."

She nodded eagerly, noticeably oblivious to every word I'd just said. "Please, sah. *Clothes,*" and then she motioned for me to take them off, and after going back and forth with her over and over again, I honestly felt so hopeless that I just surrendered and got undressed, leaving nothing but a skimpy little towel around my waist.

"Please, sah, lay down," she insisted, so I obeyed. As I was lying there, I realized how exhausted I was, and I hadn't slept too well at my dad's house, so eventually I started drifting in and out of consciousness.

After a while, she delicately tapped me on the head and asked me to flip over, so I did, and started dozing off again. Then

I remembered feeling a warm, soft sensation moving up and down my penis, but as my eyes slowly opened, I saw two, wrinkly hands stroking it, her robotically innocent grin staring back at me.

"Whoa, whoa, whoa!" I yelped, swatting her hand away. "No! Sorry, *no*, please stop that!" I shrieked, quickly snatching the towel to try and cover myself, nearly falling off of the table in the process. "I don't want that!" I said, blushing with embarrassment.

"Is okay, sah! Is okay," she reached forward and grabbed it and began stroking again, as if holding me hostage. "Happy ending, happy ending. Is okay. No bad, no bad. Happy ending," she kept repeating. "Shh, is okay. Is okay."

"No, I'm serious," I said, laughing nervously, but I felt my body slowly fall into submission, as any resistance inside me began to die. I grabbed her wrist, but she just kept shushing me. "Please stop. Please," I pleaded, but she just kept going. My nerves deflated as I laid there helplessly, my eyes fixated on her working hands.

"Shh. Yu like? *See. I know* yu like," she leaned forward and put her lips around it, moving her head up and down before coming back up for air. "See. I know yu like. Is *good*, handsome boy, yes? I make yu very happy," she said, staring at me. I was completely catatonic. Then I felt it start to build. I felt my abs tense up and my body began coiling into itself. She smiled knowingly, and moved her hands faster. I recognized the familiar sensation: it started to feel good, but I was torn, because I didn't want it to. I didn't want it to feel good and I didn't want it from her. I wanted to ask her to stop but I couldn't open my mouth. Her hands began moving quicker and quicker, until I felt myself gasp, and then it shot out of me, straight up into the air, and splashed back on my stomach, some of it hitting her clothes.

I began wheezing; our eyes locked on each other. I looked down at myself and felt limp and disgusted. I was breathing heavily, and I looked back at the woman—her wrinkles bleeding down her cheeks and connecting to the corners of her mouth—and began to gag, as I finally realized what had just happened.

"Yu see? I *know* yu like. Is *good*," she smiled and began wiping my stomach with a towel; I laid there shaking. "Yu hard still!" she said, and continued stroking it.

"Please... stop," I begged quietly.

"Yung boy always is so hard! *Look*! Still hard!" she laughed. "Is *okay*. Yu no want me stop. Yu are clean, yes? Yung boy clean, yes?" she leaned over and put her mouth over it, keeping eye contact, moving her head up and down. I felt the will being sucked out of me, my whole body being poured into a hole. Still, I couldn't move. Then it started building again. This time it was even stronger. My toes began to curl up until, finally, it released, and then her head stopped moving and I heard her cough before saying something incomprehensible, her words only coming through in vowels.

She straightened herself up and smiled. As if hijacked into involuntary intoxication, I was suddenly completely sober again, like waking up from a coma in which I was somehow conscious. She walked over to the faucet and audibly gargled some mouthwash, before walking back over and wiping my entire body with a moist towel.

Finally, she grabbed it, leaned down and kissed it and smiled. Then I yelped, "Stop touching me! Please... stop it. Why...why did you do that?" I asked, my voice cracking. "You're a fucking pervert," I whispered. "You fucking pervert, I told you to stop...but you didn't. Why did you do that?" But I knew she wouldn't answer. I felt like I was going to cry. "Please, just let me leave."

She took a step back, still smiling, and I weakly stumbled off the massage table and reached for my clothes, clumsily getting myself dressed.

"A lot inside *yu*, big boy," she giggled, proudly holding up two of her fingers. "*Two* times. *So* much in yu. Yu come back again, yes? Sucky sucky for *yu*, yes?"

"No," I said weakly. "No, I'm never coming back. You're a fucking pervert. I'm only seventeen." When I glared back at her it felt like I no longer had sole ownership or authority over my own body. It felt like all of me belonged to her as much as it did me, like she had taken something from me against my will, something that I would never get back. The worst part was that she genuinely thought she was making me happy and, based on my body's response, there was no reason for her to think otherwise.

I pulled out fifty bucks and tossed it on the table after I quickly zipped up my pants. She didn't budge or say anything, and her eyes stuck to me even as I left the room, the beaded curtains clicking together as they washed over me. When I entered the lobby all of the women stood up again and tried to embrace me, but all I wanted was to get the hell out of that place.

When I got outside, after I had gotten far enough so as they couldn't see me anymore, I started running as fast as I could. I ran and ran until my lungs gave out, and then I hunched over and rested my hands on my knees before a few ribbons of puke trickled out of my mouth, making a small splash on the sidewalk. I started picturing all of the dried cum stains from all of the old perverts who'd been jerked off in that place, and then I realized that now *I* was one of those old perverts, too. An image of that old woman washing her hands over and over and over again flashed before me, and it made me so depressed I thought I was going to break down crying right then and there in the middle of the street.

I looked around myself—nauseously penitent with the obscure, neon store fronts silently mocking me—struggling to accept that I'd just been sucked off by an old lady in a city devoted to shameless pleasure, and all too forgiving for that sort of thing.

Welcome home, Alexander, whispered Los Angeles.

VIII

When I finally got back to my dad's house, having spent the entire walk toiling with what I'd just done, I was so depressed and broken I thought I was going to collapse…then I realized I didn't have a key. For a second, I was actually relieved because now I had something else to worry about, and after several attempts at scaling the fence, I managed to jump into the backyard, feeling around in the dark until I came across an unlocked sliding door.

I quietly tiptoed into my room, which was more of a holding cell, and immediately ripped off all my clothes and jumped in the shower. I scrubbed my dick so hard it almost began to bleed, and after sitting in there for close to an hour, my skin burnt to a crisp, I finally got out.

When I got back to my room, I plugged my phone in and opened Facebook to try to distract myself. I started scrolling through previous messages between me and my L.A. friends, and it felt so weird because you can see all the messages you've sent to these people in the past, and I noticed I hadn't spoken to any of them in several years. The last conversations between us were about making plans for an upcoming weekend, or asking what the homework was, or something, and now, several years later, I was writing to let them know I was 'home' again. It's eerie to think about how you can go from seeing and talking to someone almost every day of your life, to one day suddenly becoming a complete stranger. And not because anything bad happened—like a tumultuous breakup, or something—but just because that's what happens in life, and I guess you're not meant to be as close to everyone you once were forever.

I sent out a few messages, the typical:

-- Yo, dude, I'm back

--Hey I'm home

--Are you in LA?

And so forth, and then I just laid there in bed thinking about how weird it would be to see everyone again. In my first year at Durnford, I must've gotten fifty messages a week from both guys *and* girls, asking how I was doing and saying how much they missed me, but after the first year, it completely stopped. It's quite ironic, actually, because I was so done with Los Angeles and so ready to leave that I didn't pay any attention to the outpour of love I received from everyone when I moved to England, and instead dismissed most of them; as soon as all the messages stopped, though, I found myself feeling sad and forgotten. It's funny how people work like that; when somebody's after you, you don't care, but as soon as they stop, you get this overwhelming sense of rejection, even if these people aren't anyone you cared about to begin with, you just want that emotional safety net, reassuring you that, in spite of the world's indifference, there's at least someone out there who thinks you do, in fact, matter.

I scrolled down my Facebook timeline and found all these videos that girls had posted long ago saying how much they *loved* and *missed* me and told me to come back home, and I just couldn't stop thinking about how these are people who, just a few years ago, claimed they *loved me,* whereas, now, I'm not even sure I'd stop and say hi to them if I saw them in a supermarket; truthfully, I don't think they would either. That's the weird thing about my generation: everything that kids my age ever do will literally be etched in stone for*ever*. If my parents stopped hanging out with someone back in their day, they were literally erased from their life; we don't have that same luxury. Instead, we're constantly reminded of people's birthdays, new profile pictures, and where in the world they are, and it's all just so gnarly to think about, because unless you delete *all* forms of social media and fall off the grid completely, these people will essentially be a part of you for the *rest* of your life. *Christ.* Ain't that a trip?

* * *

I couldn't remember falling asleep, but the next morning I woke up and felt surprisingly well rested for the first time in I don't know *how* long, but then I started hearing voices coming from the kitchen which immediately shattered my brief pinch of optimism. I checked my phone, and every single person I had written to the night before had replied in all caps, which felt like they were shouting at me, which was actually a bit overwhelming. I was initially so judgmental and dismissive towards everyone back home before I came, but now I was finally allowing myself to loosen up and embrace the affection that I was receiving instead of shunning it like I had been doing for the past two years. I read and replied to all the messages, and after I was done, I was actually pretty excited to see everyone, and hardly even noticed Esmeralda, along with four other surgically altered women, sitting in the kitchen as I entered.

"Axel," Esmeralda called.

"*Alex,*" I corrected her.

"Yeah, that's what I *said*," she snorted. "Don't eat any of the food in the fridge, it's for the kids."

"For the *kids?*" I asked bewilderedly. "Do they even have teeth yet?"

Esmeralda sneered, and then addressed her friends, *loudly*, making sure I heard. "This is Axel, who I was telling you about before, remember? You know, with his mom? I still can't believe it. It's just so, *so* sad." I glanced over my shoulder, and Esmeralda turned to me with a vindictive smirk.

"Is that the one you said went crazy?" one of the women asked.

"Mhmm," Esmeralda answered.

"What happened again?" another asked with forged pity.

"Well, nobody really knows but I guess she just went *cuckoo*. They even locked her *up* for it. Even poor little Alex had to go to therapy for a bit because he just couldn't handle it. Isn't that right?" she said, turning to me, smiling. "His grades failed. He lost all of his friends. That's why he was sent to England."

"Oh *no*," I heard someone else say, followed by a volley of sympathetic *oohs* and *aahs*.

"I even got kinda nervous when the kids got born thinking that, like, what if *they* got the crazy genes *too*, but then I remembered that it was only on Alex's mom's side, not the dads, so they're safe," Esmeralda let out a dramatized sigh of relief. "I feel *so* blessed."

"Let's just hope they don't get the genes that get them into the University of Phoenix," I said quietly.

"What was that?" Esmeralda called. I didn't reply.

On the kitchen counter I noticed two twenties with a note, in my dad's handwriting, which said, *for food.*

I pocketed the twenties and began to leave before Esmeralda

called back, "Oh, and Alex, make sure to bring us receipts for anything you use that money for."

I thought about saying something but I was outnumbered so I walked back into my room and asked myself why anyone would want to marry someone like that. I wondered if my dad even cared what a witch she was, but I figured he probably didn't, because I truly don't think he cared about anything other than money, and all I could wonder was what the hell they ever spoke about. But that's my theory with middle-aged men: I think that after their first marriage with a *real* person—someone who they struggled, and, eventually, succeeded with—they just can't be bothered to do it all over again. I think these men have done the whole 'real marriage/real love' thing once already, and now they're tired and old, with lots of money but no time or energy, so all they want is some brainless young chick with big tits, who doesn't ask questions, gives blowjobs, and that's it. I don't think that holding an intelligent conversation carries the same value as it once did for them back in the day. Sadly enough, though, whenever I've brought this up with my dad, he dismisses it, or snaps at me, and claims I'm badmouthing Esmeralda. Sometimes at night, before Esmeralda moved in, I'd hear him play the guitar alone in his room, but if I ever came in on him and wanted to join, he'd get embarrassed and immediately put the guitar away, dismissing it as a childish, unrealistic hobby. When Esmeralda finally moved in, she threw out the guitar because it *'took up too much space.'* All I can pray is that I don't do what he did when I get older: sell my soul for a big house and a gold digger, while playing golf on the weekends. But who knows? When I think about it, I probably will.

I wrote to a few friends on Facebook, asking if they wanted to

139

meet somewhere, eventually deciding on Cross Creek, which is this little, outdoorsy shopping center in Malibu with overpriced smoothies, handbags, and the occasional wild, celebrity sighting. When we were younger, my friends and I would joke about how every mom's upper lip cost more than a full college tuition. Some of them actually looked so gnarly we couldn't even recognize them anymore. My mom used to hang out with this histrionic blonde lady who was married to some real estate extraordinaire, and one day we ran into her on the street, and I stuck out my hand as if meeting her for the first time, because I literally didn't recognize her from all the surgery. She tried her hand at a singing career not too long after that—she had a couple of shows at some obscure venues around Los Angeles, with production costs through the roof, despite there being no more than like ten people in the audience—but, eventually, she gave up, blaming the music industry and Lady Gaga for stealing, what she claims, would have been her spotlight. Now she's become a stage-mom for her three kids, forcing them to home-school so she can take them to auditions every day, hoping they'll get famous. You meet a lot of those kids growing up in L.A., kids with no social skills or real hobbies or personality because they've never spent any time interacting with normal kids their own age, their entire identity just a mishmash of all the different roles they've spent their short life auditioning for. If you ask them what their favorite movie is or if they play any sports, or something, they don't even understand the question, and instead they'll just respond by tap dancing, or awkwardly start singing, "The sun will come out tomorrow," as their mom stands proudly in the background next to the other parents, pointing, "Isn't she amazing? Everyone says she's a natural. She's auditioning for Disney Channel tomorrow, just you wait." Most Malibu moms are like that: always up to some new business venture, whether it's jewelry or reality television or interior design or opening a pilates studio or whatever they can do to pass the time when they're not enslaved to the couch, guzzling wine and popping Xanax, trying to convince themselves that their husband isn't fucking his secretary or the family au pair who, coincidentally, just moved into their guest house.

When I first moved to England, some kid told me he had been to Malibu once before but found it quite disappointing, saying that all he really saw was 'lots of silicone and lots of sand,' and that always stuck with me.

I took an Uber to Cross Creek and bought a smoothie that almost cost as much as the hand-job from the night before. I always get anxious when I'm spending too much money, but for once in my life I actually had quite a bit, so I didn't worry about it too much. I went and sat in the park—the same park that I used to play in all the time as a kid—and watched all the little kids on the swings and the jungle gym and the dogs running around, and this giant red hammer statue that stands in the middle of the grass. That statue has been there for as long as I can remember and it's huge, and the coolest thing you could do if you were a kid, was to climb all the way to the top, but nobody ever succeeded because it was way too tall and slippery. Ironically, Ocean was the one who'd always bet me that he'd be able to do it, but I always ended up winning because, like I said, nobody ever got to the top.

Suddenly, an eruption of shrieks exploded on the other side of the park hijacking the attention of everyone within range, myself included, just to find that it was just one of those Kardashians walking by. I saw a swarm of Paparazzis, followed by more screaming, and I swear I think I heard somebody say,

"You're my hero!" Hero for *what?*

After the commotion subsided, I heard somebody call my name, and I recognized the kid from my old high school, but for the life of me I really couldn't remember his name.

"Alex?! *Duuuude.* I haven't seen you in forever. " He stuck out his hand.

"Heeeey," I said.

"Where have you been?"

"I…moved to England," I said, simply.

"What?" he said, shocked. "That's so gnarly. So are you, like…have you moved back now?"

"I'm just here for Christmas."

"Oh, for sure."

A long, awkward pause.

"'Boutta go hit this spliff in my car," he paused. "Wanna come?"

"Uhm…" I said, not hiding my hesitation.

He shamelessly produced a large joint from his pocket and waved it in front of me. "Come on, bro."

"Okay," I said reluctantly.

"Sick…"

Weed hadn't been legalized yet, but from his unapologetic display you would've assumed that it was. I sat next to him in the passenger seat and he handed me the glowing joint and I brought it to my lips and inhaled carefully. I instantly began coughing.

"What is this?"

"Mainly sativa, but there's a bit of salvia in there."

"*Salvia?*"

"It's nothin', dude. You're chillin'."

"That's not gonna fuck me up, is it?"

142

"Nah, dude. You're fine."

My eyes started vibrating and, suddenly, I felt very sick.

Don't panic...don't panic...don't...

"I need some air," I said.

"Cool. Good seeing you, dude."

I looked over at him, unable to make out what he was saying, and then I quickly stepped out of the car. I sat down on the asphalt in the parking lot, holding my head in my hands, until I heard someone shout, "Alex!" and I looked up to see my friend, Riley, who had grown about a foot since I last saw him. "Dude, what-is-up," he called as he approached me, and when he got closer, he leaned his head down worriedly, and asked, "You good, man?"

"What?"

"You look kinda sick."

"I just... smoked."

"Where?" He laughed and looked around curiously. "With who?"

"I don't remember. He...went to our school," I shook my head. "Fuck, man. This sucks. What is this?"

"Dude, you're gonna be fine," he said dismissively. Come on."

Riley and I walked over to his car, but as soon as I got in and fastened my seatbelt and turned back over to him, he was waving a joint in my face.

"*What?*" I said, emphasizing the reluctance in my tone.

"Dude, this is *indica*, this'll calm you down."

"Dude, I don't need any more weed. I need some water."

"Trust me, dude. This'll mellow you out."

Riley rolled down his window, and began puffing away. I

was looking out the window until I felt him nudge my shoulder.

"Here."

I sighed, and took it. I felt the smoke enter my lungs but when I exhaled this time, I didn't cough. What a relief.

I still felt sick, so I rolled down the window, my eyes squinting in the sun, and I was suddenly reminded of the first time I smoked weed, which was with Ocean and Beau, under the Santa Monica pier amongst the crackheads and gutter rats. When I felt the weed take its effect, the sound of the roller coaster grinding above us got me so nervous that I ripped off all my clothes and sprinted away until I was back out into the open. When I finally calmed down, we walked up Broadway and stopped at this French crepe place that doesn't exist anymore, and spent like a hundred bucks on Nutella crepes. The food hadn't even arrived before I passed out on my plate, and Ocean had to pull me up by the hair to keep us from getting kicked out. Afterwards we took a cab back into Malibu, but the driver was some insane Russian, with a KGB sticker on his window, who pushed ninety all the way home, and by the time we had finally arrived I'd thrown up three times on the backseat, but his deafening euro-disco was so loud that he didn't hear anything.

"That guy's car smelled like terrorism," Ocean had chuckled, as the cab pulled away.

We pulled up to a massive house on PCH that I didn't recognize, and I waited for Riley to reveal whose it was, but he didn't say anything. The front gates resembled the entrance to Jurassic Park. They slowly opened in front of us and we started driving up the driveway which covered more ground than most houses. On the left there was a tennis court and guest house; on the right there were black and white Range Rovers leading up to the house like inflated piano keys.

"Whose house is this?" I asked, as we approached the front door.

"It's a surprise, man," Riley said.

The door swung open and it took me a second to register, but I finally noticed that it was Beau standing in front of me. I quickly realized how much weight he'd lost, but, as I looked closer, it looked like someone had sucked it out of him far too quickly; if not unnaturally. The skin around his throat folded into itself like a used condom, and his head was completely shaved, with dark grooves under his eyes, but I couldn't tell if it made him look younger or older. Somehow it just made him look plain, a faceless figure, like a manikin, or something. I tried to absorb this new image of him, but before I could speak, he swung his arms around me. Eventually I snapped out of it, and began hugging him back.

"Good to see you, man," he said, a bit wearily "I bet you had no idea where you were, huh?" he said, as I followed him inside.

"Yeah," I said, anxious over whether or not he could tell how shocked I was by his new appearance. "When did you move?"

"About a year ago."

"How do you like it?"

"It's okay," he shrugged.

I followed him in through the door, staring at the deep indents on the back of his skull as he walked, the fuzzy shell of hair coating his head like a dark peach. He led me down a cavernous marble hallway—the walls draped in expensive oil paintings and black and white photos of his dad with people like Tina Turner and Frank Sinatra—and then halfway through the living room there was a metallic, blue aquarium erupting through the floor, several prickly, exotic fish swimming around inside.

I followed Beau out into his backyard, where these guys, Bryan and Rocky—two guys I *kind* of remembered from high school—were sitting in the Jacuzzi, both wearing sunglasses, smoking out of a bong.

"Look who's here," Beau said calmly. Both of them slowly turned around and pushed up their shades, revealing two pairs of red, glossy eyes staring back at me bewilderedly.

"*Alex?*" Rocky asked, carefully placing the bong down next to him.

"Yeah," I answered, followed by an awkward laugh. "What's up?"

"Duuuuude," Bryan moaned in disbelief. "What the fuuuuck. You look so different," followed by a laugh.

Yeah, well, you guys look *exactly* the same, I thought. I smiled back at them, struggling to see them clearly in the invasive sun. I dragged my feet along the grass and gave each of them a moderately enthusiastic high-five, before taking off my shirt and laying down on my back. I heard laughter in the background, but nobody was coming towards me, so I just laid there for a while and glanced out across the ocean and the palm trees. You could see every other house and its backyard, stretching along the coast for miles; each house flashier than the next but, as I laid there staring, I saw that every house and backyard appeared completely empty.

Clouds of weed smoke, followed by fits of coughing, would erupt from behind me every other minute or so, but all I could think about was that I had barely eaten all day and, slowly, I felt my body shriveling up like a beached jellyfish drying out in the sun.

* * *

I woke up on a spotless, white couch with an icepack on my head, and when my eyesight finally stabilized, I saw Beau sitting across from me looking relieved, several chips bags and Snickers wrappers scattered around him.

"You passed out, man," he said.

"I passed out?"

"Yup," he nodded. "Bryan said he saw you stand up and then you just nose-dived straight into the ground," he said, chuckling. "You're lucky you were on the grass. You're probably super dehydrated, dude."

"Shit," I said, tracing the surface of my head. "Yeah, you're probably right."

"I got you some Gatorade and some crackers."

I looked around and noticed that we were the only ones there. I didn't hear any other voices.

"Where'd everyone go?" I asked, still rubbing my head.

"Everyone drove home."

"Ah," I said softly. "Cool."

"Bryan didn't even know you'd moved until I told him," Beau chuckled. "He was like, *why hasn't he been in school?*"

"Oh," I smiled awkwardly. "That's…funny."

Beau stood up. "But why don't you just, like, sip that Gatorade and I'll go order some pizza. Just… you know… just lay down for a bit."

I heard the sound of Beau's footsteps slowly vanish as he left the room, as I continued delicately tracing the back of my head.

I sat up in the couch and began slowly sipping the Gatorade, each drop echoing its descent down my empty stomach. I started looking around, and finally began to register just how massive his house really was; despite its size and all the rooms and the pool and marble staircases and aquariums and the photographs, it seemed like we were the first ones to ever step foot inside. After a while Beau came back with a vacant smile and told me he had just ordered pizza and that it should be here in less than an hour which sobered me up because I realized it would be my first meal all day. Beau began aimlessly flipping through channels on the TV, eventually landing amongst the porn channels, to which he started giggling immediately. Channel after channel, the material got more and more graphic, until he finally landed on a skinny blonde girl getting fucked from behind, to which Beau's face dropped, shouting, "Holy shit, dude, that's Samantha!"

I sat up in the couch and looked closer, and although something about her face seemed familiar, it was hard to recognize her with tear-soaked mascara bleeding down her cheeks, and thick fingers fish-hooking her mouth.

"Oh—My—God," Beau gasped, completely petrified. "Don't you *remember* her? We had freshman seminar with her!"

"I…think so?" I stuttered. I started to feel sick and yet it was impossible to look away.

"Man," Beau said, as he reached for the remote and quickly turned off the TV. "That's the most depressing thing I've ever seen in my life," he continued, shaking his head. "Did you see the size of that thing she was choking on? '*Don't tell my boyfriend.*' Fuck, man. I wonder if her parents know."

I didn't say anything. I tried to remember what she looked like from before, scanning my eighth-grade yearbook in my head, but the only image that appeared was the one I'd just seen, one that stayed in my head for many days after. I wondered if her parents knew.

Eventually, the pizza arrived.

"Is your dad coming back tonight?" I asked, through a mouthful of pepperoni.

"No," he reached for a slice. "I'm usually here alone," he said indifferently.

"What do you mean?" I asked. "Where is he?"

"I think he's in Japan—I'm not sure *where* exactly, probably Tokyo—but his assistant was supposed to come by today or tomorrow and check in on me and make sure that I hadn't burned the house down or something," he said, with an awkward chuckle. "He's kind of a fag though. I don't really like him."

"His assistant?"

"Yeeeah," he sighed, as if embarrassed by his own disdain. "He's just, like, such a kiss-ass. If I took a dump on the floor and asked him to lick it up, he'd do it. And like, I dunno... knowing he's doing all of that just for my fucking *dad* is kinda annoying."

Throughout our three years in middle school Beau's dad ran through nine different assistants; apparently, he was notorious in the music industry for that. In sixth grade Beau asked one of the assistants—I think his name was Michael—if he could do his mitochondria project for him, and he didn't even hesitate. One time I spoke to him, to Michael, and he told me he'd studied marketing at some Ivy League school, and that he hoped to be a music manager one day, hence his joy over becoming Beau's dad's assistant. We spoke about music for hours that night, and I honestly really enjoyed his company. About a week later he was fired, and I never saw him again. I asked Beau why his dad never had female assistants, and he said that he used to, but, recently, he kept getting sued by them for some reason, so now his lawyer advised against it.

Eventually we started talking about winter break, and I asked if he had any plans for Christmas or New Years, but he said he wasn't sure yet. Finally, it started to get late, and I think Beau could tell I was passing out, so he walked me upstairs to one of the guest rooms, which was bigger than any room I'd had in my life, with a plasma screen hanging from the wall across from the king-sized bed.

"You've lost a lot of weight," I said suddenly.

"Huh?" Beau asked.

"Yeah," I said. "You've lost a lot of... you look good."

"Oh. Yeah, I guess," he paused. "Thanks."

Beau turned around quietly and disappeared down the hall, and I waited for the sound of his door shutting from the other end of the house.

Despite all my jetlag and how tired I was, as soon as I climbed into bed, I felt wide awake. Changing positions every five minutes for hours did nothing to help my pursuit of sleep, so eventually I grabbed my phone and as I was scrolling through messenger, I noticed Bardot's name, the intimidating green dot flashing next to it, indicating that she was online. I clicked her chat-box and laid there with the blue light illuminating my face in the darkness, just staring at her name. Seconds, minutes—maybe even an *hour*—went by, until eventually I mustered up the strength to write something—it wasn't very impressive though...

Alexander: 1.46 a.m.: heyy

Nothing happened for several minutes.

Bardot: 1.57 a.m.: helloo Alexander

Instantly I felt the butterflies in my stomach.

Alexander: 1.59 a.m.: whatre you up to?

Bardot 2.00 a.m.: im having breakfast with my mother. What are you doing?

Alexander: 2.01 a.m.: im at my friend's house but I can't sleep.

Bardot: 2.01 a.m.: how does it feel to be back?

I wasn't sure how honest I should be.

Alexander: 2.03 a.m.: its good, but I've been thinking about you a lot...

I started to type, but I deleted it.

Alexander: 2.04 a.m.: its a bit weird but its not bad

Bardot: 2.04 a.m: what kind of weird?

Alexander: 2.05. a.m.: I dunno, its like nothing has happened. I feel like ive changed, but nothing here has.

Bardot 2.07 a.m.: do you wish your friends and family had changed like you?

Alexander: 2.07 a.m.: well I guess a bit. Theyre all just doing the same thing

Bardot: 2.08 a.m: whats that?

Alexander: 2.09 a.m.: smoking weed… nothing else really

Bardot: 2.11 a.m.: do you do that?

Alexander: 2.12 a.m.: noo. Ive tried it a few times but I dont do that type of stuff

Bardot: 2.13 a.m.: I think your brain deserves better than that

Alexander: 2.15 a.m.: I think youre right. Hows Sweden?

Bardot: 2.15 a.m.: its very nice. Very white and snowy and very cold. Nobody likes being out when its this cold but I dont mind it. I think its nice as long as you keep yourself warm

Alexander: 2.17 a.m.: how do you do that?

Bardot: 2.18 a.m.: with ice cream of course

Alexander: 2.19 a.m.: haha what? Ice cream in that weather?

Bardot: 2.20 a.m.: I know its maybe a bit strange but I love ice cream no matter how cold it is. Most girls like chocolate or drinking wine. I prefer ice cream

Alexander: 2.21 a.m.: what flavor?

Bardot: 2.22 a.m.: hmmm. That is a good question. Depends on the brand and where you are. Unfortunately it is hard to get some of the good brands on my little island, but haag n dazs cookies n cream is my favorite

Alexander: 2.24 a.m.: I dont think ive ever had that one

Bardot: 2.25 a.m.: well then youre clearly not as smart as you think you are

Bardot 2.26 a.m.: but dont worry, I have faith in you. Even if you are American ;)

Alexander 2.27 a.m.: very funny. what are you eating for breakfast?

Bardot: 2.28 a.m.: do you know what filmjölk is?

Alexander: 2.29 a.m.: nope. Whats that?

Bardot: 2.29 a.m.: its a Swedish yogurt. Its very good and has very high protein. The vikings ate it.

Alexander: 2.30 a.m.: does that mean youre a viking?

Bardot: 2.30 a.m.: of course. Havent you seen my muscles?

Alexander: 2.31 a.m.: I shouldve guessed that was your viking ship sitting across the lake

Bardot: 2.32 a.m.: I built it myself too. All thanks to the filmjölk

Alexander: 2.33 a.m.: youre gonna have to bring me some back after christmas.

Bardot: 2.34 a.m.: that will be my present to you. But what are you going to get me?

Alexander: 2.35 a.m.: I bought you an in and out burger as soon as I landed. its wrapped up in my suitcase waiting for you.

Bardot: 2.35 a.m.: ew!

Alexander: 2.36 a.m.: haha dooont worry. But id never tell you anyway.

Bardot: 2.36 a.m.: youre mean

Alexander: 2.37 a.m.: itll be worth the wait. promise. so whatre you doing for christmas?

Bardot: 2.38 a.m.: it better be. And well for christmas we will probably just spend it with family. And new years I would like to spend with my friends but my mother has actually not been feeling so well lately so I might have to stay home and take care of her

Alexander: 2.39 a.m.: Is she gonna be okay?

Bardot: 2.40 a.m.: I think so. Shes just getting older and since shes drank her whole life it has not helped. Maybe if we give her enough filmjölk she will be okay

That made me laugh.

Alexander: 2.41 a.m.: if it helped the vikings maybe it can help her. Does your dad know about her condition?

Bardot: 2.43 a.m.: no not really but its okay.

Alexander: 2.44 a.m.: does he live in Sweden?

Bardot: 2.45 a.m.: Im not sure actually. I met him once when I was small and my mother just said he was an old friend and didnt tell me that he was my father until many years later. I just remember him looking like an angry little cat with almost no hair. Im not sure I would like him to be my dad anyway. When I was small I always imagined my dad as a big strong man with pretty hair. So I prefer to keep it that way. What about your dad?

Alexander: 2.47 a.m.: I think thats a good way to think. I know my dad, but lately I feel like thats not the case any more

Bardot 2.48 a.m.: why is that?

Alexander 2.51 a.m.: well he has two new kids and he married this girl who... this may sound messed up... but if she died I would throw a party

Bardot: 2.53 a.m: haha oh really? Whats wrong with her?

Alexander: 2.56 a.m.: shes just...i dunno...a bad person. And now they moved houses and he didnt even tell me and all my stuff is gone and I havent even seen him yet since ive been home

Bardot: 2.57 a.m.: and your mom passed away?

Alexander: 3.00 a.m.: yeah. But it's okay.

Bardot: 3.02 a.m.: You know something Alexander? Sometimes as I grow older I feel like I don't need all the people I thought I needed when I was growing up. I start to feel that I can actually take care of myself quite well and I dont need help from stupid grownups who think they know everything. When I was little I was always so jealous of my friends who had a dad but now I almost never even think of him at all but whenever I do all I see is that angry little cat in front of me and that makes me feel better about not knowing him

Alexander: 3.03 a.m.: that's a good way to put it. Youre quite poetic you know

Bardot: 3.04 a.m.: it's because I was raised by vikings

I began to hesitate over the next line.

Alexander: 3.07 a.m.: Bardot

Bardot: 3.07 a.m.: yes?

Alexander: 3.09 a.m. this may sound weird, but whenever I talk to you it feels like ive opened up a window and hung out my brain for some fresh air

Bardot: 3.10 a.m.: that doesnt sound weird

Alexander: 3:11 a.m.: it doesnt?

Bardot: 3.12 a.m.: nope. Whenever I talk to you it feels like the first time I ever took a shot of wheatgrass

Alexander: 3.12 a.m.: what! That doesnt sound good at all

Bardot: 3.14 a.m.: haha. I mean that it is intense at first and a lot to handle, but once it sinks in it feels like the sun is shining inside of you

Alexander: 3.15 a.m.: I wasnt expecting that. Thats maybe the nicest thing anyones ever said to me

Alexander: 3.16 a.m.: but you think Im intense?

Bardot: 3.17 a.m.: yes. But mostly I think that you are angry. And a little bit lost

Alexander: 3.18 a.m.: you do?

Bardot: 3.20 a.m.: yes. But its okay. Because I think Im angry too. And probably also a little bit lost. But maybe its better to be lost together than found and alone

Alexander: 3.21 a.m.: well Id like to think so

Bardot: 3.22 a.m.: but Alexander my little hamburger boy unfortunately I need to take my mom for her checkup now. And you need to sleep!

Alexander: 3.22 a.m.: youre right I probably should. Well...it was nice talking to you. I hope the checkup goes well and your mom feels better. Good night Bardot

Bardot: 3.23 a.m.: It was nice talking to you too. Good night Alexander. Have sweet dreams about me

IX

The next morning, I woke up and found my clothes washed and neatly folded on the nightstand next to me, with a massive Fiji bottle placed next to them. Probably the maid, I figured. It was December 23rd, and that unsettling Christmas feeling was burning a hole through my stomach.

Beau came in through the door in nothing but boxers, and he was so skinny the indent in his chest was more reminiscent of a salad bowl than a torso. His shoulders were so bony they resembled the pointy edges of an umbrella skeleton; his collarbones looked like car door handles.

"You wanna come with me to Venice?"

"Venice?" I asked.

"Yeah, Mason just got a new place. I said I'd come check it out. He always has a bunch of weed," he continued, his enthusiasm lukewarm at best.

"Okay."

"Cool."

Before we left, Beau grabbed an orange pill bottle and threw two of them in his mouth.

"What are those?" I asked.

"Huh?"

"*Those,*" I repeated, pointing.

"Oh," he said pensively, as if he'd never considered it before. "It's just Prozac."

"Why do you take that?"

"They say it's for depression."

"*Are* you depressed?"

"I dunno," he paused. "I guess."

As soon as we got in the car, Beau habitually lit up a joint and handed it to me; the first puff showed that my lungs had become initiated after yesterday.

"What happened there?" I asked suddenly, pointing to several long, striped scars on his wrist.

"What?" he said distantly.

"There," I said, and reached for his hand.

"Nothing!" He snapped, and pulled his hand away. "Sorry it's... it's nothing. I fell."

I realized I was still holding the joint, and instead of asking him again, I inhaled deeply and just stared out the window.

We took PCH all the way down to Santa Monica, then took Main Street down past Venice Boulevard, and pulled into one of those little alleys on Speedway where you're not actually supposed to park unless you have a permit, but Beau did anyway.

"Where is it?" I asked, stepping out of the car.

"Around the corner. There's like a weird entrance, I guess," Beau said.

"So Mason's dad moved?"

Beau laughed, "No, no. If Mason went to rehab for a month his dad said he'd get him a place."

"Rehab? Didn't you just say he has a bunch of weed?"

"Yeah," he said, shaking his head. "It's always been over for Mason, dude. He's an idiot." *Rehab*, I thought. Every kid I've ever known who's been to rehab is back on drugs within a week upon their release. Most of their parents even brag about it: the more expensive the rehab, the more they gloat.

We walked up to a big, concrete house with a metal gate, but knowing the hipster pretentiousness of modern Venice architecture, I could only assume the inside more than made up for the bland exterior. There was a telecom next to the door, and Beau pressed it and spoke into it, but all we heard on the other end was a bunch of coughing, and then the gate buzzed open. The inside was a complete 180 from the outside: glossy, wooden floors; iron handrails leading you up the stairs; and pristine, white walls with exposed ceiling beams to enhance the aesthetic, with a bunch of surfboards lined up against the wall. Must've cost a fortune.

As we walked further in, I could see the back of Mason's long, blonde, ratty hair enveloped in a big cloud of smoke.

"What up nigga," he called, without turning around. He started waving his hand for us to come over. Beau leaned over and skinned Mason's hand, but I already knew how he was going to react at the sight of me based on my experiences with him in the past.

"Holy *shit.* Are you fucking *kiddin'* me? Dude, what the fuck is up, you faggot?" Mason exclaimed. I stuck out my hand and he slapped it so hard it actually hurt.

"What's up," I replied, wincing.

"Dude, I haven't seen you in forever you big bitch," Mason punched me in the arm, but my reaction was interrupted when I noticed a big bowl of, what looked like, pure cocaine, on the table in front of me.

"What is that?" I said, pointing to the bowl.

"Flour. I was baking earlier."

"Really?"

"*NO!*" he shouted and laughed, slapping me on the leg.

"You fucking *idiot*! You think I bake? Uh, I'm not a *faggot,* bro."

I let out a weak, contemptuous laugh. "Is it coke?"

"Obviously it's fucking coke, bro. What's it look like? Jesus, dude. Don't they teach you anything over in fuckin' France, or wherever the fuck?"

"Apparently not," I said calmly.

"Want a bump?"

"Of coke?" I asked, instantly regretting my choice of words, having to brace myself for his inevitable reaction.

"No, uh… of *flour*. Dude, we *just* went through this! Are you fucking retarded?" Mason was wearing a Tupac t-shirt, had diamond earrings, and a knife shaped necklace dangling from his neck, and he leaned forward, scooped some coke on it and brought it up to his nose with a loud snort "Come on, dude. Don't be a pussy."

"I'm okay," I said.

"Well Beau's not a *bitch,* right?"

He turned to Beau, who I'd momentarily forgotten was even in the room.

"Uhm," Beau hesitated. I could tell he didn't want to, but I knew he wasn't going to say no. "Yeah, okay."

Beau leaned forward and Mason handed him his necklace.

"Good shit, right?" Mason asked proudly.

"Yeah," Beau said, and leaned back down on the couch, gently rubbing his nose.

"Are you seriously not gonna have any?" Mason asked again, as if it were a personal insult to deny his offer.

"I really don't want any."

"Bro, you are such a bitch," he grabbed his bong and handed it to me. "You better at least take a snap."

I sighed, making no effort to hide my reluctance. "All right,"

I submitted. The bong was much stronger than the joint and I began coughing almost instantly, smoke pouring out of every hole in my face.

"Snap it, pussy!" Mason laughed obnoxiously. "Are you serious? Bro, you can't even clear it!"

I placed it down next to me, and struggled to contain my coughing while wiping the tears from my eyes.

"Bro, like... I always thought you were straight, but I guess France has made you a faggot or something. I'm like... kinda disappointed, man. Like... for real," he said theatrically, before turning to Beau and snickering again.

"Siri," Mason shouted. "Play Snoop Dogg."

Music immediately started blasting from the speakers fastened in each corner of the ceiling, and I just sat there, uncomfortably high, staring at the bowl of coke in front of me.

Despite the deafening music, which Mason didn't even seem to notice, he turned on the TV and started flipping through channels until he came across a soccer game. Immediately, the hectic chatter of a couple of European sounding commentators blasted from the TV: the soccer game, and rap music now just one big mesh of noise.

"That guy's so bad," Mason said.

"Who?" I asked vacantly.

"Balotelli."

"What?"

"*Look* at him," he said, pointing to one of the players dribbling a ball across the field.

"Oh," I said.

"You know I beat him right?" Mason said.

I laughed, waiting for the joke, but he remained stolid.

"You beat him?" I asked incredulously.

"You're such a fucking idiot, dude," he snorted. "How do you think I paid for all this?"

"What are you *talking* about?" I began, getting frustrated. "*Paid* for all this?"

"Dude, are you fucking retarded? I've been a professional soccer player since I was, like, nine."

"*What?*"

"Yeah, when I was eleven, they sent me to Portugal and I trained with Ronaldo's trainer, who said I was a prodigy."

"*What?*" I repeated.

"Bro, I lived there for like *all* of seventh and eighth grade just playing soccer," Mason said, as I scanned my memory, a clear image of Mason in seventh and eighth grade sitting in my classes, with no talk about ever going to Portugal.

"Dude, we had classes together in seventh grade," I said.

"Yeah, okay, like *one* maybe. But then I left for Russia and…"

"You said *Portugal*," I said.

"Yeah, Portugal. That's what I said," Mason scoffed, inhaling the milky bong smoke from between his legs. Suddenly, Beau kicked me discreetly, put a finger to his lips and shook his head.

"*What?*" I whispered.

"*Dude,* just drop it," he wheezed. "I'll tell you about it later. Just stop *asking* about it."

Mason didn't hear our whispering, and exhaled proudly before setting the bong back down next to him.

I knew I should shut up, but I couldn't resist. "So, you're a *professional soccer* player?" I prodded again.

"It doesn't surprise me that you don't get it, bro." Mason

flipped the channel and landed on a basketball game. "These faggots don't know how to dribble either," he snickered, and continued flipping. "Fuckin' bitches."

When Mason was fourteen, he stole his dad's Bentley and crashed it on Sunset, but all his parents did was ground him for a week. On his fifteenth birthday, he got an Escalade that his parents said he couldn't drive until he got his license. Three weeks later, he crashed that one too.

After a while I raised myself from the couch. "I'm gonna get some air," I said. Beau and Mason were so violently stoned that it didn't even seem like they heard me.

I left through the back door and came out to the alley and began walking north towards the boardwalk. The sun was setting at this point which made me realize how long we'd been inside Mason's place. My vision was hazy and my eyes were still a bit vibrant, and each step I took felt lighter than the next. I hadn't eaten anything all day, so I walked and walked until I came to this little pizza place on the boardwalk and bought a slice. When you're high, you're never really present but you're never entirely detached either, instead, you're just hovering between reality and deception, and everything takes just a little bit longer to process than it normally would.

I watched as the skaters carved their boards up and down the pavement, each turn followed by howls of tortured rubber screaming against the cement. Like an outdoor museum displaying the weirdos of L.A., I observed the freaks as I walked along. Some were dancing barefoot on glass; some juggling knives and chainsaws; some selling distorted paintings of the Los Angeles skyline; others handing out medical marijuana cards.

I finished my slice, threw my paper plate in the trash and

continued walking down the street as the bright red sun slowly sank into the ocean, like a fat girl tentatively lowering herself into a pool.

As I stood there watching all these bizarre creatures perform, desperately bleeding for any and all pocket change, I noticed an old man walking down the street wearing nothing but one shoe and a crop-top, his whole package on display, carelessly fluttering in the wind. I stared at him as he wobbled with each footstep, trying each and every door handle he came across, to no avail. He would knock, bang, and tug on every single knob for a few seconds, and then stumble down the road until he got to the next one.

Just beyond him I noticed a couple of Mexican kids playing soccer with a ratty old ball that looked like it was about to deflate at any second.

I continued walking and saw two hulkish men walking towards me, and as they got closer I recognized them as these twins I used to go to school with.

"Nathan? Tyler?" I asked, as they got closer.

"Alex!" one of them shouted. I really couldn't tell them apart.

"Wow. You guys are huge!" I said bashfully, poking one of them in the arm. I realized I was still pretty high, so I tried to keep it together, their neck veins wiggling as they laughed proudly.

"Thanks."

"Yeah, we know."

"Man," I said, still shocked. "I can't believe how big you two are." They dwarfed Dwayne Johnson, I swear. "Are you guys like bodybuilders, or something?"

"Yeah."

"Yeah, IFBB pro. We compete."

"We just had a photo shoot down at the beach."

"Wow," I said, meaning it. "Good for you two."

"Thanks, man."

The conversation suddenly stalled, and I tried to think of something. "So uh, how's your sister and stuff?" I asked, as I remembered they had an older sister who used to drive them to school when we were younger.

"Who, Brooke?"

"Yeah. *Brooke*! How's she doing?"

"Ah..." one of them began shaking his head.

"Yeah, she uh... she's a fuck-up," followed by a sick laugh.

"*What?*" I asked.

"She stole forty grand from our dad and crashed his car so he kicked her out and now she's living with some meth head in Camarillo who she just shoots up with every day."

"*What?*" I gasped.

"Yeah, it's pretty gnarly."

"Yeah, we haven't seen her in a while."

"Fuck. I-I'm sorry to hear that," I said.

"Don't be."

"Yeah, she's a bitch. Nobody speaks to her anymore." They both snickered indifferently.

"Man... I uh..."

"Who cares, dude?"

"Yeah, she's a loser."

"Well, I'm happy to see you two are doing well, at least," I said sympathetically.

"Thanks."

I couldn't stop staring at their arms.

"I still can't believe how big you two are. You look like

you're on steroids," I said jokingly.

"I mean, we are, but so is everyone."

"Yeah, exactly."

"*Steroids?*"

"Yeah, so?" one of them said, instantly triggered.

"No-no. I didn't mean it like that, I just... I mean... doesn't that stuff like... don't your *balls* shrink?"

"Dude. I can bench four-twenty and my balls are fine."

"Yeah, that's just a myth."

"Yeah. We're *fine*."

"Oh, okay. I just didn't know," I nodded with nervous agreement, trying to hide my skepticism.

"You're *super* skinny," one of them said.

I visually compared the width of our biceps. "Yeah, I guess I am."

They chuckled pitifully, before marching off in unison.

"*God is the answer! Jesus saves! God will free you from your sins!*" I heard someone shout from a megaphone, while riding down the street on a bicycle, his shoulders draped in a handwritten cardboard sign with Biblical inscriptions.

A bearded dude on roller-skates, in a turban, who I recognized from years before, skated by, a miniature amplifier dangling from his waist, while he soloed on an electric guitar.

"You gotta buy one of my t-shirts, man," he said as he got closer; skating around me in circles, pulling out a t-shirt from his bag.

"Sorry," I said, holding up my hand.

"No apologies in the jungle, brotha," he smirked, and then he rolled away down the boardwalk.

I began walking back to Mason's place, passing all the tattoo parlors on the right, guys tattooed from head to toe waiting outside, trying to attract any tourist naive enough to spend fifty bucks on a badly drawn *Carpe Diem* tramp stamp.

A bunch of personified tourist traps were shouting in all directions, aggressively imploring me to listen to, and buy, their mixtape , so I took a back alley out from the boardwalk to avoid them. As I wandered through the alley I saw an old man, almost naked, smoking something out of a dirty glass pipe. I grimaced at the sight of him, and when he saw me, he tilted his head back and smiled proudly, flaring his remaining brown teeth, before resuming his smoking. I thought about the man who had been trying to open all those doors, and the man sitting in that alley, and Brooke and her meth-head sugar-daddy and what must've happened for them to end up like that—all these different people, completely messed up with no place to go. Then I thought about Bardot, and how I never wanted to bring her here.

When I got back to Mason's place, Beau and Mason were in the exact same spot I left them in, playing FIFA. I said hi to them, and Beau answered vacantly; Mason didn't even notice.

"Oh, dude, by the way," Beau started. "Oceans here."

"What?" I asked.

I heard a toilet flush behind me, and as I turned around and the door opened, it felt like meeting someone from a dream in real life; someone you didn't know, yet were oddly familiar with.

"Hey," I said awkwardly. He had grown out his hair, like Jim Morrison, and had a five o'clock shadow and a lit cigarette taped to his bottom lip. He had rings, and some of his nails were carelessly painted black.

"*Huh*," he said indifferently, zipping up his pants. "What's up?"

"W-what's up, man," I said nervously, like seeing an ex for the first time in years.

He walked right past me and slumped over in the couch. "I'm next," I heard him say to the others. I just stood there, staring at him. His face was much thinner, and in the span of him exiting the bathroom to cementing himself in the couch, he must've smoked three full cigarettes. I approached the couch and tentatively sat down next to him, but he said nothing. Finally, eyes still glued to the TV, he asked, "How's England?"

The question startled me. "Good."

"Cool."

"How's everything in L.A.?"

"S'all right," he said, followed by an extended pause. "How long're you here?"

"Just for the break."

"Cool."

I wasn't sure if time was moving either too slowly or too quickly, but eventually everybody seemed to get up and discuss their plans for departure. I sat there quietly, unsure of what to do.

"Dude, my dad said I can't have anybody sleep over tonight because they're cleaning the house tomorrow," Beau said to me, which took me a second to register but, when I did, I got nervous because the last thing I wanted to do was go back to *my* dad's house.

"What?" I asked.

"Yeah. He's being a dick," he answered.

"You can sleep here if you—" Mason began.

"—you can sleep at my place," Ocean interrupted.

"Really?"

"Sure," he answered.

170

Before we left everyone said goodbye to Mason and I lied when I said that I'd call him soon again. Ocean and I walked over to a sparklingly new BMW parked on the street.

"Are you hungry?" he asked, starting the ignition.

"Not really."

"Me neither."

"What's the deal with Mason?" I asked abruptly, as we drove past the Malibu sign on PCH, dusk rapidly invading the horizon.

"Huh?"

"He said he's like...he said he lived in France and plays soccer and..."

"Ah, he's lost it," he chuckled dismissively. "Don't listen to anything he says."

"What happened? He wasn't always like that."

"All that ketamine, man. Been to rehab, like, five times."

"*Five* times?"

"It's not *that* many."

When we got to the front gate of Ocean's house, I realized that he'd moved, since I didn't recognize anything. Before we got out of the car, I caught a furtive glance at his long, dark hair, and then noticed my own, preppy haircut in the rearview mirror, and, suddenly, I felt very awkward and out of place.

"My girlfriend might come over later," Ocean muttered, as he rummaged through his fridge.

"You got a girlfriend?" I asked.

"Yeah," he said, showing no enthusiasm.

"What's her name?"

"Karen."

"Cool…" I paused. "Is she cute?"

"Fuck no," he said, shutting the fridge.

I began laughing, assuming he was kidding, but when I noticed his stiff expression, I quickly shut up. "I can't tell if you're kidding."

"I'm not. She's beat."

"Why're you with her?"

"I dunno…" he shrugged and poured himself some cereal. "Convenience, I guess."

"Oh."

We sat silently, feeling very small in the massive kitchen, eating cereal on the marble countertop.

"I was at Cross Creek today," I blurted.

"Oh yeah?"

"Yeah. I saw the red hammer statue. Remember when we'd always try to climb it?"

"Yeah," he smirked.

"Did you ever end up getting to the top?"

"No."

"Me neither."

He poked at the remaining cereal with his spoon.

"I hate Froot Loops," he said suddenly. "Lupé always gets the wrong cereal."

Karen never ended up coming over.

X
Christmas

Like a library book that had been re-shelved in the wrong section, I was sitting on the couch wondering what the hell I was doing there. Esmeralda's hysterically drunk relatives were obnoxiously parading around the living room like they owned the place, my ears were bleeding from the deafening sound of Pit-Bull on the speakers, and Esmeralda and my dad's new kid was opening his umpteenth present under the tree. Lying next to him was a mountain of half-opened presents with most of the tape and wrapping paper still attached, a shameless display of this kid's feverish gluttony, a trait undoubtedly inherited from his mom, although I did see a bit of my dad in him, too. As he had done with each previous present, as soon as a fourth of the wrapping paper had been violently torn off, he began to bawl, but my dad and Esmeralda only laughed, and smothered him with kisses, while the rest of her family members smiled and drank sangria. Even though Esmeralda can't speak Spanish, everyone else spoke it fluently, including my dad, so I guess they didn't care that I couldn't talk to anyone.

"Alex!" my dad called, the first time he'd acknowledged me all evening. "Come help me in the kitchen."

I reluctantly stood up and followed him into the kitchen.

"So, have you gotten to know Esmeralda's family? Aren't they friendly?"

"Well, I wouldn't know, they don't fuckin' speak English."

"*Hey,*" he snapped, turning to me irritably. "What's with the attitude? They're nice people. *Get* to know them," he commanded.

"How? They-do-not-speak-English," I repeated, my frustration evident. "And no one's said a word to me. They just glare at me."

"Whatever, Alex," he sighed. "If you refuse to even make an effort, then this conversation is pointless..." I swear, sometimes I think he's genuinely delusional. "But do me a favor and bring this sangria out to the living room and ask if anybody wants some more."

"Dad," I said firmly. "Can I ask you something?"

"Mhmm," he mumbled, preoccupied with the sangria.

"Why did you ask me to come here?"

"What?" he asked, shifting his body towards me.

"Why did you bring me here? I mean, like, why did you *force* me to come home? What's the point of me even being here? It's Christmas Eve, and do you know what I've done today? I've watched your new kid open presents for the last three hours, the entire house is overrun by people who don't know I exist, and this is pretty much the first time I've even seen you since I've been home, and I don't even think you've realized that. I literally haven't seen you until today. And do you know that the *day* I landed Esmeralda literally asked me how much time I would be spending here because she didn't want me around the house, and then it just hit me... does *any*one? Because it doesn't seem like *you* do."

He put one hand on his hip, and stared at me perplexedly.

"What the hell are you talking about?"

I sighed. "The first time you've talked to me all day is *now* when you're asking me to be a waiter for Esmeralda and her family."

"*Waiter*?" he scoffed. "You're just like your mother—everything's gotta be *so* fuckin' dramatic. How 'bout you show a little gratitude instead. *Hey dad, thanks for paying my forty-thousand-dollar tuition.* Ever consider that? Now stop being such a spoiled little brat and help me bring this out to—"

"—You didn't answer my question."

He paused. "And what was that?"

"Why did you ask me to come?"

"I *did* answer that. I told you to stop being so fucking dramatic."

"Still not an answer, dad. Why do you want me here? You know Esmeralda hates me, and I hate her too—"

"—There you *go* again!" he threw his hands up frustratedly. "She does *not* hate you. Cut it out with your self-pitying *bull*shit, Alexander! This Oliver Twist routine is getting old. You're a spoiled little shit from Malibu who goes to one of the most expensive boarding schools in Europe, so stop moping around like you don't know where your next meal is gonna come from."

"If you can't even answer a question then I don't need this shit," I interrupted, turning away.

"What?" he snorted. "And where the hell are *you* going?" but I didn't answer.

I started gagging, as I raced through the living room, and I heard Esmeralda shout, "What's taking so long?"

I ran out into the middle of the street, shaking, and then it finally came, and I puked all over the sidewalk. I keeled over, hands on my knees, and tried to expel whatever was left inside of me, and then I tried ordering an Uber, but I couldn't get one so, eventually, I just called a cab.

* * *

The valley is always pretty quiet, especially during the holidays. The neon lights are all still on, but you get a feeling of loneliness that you can't shake off when you're driving down those desolate valley streets late at night, knowing that most people are inside with their families celebrating a wonderful holiday, whereas here you are, stuck in the backseat, with some depressing, stinky old man driving you around. We drove past the massage parlor where I was molested on my first day back, and I wondered what that little old Thai woman was doing tonight, and if my driver had ever spent any money in there and if she knew him, or any other cab drivers around town who didn't get any action aside from her hand or their own.

When I was younger, my dad would usually work on Christmas day since he was divorced and the only person to celebrate it with was me and I guess he didn't see the point in that, so my friends and I—most of my friends are Jewish so they didn't even celebrate Christmas in the first place—would take the bus out to the valley from Malibu or Santa Monica and find some old, rundown bar that hadn't been remodeled since the '70s, and even though we were only around fourteen years old, we'd never get carded—probably because they desperately needed the business—so we'd just sit there drinking, surrounded by all the other lonely alcoholics who had no body or place to go home to. It's real sad, too, because those bars that we'd get into would always make the slightest effort to participate in any Christmas spirit, too, if you know what I mean. There'd be a couple of red and green lights in desperate need of a change draped around the TV, and they'd usually have that fake, washable snow spray painted across the windows reading *Merry Christmas*, a sight so miserable it just made you want to cry. When I was a kid, I thought that going to those places with my friends was awesome because we could get drunk and blaze in the parking lot and nobody would say a word, but now that I was a bit older, thinking about all that made me want to jump off a bridge.

Even though I knew the exact directions, I asked the driver to just drive around a little extra since I hadn't driven around this area at night for quite some time, and besides, I felt kind of bad that he was forced to drive a fucking taxi on Christmas day, so I thought the extra fare would be a nice gesture. I even tried to talk to him a few times and ask him how long he had been a driver for, and whatnot, but every time he opened his mouth, he began coughing so violently it sounded like he was having a heart attack, so I quit talking out of fear of him passing out at the wheel, or something, and killing us both.

After about ten extra minutes of driving around, I noticed the meter had crawled up quite a bit so I thought it'd be best to stop aimlessly driving around and actually take me where I needed to go, so I told him the address and we headed down towards Van Nuys boulevard. As we got further and further down Van Nuys, I started recognizing the buildings and the houses and the park benches and jungle gyms that had now become a nursery for the homeless, the flickering street lights desperately crying out for a change. When we got to my stop I thanked the driver, gave him the fare, with a pretty healthy tip, and stepped out.

The tan, water damaged building stared back at me as I nervously approached the ratty old steps leading to the apartment. I recognized the golden 42 on the door, but the 4 had fallen off and now you could only make out the shaded outline of where it once hung. I was so anxious I thought I was going to throw up again, but I regained myself, bit the bullet, and rang the doorbell.

I waited for at least a minute, then I rang it again, three times in a row. I put my ear up to the door to see if I could hear anything, and suddenly I heard a bunch of scrambling on the other side, followed by heavy footsteps wearily approaching the door. I instantly stepped back, realizing they were coming near, and I licked my fingertips and tried to fix my hair to look presentable.

The door slightly cracked open, and a boozy voice called out, "Who's there?"

I hesitated at first, but then I answered, "Mom, it's me."

I could feel the hesitation in her voice too, but, finally, she unlocked the chain and opened the door completely, seeing each other for the first time in almost two years.

"Hi mom," I said.

"Oh…Alexander," she said, as she covered her mouth with her hand, a wine bottle tightly clutched in the other. She swung her arms around me and when I hugged her back, I could smell the stench of cigarettes and wine on her breath.

She finally loosened her grip, stared me up and down, and told me to come in. The apartment looked like hell, and scattered across her coffee table were three empty wine bottles that she had probably finished within the last hour. A bunch of prescription pill bottles were sprinkled around the floor, and as I struggled to absorb it all, I looked over and noticed that she was already falling back asleep on the couch.

"Mom!"

She jolted, her eyes popping, and then looked up at me and smiled, "Oh Alexander, hunny. I'm sorry, baby, it's the Xanax. Come. Sit down, please, please. Tell me, darling, how is school? How is everything?" she asked casually, as if I'd just come home off the bus.

"School's nice, mom. I'm—"

"Did you see my tree?" she interrupted, proudly pointing to an apologetic, undecorated tree in the corner.

"Yeah it's—it's nice," I stuttered. "Is it fake?"

"Well of *course* it's fake, baby. Got it a few years ago. *Such* a bargain. But packing it back into the box is such a hassle—oh, those boxes they come in are so small, you can't understand how they even fit the damned thing in there in the first place, and what for *any*way? *Just* to unpack it again in a few months? So I just leave it up all year long. Isn't that great? That way it's *always* Christmas at mommy's house," she hiccupped and fell backwards onto the couch.

"That's nice," I said.

"Did you cut your hair?" she asked, adjusting herself.

"What?"

"Hunny, it's gotten so short, when did you cut it?"

"Mom, I cut it years ago."

"What?"

"You've seen it like this. It's been short for a while now."

"Mm, yes, I remember now. So handsome. How's school?"

"Schools really good."

"Mmm...made any friends?"

"Yeah, I have. They're a great group of guys. You'd really love them."

"I'm sure I would," she said, downing the rest of her glass. "How long have you been back, baby?"

"Just a few days."

"You waited that long to see your mama?"

"I meant to come sooner, I'm sorr—"

"Hush, I'm teasing. Hunny, wait," her glossy eyes began to widen as she sat up on the couch. "What are you doing for New

179

Years?"

"Uhm…I'm not su—"

"Why don't we go to Miami… no…*Paris*! You and me. It'll be wonderful. Oh, I love Paris. Remember when we were there?"

"Mom…I've never been to Paris."

"Even better! Oh, imagine the two of us in Paris. Would you do that with me, baby? Would you come to Paris with your poor old mama?" she continued with childish naivety, her wine glass rattling in her hand as she fervently shifted around on the couch.

"Mom, I… I don't know if—"

"Come! Just imagine it! Oh, *Paris*. I spent *so* many years in that city when I was young. All those festive nights—*Paris…* little did I know," she stopped talking, thinking, as if trying to remember the taste of some forgotten childhood sweet. "I have friends there, you know," she said proudly, her tone shifting. "*Photographers*. They always told me what a perfect canvas my face was; what a luxury it was to shoot me. We wouldn't even have to find a hotel. Oh, Alexander. We could stay with them. We would have a fabulous room overlooking the Champs Elysée and drink coffee with croissants every morning and in the evenings we'd go dancing in Montparnasse and…"

"… *Mom, I…*"

"Oh…" her tone suddenly deflated. "Oh, yes of…of course. What was I *thinking*," she playfully slapped herself on the head. "You have school. You have to study. You can't be off in *Paris* with some old lady like me. You need your edu*cation*. No time for dancing, isn't that right, baby?"

I nodded, as I reminisced over all of the stories and adventures she'd promised me as a child: *'We're going to Disney World for your birthday and I'm going to get you anything you want and we're going to buy a house in New York. And one day,*

*you and I are moving to Naples, Alexander. Oh, hunny, it'll be
just the two of us. Just you and me, forever, the way we always
wanted.'* But we never went to Naples. We never went to Disney
World. We never did any of it.

"You look just like Robert Redford, you know. Anybody
ever tell you that?"

"No," I replied bashfully. "No one's ever told me that."

"I met him, you know. In Cannes when I was a young girl.
He asked me to marry him. *Bobby,*" she giggled, becoming
distant. "Your father didn't like that story. Claimed I was *lying,*"
she snorted. "But he knew it was true. Oh, he *hated* it when I told
people that story at parties—he was always *so* jealous of me at
parties—but it's true, you know. You could've been Alexander
Redford," she said with a sneer. "The men I rejected for your
father. You think I ever got any gratitude for *that?* I rejected
Robert Redford. He wanted *me,"* she snapped. "Oh, and don't
even get me *started* on Warren Beatty," she said, reaching for a
cigarette.

"Mom, I thought you *quit,*" I said, intercepting it.

"Oh, hunny. Spare your poor old mother. Let her have her
cigarette, it's Christmas."

"All right," I sighed, retracting my hand.

"How is your father?"

"I couldn't care less," I blurted. But I did mean it.

"*Hmpf,*" she said, rolling her eyes. "How's that little whore
of hi—"

"—*Mom,* please."

"You're right," she sighed. "You're right, you're right."

"I'm not...*defending* them, but they just make me mad, and
I don't—I came here to see *you.*"

She smiled and began eying me up and down again with

careful steadiness, as if to see how her investment had turned out.

"Oh, Alexander. Look at you. You've gotten so handsome. My little baby," she said. "Oh, how I've missed you."

"I missed you too, mom."

She smiled at me, flashing her crimson teeth yet again, but I could tell her eyes were starting to shut so I tried to think of something stimulating to say.

"So... how've your holidays been? Any company?"

"What?" she said, as she came to again.

"I asked if you've had any company."

She laughed, rolled her eyes and dismissively waved her hand through the air. "*Me*? No, no. *God*, no. Pigs. Bunch of fucking *luuu*natics. And you know *what*?"

"*Mom*."

"Yeah, okay, okay. But no, sweetie, I'm not seeing anyone. At least not any more. I was for a while—hmpf, *Randy*—up until a few months ago. He came barging in here and *stole* my DVD player!" She scoffed. "Would you bel*ieve* that? Com*pleeeete* lunatic. Then he proposed to me a week later. Oh, you should've *seen* the little ring he had. Tragic. Abso*lutely* tragic. I told him I'd think about it, but I never called him, and now he's left me about eight million voicemails and texts—he's even come banging on my door in the middle of the night a few times—but lord knows why I'd ever give him another chance. He's puh-*theh*-tic."

My mom continued talking about all the men who wanted her, and I just sat there and listened because at the moment that was all I could give her, even if the excessive personal details made me gag. She used to go to a therapist when I was younger, and to be honest I actually noticed a difference in her behavior, but I doubt she could afford him anymore, because if she could,

I don't think she'd be living like *this,* or seeing the kind of guys she'd been seeing. When I was a kid, and before my dad got rich and we still lived in that shitty little apartment on Venice Boulevard I had this old photo album of my mom when she was a teenager, and I remember thinking how beautiful she was and how proud I was to have a mom who looked like that. But now, when I was sitting across from her on the couch, there was nothing left but an abandoned, old shell that carried no resemblance to that pretty girl from all those years ago. Although she was older now, her wrinkles stretching across her face like spider webs, in some ways it felt like I was listening to a little girl, lost and deserted, praying that someone would come pick her up so she wouldn't have to try and find her own way home. I studied her face and listened to her lavish stories, her delusions of glory having smashed against the rocks of reality for so long that eventually there was nothing left at all.

In the middle of her speech, she started dozing off, eventually falling asleep, but instead of trying to wake her up I just covered her with a blanket and kissed her on the forehead. I walked into the kitchen where the sink was overflowing with dirty dishes, and as much as I hate getting food on my hands, I'd rather help out my mom than be back at my dad's Christmas party.

After all the dishes were done, I cleaned the countertops with this ratty old sponge I found under the sink, doing my best to make it look as habitable as possible. I went out into the living room and threw away the empty wine bottles and tried to find any discarded pill bottles that needed to be trashed.

I went into her bedroom and tried to clean up a bit in there too, until I found a couple of used condoms on the floor, sadly realizing that no good deed goes unpunished. I found a Xanax and a couple of Valium on the nightstand next to her bed and swallowed them, and then I walked back out into the living room. I stared at my mom sleeping for another minute or so and couldn't help but pray that hopefully her dreams were better than her reality, because staring at the life she had made for herself wasn't much of a life to live. I thought about waking her up and saying good-bye, but it felt hopeless, so I kissed her good night and then I left.

When I stepped out into the street I glanced back up at the forlorn apartment, and it felt like nothing but emptiness had ever existed behind those doors, and if I would ever return, I was sure that I wouldn't find anyone living in there again, like entering a nostalgia shop that only sold you back your own nightmares. I thought about when those apartments had been built and how much effort must have been put into making them look pretty and livable, but now, much like my mom, maintenance and effort had ceased entirely, and now there was nothing left but a decaying old artifact, memories of a time that would soon disappear.

I wished I'd known her when she was young and pretty and full of confidence and charm, just the way she was in that old photo album I used to have of her as a kid. I wish I could've spoken to her and sat down with her, before her descent into this hell that she'd created for herself, and just give her a hug and tell her that it didn't have to be like this. I wished I could've seen my parents when they were kids and met each other for the first time. I wondered what my parents were like when they were young, and if my mom had the same effect on my dad that Bardot had on me, and I wondered if he was a gentleman and if he treated my mom like a princess and if they made each other smile, and I wished I could've known the look on their faces when they were happy and in love, before all this money got in the way. I wondered if, on days like this—when my dad was blinded with the fallacy that some young gold digger made him happy, and my mom was alone and unconscious from another wine and Xanax induced coma—they thought about each other. I wondered about a lot of things, I realized, but after a while it just felt hopeless, like punching in a dream.

I walked down the desolate valley street for several blocks until I came across Twain's Deli that's open 24/7. Most delis in L.A., especially the Jewish ones, have this thing called a black and white cookie, and when I realized I hadn't had one for over two years I almost forgot everything that had just happened because of how excited I got.

The ceiling fans were crackling and felt like they could've fallen off at any second, and the lights emitted this mustard-colored angst, and the '70s stone covered walls didn't exactly aid the aesthetic either, but despite the tacky interior, I felt unbelievably calm. Some haggard old man with a red, bubbly nose asked me what I wanted, but just then the drugs began to take hold and I felt my desire for a cookie suddenly disappear, so instead I just waved at him, and wobbled back outside.

I thought they were just going to put me to sleep, but instead I actually felt pretty buzzed, so I decided to call up Beau to see what he was doing, since he was Jewish and didn't celebrate Christmas.

He picked up pretty quickly, which was unusual for Beau, "Hello?"

"Yooo, iss Alex. Wassup?" I said, slurring my words

"Alex?" I heard music in the background. "Why're you calling me? It's Christmas."

"Nah, nah. Not for *meee.* I took some bars. Where you at?"

"Dude, I can barely understand a word you're saying," he

laughed. "But if you can understand *me*, we're at the Viper Room. Come."

"The *Viper* Room? *Duuude*, we're not twenty-one."

"Ocean knows the bouncer," Beau chuckled. "It's chill."

"Oh, sweet. All*rightey*, then. Peace."

"Peace."

When I opened my phone to call an Uber, I saw that Bardot had texted me: *God jul Alexander.* I didn't know what it meant, but it made me smile. I was going to write something back but the screen started to get fuzzy, and my fingers weren't obeying me so I stuffed it back in my pocket and waited for my ride, the valley breeze comfortingly tousling my hair, letting me know that I wasn't alone.

XI

I always had a weird thing for The Viper Room, because River Phoenix died on the sidewalk right outside the club and whenever I walked past it, I'd always have to stop and take a second to stare at the sidewalk and try to imagine what it was like seeing him there, on Halloween, over twenty years ago, squirming and convulsing in front of his younger siblings who could do nothing but panic as they helplessly watched their older brother die. Thinking about that always made me sad, but I also wished I could have been there, just so I could have seen what it was like.

When I arrived and stepped out of the car, I realized how loopy I was. I guess I was wobbling as I walked, because before I even made it to the front door this behemoth of a bouncer just shook his head at me and grunted, "Ain't gon' happen."

In any other situation my tongue would've gotten the best of me and I probably would've gotten punched in the face, but thanks to the state I was in I just called Beau and told him I was outside waiting.

When Beau and Ocean came outside, I could already tell that they were more fucked up than I was, but Ocean just fist bumped the bouncer and then he immediately let me in.

There was this terrible Sublime cover band on stage which really made you envy the deaf but, after a while, the music itself slowly faded out and all you could hear, and feel, were noises and vibrations. Ocean and Beau led me to a booth in the back where a bunch of people were sitting that I had never seen before, but I could only assume that one of them was Karen by the air of entitlement in which she carried herself, glaring when she finally caught sight of me.

"Alex, this is Karen," Ocean said. Karen stuck out her limp flipper of a hand and waited for me to take it.

"It's nice to meet you. I've heard a lot about you," I said, my tongue struggling to find its rhythm in my mouth.

"Aw, *really*?" she smiled, and slowly retracted her hand. "That's so cute."

"Alex," Ocean grabbed me. "*Alex*. This is Zeus."

Next to Ocean I saw this short, coked out Smurf of a man who must've been close to forty, wearing a pinstriped blazer, sequin embroidered converse, and a budget Mick Jagger haircut that wasn't so much brushed, as forced into submission. He looked like one of those generic, old roadies who linger around rock concerts with a VIP pass dangling around their neck, hounding young groupies and fabricating stories of their days partying with Robert Plant in the '70s. For some reason those guys are always sweaty and always in a hurry, and Zeus fit the description perfectly, as I watched pearls of sweat slowly shimmy down the side of his temples.

"*Alex*. Great name," he slapped my back with aggressive friendliness. "That short for Alex*ander*?"

"Yeah," I said.

"Nice, nice. Clean, classic, biblical. The *Maccabees*, man. Alexander the Great. Fuckin' hero. You Greek, man?"

"No."

"No worries, bro. Don't sweat it. My names Zeus and I'm not fuckin' Greek either, bro. But who cares? You know what I

188

say to anyone who cares? Fuck 'em! That's a great name, man. *Great* fuckin' name," the words were firing out of his mouth like a machine gun. This dude looked like he was about to pass out, or have a heart attack, at any second. I stuck out my hand and tried not to yelp as his shaky, sweaty fingers enveloped my own. After Zeus sat back down, Ocean came over to me and whispered proudly, "He can literally get us *any*thing we need, dude."

Ocean pulled away, and waited for me to mirror his enthusiasm, but I just nodded blankly, "Cool."

I took a seat in the booth, and Zeus slid a perspiring beer across the table, shot a finger gun at me, and tried to wink, which really just looked like he was having a stroke. In all honesty, he seemed pretty harmless, but I just had no idea why the hell a guy that age was hanging around a bunch of teenagers, but then I figured it was probably because he wanted to get closer to their parents.

"I'ma go skiing really quick," Ocean hollered, followed by a loud snort. Then he turned to me, "Alex—*down*?"

"Skiing?" I asked. Ocean poked at his nostril.

"Oh, uh…I'm good," I said, but Ocean just shrugged, took Karen and Zeus by the hand and left, leaving Beau and I alone, which was actually a relief.

I leaned over to Beau and whispered, "Dude, how old is that Zeus guy?"

Beau laughed and shook his head, "He's, like, pretty old, but he gets us in anywhere and has free coke," followed by another laugh. "You want a bump?" he asked.

"Here?" I asked with a gasp.

He shrugged, "Yeah, *here*."

The fact that it was apparently such a *given* almost convinced me that it wasn't such a bad idea after all. And I had started feeling a bit tired from the bars I took earlier, and that beer was becoming an anvil in my stomach, so I caved, and followed Beau to the bathroom.

"Go to the stall next to mine, and I'll pass it to you underneath," he whispered before we stepped inside. I was pretty nervous, and I don't think I said anything aside from a quiet nod. He pushed the door open and there were a couple of guys peeing in the urinals, but they were struggling to stand up, so I figured I shouldn't concern myself with their opinion.

I went into the adjoining stall and listened to see if I could hear anything, and then it came: a thunderous snort that echoed throughout the entire bathroom. His nose was like a vacuum, because the snorting just continued until he finally knocked on the cheap plastic divider, and I saw a sweaty hand peak out underneath with a little plastic bag half-filled with some white stuff. I heard him exit the stall, wash his hands, and leave the bathroom, and then it appeared that I was completely alone in the bathroom because the other guys had left, so I turned my back towards the door, took out my Highland key, dipped it in the bag and brought it up to my nose.

I had never done it before, so I didn't know what to expect, but I didn't expect it to be as overwhelming as it was. The first bump was like a fast rush of carbonated water up my nose and down my throat. I felt my eyes clench together and then I started rubbing my nose, but all the movies I'd seen told me to dip the key in the bag and do some more, so I did. Then, out of nowhere, I got this sudden urge to shit, so I quickly pulled down my pants and sat down on the toilet. I sat there for a few minutes, feeling a weird, dripping sensation in the back of my throat, like I couldn't swallow. Finally, I finished, wiped, stood up and sealed the bag and stuffed it in my gooch, because I knew that bouncers wouldn't search there, and then I left the stall.

When I looked into the mirror in front of me, I was suddenly introduced to someone I'd never met before. The guy staring back at me had big, bloodshot eyes with pupils the size of saucers; a clenched jaw that had horizontally expanded several inches; and, based on his frail appearance, he hadn't eaten in weeks. And yet, despite seeing that mess of a man staring back at me, I felt like I needed to fuck, fight, or dance.

As soon as I started washing my hands, I felt my stomach start to fold into itself, and then the back of my throat suddenly opened up and I spewed all over the sink in front of me, yellow droplets splattering across the mirror. A flush of snot soon followed, and I tried to wipe it off with the sleeve of my jacket, but then it kept coming and coming, and I recognized the taste of bile slithering up and out my throat, reminding me that I hadn't eaten all day. Finally, I managed to straighten myself back out before walking over to a different faucet and washing my hands, gargling with some water that tasted like gasoline, and then I left.

"Dude, you took fucking forever," Ocean called, as I approached their table. It was clear he was drunk because he was a lot more animated than when I saw him for the first time a few days ago.

"Sorry," I said, still shaky.

"Stuff those sorries in a sack, bro! No room for apologies on this train, my friend. Good vibes only," Zeus said, rubbing his nose, as he attempted to stretch over the entire table in the hopes of giving me some drunken handshake/hug hybrid which didn't have the intended effect he'd hoped for. He struggled for another second while I just stood there and looked at him, until he finally retracted himself back into his seat and dismissively waved his hand in the air, as if to say, *forget it.* He laughed nervously and nudged Beau in the shoulder, seeking validation, like, 'I didn't look *completely* retarded there, did I?' But the only thing I was thinking of was how he could've been my dad. I glared at him sitting there, sandwiched between Ocean and Beau—both at least two decades younger than him—swinging his head back and forth between the two of them like a kid in a zoo standing in-between the lions and the gorillas, so conflicted over which animal to focus on, that he starts jerking his neck back and forth so violently, eventually snapping it in half.

Sometimes, when I got older, I'd still think about Zeus, and wonder what he was getting up to, and if he had found another group of rich, young brats to leech onto, or if he was bleeding out in a bar somewhere, sitting next to some elephant girl with *Mike* tattooed on her tits, telling her about all the famous people he'd done coke with back in the day.

* * *

"Alex!" I heard someone shout, followed by two hands firmly gripping my shoulders and shaking me. "We're here, dude! Wake up!"

I opened my eyes and noticed we were in a car, and my head was hanging over the back of the seat and as I stretched out my neck, it felt like it was about to break.

"Dude, wake the fuck up! We're here!" I heard someone shout again. I tried to piece myself together, everything slowly coming into focus, and I noticed a concerned Beau staring at me as I muscled my way up and out of the car, trying to stabilize my legs when my feet touched land.

"You okay, man?" I heard and felt Beau's affectionate hand patting me on the back. I nodded weakly, which produced a

192

laugh, followed by, "Okay, man. I think you need another bump. That'll wake you up."

Finally, my mouth opened, "Where are we?"

"The hills."

"Whose house are we at?"

"I dunno. Ocean knows him, I think."

As my eyes cleared up, I finally gauged the size of the house we were in front of—two Maseratis parked out front—and I could hear the music pulsating through the walls from inside. I saw Ocean, Karen, and Zeus already ascending the hill towards the stairs, but Beau kindly waited for me, carefully grabbing my hand, leading me towards the entrance.

"You sure you're cool, dude? Just lemme know if you wanna leave, okay?"

"I'm cool. Just a bit… tired."

"Okay, man. I'll be here."

The house was slammed. I didn't know, or recognize, anyone, and Ocean, and the rest of his entourage, had vanished completely. Everyone there had at least a decade on me in age, maybe more, but everyone looked identical, like they'd all been given the wrong address to the Johnny-Depp-lookalike-contest. Most of them were wearing those wide brimmed hats that all the influencers wear to Coachella, and it made me nauseous to look at them. In the middle of the living room, this shirtless dude with a pink ponytail, half of his head completely shaved, was desperately trying to make it look like he knew what he was doing at the DJ table.

"Dude, come on," Beau said, leading me upstairs. People were sprinkled all along the staircase, and I could make out about three to five seconds of each of their conversations:

—I got a call-back for a *Papa John's* commercial

—I don't *eat* meat

—Do you have any ketamine?

—How many followers does he have?

—I'm kind of, like, between agents right now

—This coke is so bad

—Technically I'm from Cleveland, but I've been here for eight months.

It felt like I made eye contact with each and every person, each one staring back at me as I struggled to put one foot in front of the other while walking up the stairs. I followed Beau into a room where we found Ocean, Karen, Zeus and a bunch of others, all bent over a cupboard snorting coke off of a mirror; everyone else in the room looked bored.

Ocean poked up his head like an ostrich, his eyes lighting up at the sight of us. "Where the fuck have you guys been? I got a fat line for you both."

"Alexander, my brother. Get over here," Zeus said as I got closer, throwing a brotherly arm over my shoulder. He handed me a rolled-up dollar bill and I robotically bent over and snorted the lines laid out in front of me, my eyeballs getting wet and heavy.

Then, completely resurged, I started bouncing on my toes, suddenly feeling great again. My jaw was clenched so tightly I could feel my teeth squeal. I hadn't even noticed that I had started dancing, but there I was, dancing alone in the middle of the room, before I reached down and grabbed my dick and noticed how tiny it'd become, but I didn't care. Ocean came over and put his arm around my shoulder and started dancing with me, and I felt his sweaty armpit breathe into my shoulder. As we were dancing, I suddenly felt my nausea start to creep up again—within a second it was at the top of my throat—and I quickly sprinted into the first room I saw, kicking open the door and hurling into the toilet.

"What the fuck, man!" I heard someone shout behind me. I let out an agonizing groan as I turned around, noticing a tall, blonde, figure snorting lines off a dresser.

"Shit, sorry, man. I-I didn't mean—"

"—Get the fuck out, bro. Do you know who the fuck I am?"

"Sorry, I'll leave," I said, and wiped my mouth with some toilet paper, before stumbling out the door and finding Ocean.

"Dude," I said, fumbling the words. "There's some big, blonde guy in the bathroom. I think I pissed him off."

Ocean laughed dismissively, "That YouTube faggot? Don't trip, dude, he won't do shit."

"*YouTube?*" I asked.

"He makes gay videos for eight-year-olds and now he thinks he's famous."

"Is this your fucking friend?" a voice behind me interrupted, as I felt a hand dig into my shoulder.

"What's it to you?" Ocean said, and I turned around and saw it was the guy from the bathroom.

"He just puked on my fucking shoes. Do you have any idea how much these cost?"

"You should thank him," Ocean said, glaring at his shoes. "Those things are ugly as fuck."

The guy laughed, insulted. "You really don't know who I am, do you?"

"Am I supposed to?" Ocean asked callously.

"*Bro,*" he said, and then he pulled out his phone. "*Look,*" and then a video popped up and it was a montage of him boxing and jump roping, as if that was supposed to answer any questions.

"Wait," Ocean said, taking a step back. "Are you seriously showing us YouTube videos of yourself to prove that you're *famous*?"

The guy's face went limp.

"*No,*" he said, embarrassed.

"Dude," Ocean said with an eye roll. "You're even more pathetic than I thought. Just go home, man. You clearly showed up to the wrong party."

"You know what, man?" He got in Ocean's face and dug his finger in his chest; Ocean remained unfazed. "You're a bitch, bro. You should be grateful that I didn't knock you *and* your boy out," he continued, and walked off.

"What a loser," Ocean said and shook his head, before turning back to me. "Yo, Zeus can get us some more coke, but don't tell anyone 'cause then everybody's gonna want some."

"Okay," I said.

Ocean grabbed Zeus, and I followed them downstairs. We came out the back and into the garage where there were a few other people subtly bobbing to the low sound of music bleeding through from the main house.

"Alex, my fuckin' man. Come here," Zeus exclaimed, his teeth gnashing. "I was lookin' at you earlier, and you got that jawline, man. You really do. I was lookin' at you and I was like *fuck*, I bet this kid gets some pussy. I bet you do, huh? How many bitches you fucked, huh? Hundreds, I bet. I bet it's hundreds. I know your kind, man. You're a fuckin' dog, huh? I fuckin' knew it, man. You know my boy, James Osterberg?"

"Uh—"

"—He goes by Iggy Pop. Ever heard of him? He's a good friend of mine. He's a fuckin' rock god, man, and you got that same look, I'm tellin' ya. You got that Iggy look, man. *Nobody* parties like Iggy, but I can tell *you* fuckin' party. *Fuck*, man. Fuckin' love you, bro. You're a fuckin' legend," Zeus continued, swaying back and forth, his sweaty fingers massaging my right shoulder.

Then he took a deep breath and pulled out another bag of coke and he emptied most of it on the table and I felt someone tap me on the shoulder and ask, what sounded like, *'can I have some?'* and she smiled and walked past me and hugged Zeus who she was clearly acquainted with and then she leaned down and did a couple and then Ocean did a couple and then it was my turn but I'm not sure how many I took but when I was walking back up the stairs my nose started to bleed.

"Dude!" I heard Ocean shout when I was sitting in the couch blotting my nose. "Come here!"

I got up quietly and followed Ocean who was standing outside a bathroom, proudly pointing at whatever was inside.

"There he is, that punk bitch," he said, and I saw that YouTube guy passed out on the floor by the toilet, the toilet seat covered in puke.

"Watch this," Ocean whispered as he unzipped his pants and began peeing all over him, but the guy didn't move. Then he took out his phone and snapped a few photos of him lying there covered in piss.

"If I ever see that blogging faggot again, I'ma send this photo to TMZ," he said. Ocean stuffed his phone back into his pocket and walked off, and I returned to the couch and sat back down, stuffing another ball of toilet paper up one of my nostrils.

As I sat there, aimlessly scanning the crowd, I saw Beau talking to that girl who had asked me for coke earlier. They seemed familiar with each other due to the way she moved around him—playing with her hair, stroking his face—but then she suddenly walked off, and Beau noticed me staring, and ran over.

"That's Ximena, man," he said, excited.

"*Ximena*? Never heard that name before," I said.

"So," he began nervously, ignoring my comment. "What, uh, what do you think of her?"

"Yeah, she's really hot, man. How'd you—"

"Yeah! Yeah, she's super-hot, right?" he said, his tone escalating.

"Yeah, super," I agreed. "Who is she?"

"Her dad's someone at The Weinstein Company. At least I think so."

"But how do *you* know her?"

"Well, she goes to Wildwood, but we've met at some parties a few times," he paused, his face turning serious. "I really fucking like her, man."

I tried to act surprised, even though I wasn't, considering how shifty he was when he spoke about her.

"Yeah, I can kind of tell."

"Shit, really? Don't say that, man! Is it obvious?"

"No, no," I lied. "No, you're fine, man. Don't be so nervous."

"Okay, okay. Shit," he said, struggling to calm himself. "Fuck, I think I've done too much coke. Do I look fucked up?"

"No, man. I promise," I said reassuringly, and patted him on the shoulder. "You look good, don't worry."

"Okay, cool. Thanks, dude," he said, desperately. "Fuck. I dunno, though, man. I just dunno what she wants, you know? She's like... *really* confusing."

"What do you mean?"

"No, I dunno. I-I just…fuck, I dunno, man. I dunno," he paused. "What should I do, man?" I could tell he was getting anxious, and I wasn't sure how to react.

"Dude, it's fine, just calm down."

"Yeah, yeah. I'm fine, I'm fine. Just… just don't do anything with her, okay?"

"With *her*?"

"Yeah, *her!* Okay!" he said, almost shouting. "Just don't do anything with her, ever! Promise?"

"Of course, man. *Chill.* I don't even know her. Why would you say that?"

"Good," he replied, as he anxiously stood up and vanished into the crowd.

With the taste of coke still itching in the back of my throat, I resumed my people watching, and I couldn't help but wonder if anyone at this party was actually having any fun, because it didn't look like it.

There was no real joy anywhere, just a sea of bored, misplaced, faces thinking about nothing other than their impending Instagram hashtags—some unoriginal caption like '*about last night*' with a photo of them preening in front of the L.A. skyline—wondering if there was someone more important to who they should be talking, rather than the one they're currently engaged with.

Nobody ever has any fun in L.A., people just want you to think that they do.

Beyond the people over by the bar in the kitchen I noticed Ximena again, now openly making out with someone, and right next to them I saw Beau staring straight at them, and then he chucked his red solo cup at the wall and stormed off.

"This party sucks, let's leave," he barked, coming towards me.

I nodded and stood up and followed him out the front door, and when we stepped outside, I couldn't have been less prepared for the blinding sun, having completely lost track of the time since the inside of that house was like a casino.

"Fucking bitch," Beau muttered under his breath, as I struggled to shield my eyes and regain my vision. "She's not even that hot, man. Like, she's *really* not." But she really was. She had long dark hair that grazed the top of her shoulders as she walked, her eyes were shrink-wrapped in dark mascara, and she floated through the universe well aware of the power she had over men. "She thinks she's all that, but she's just a slut and I don't even like her, man. I really don't."

Beau started pacing anxiously, but after having seen the cause of his heartache, I really couldn't blame him. She was the kind of girl whose life was defined by climbing in and out of the passenger side of expensive cars belonging to handsome men who had seemingly never spent a single day as a boy, the kind of man who could slap a goddess like Ximena and tell her to *fuck off* and not think twice about it, the kind of man most of us idolized, but knew we would never be.

"Let's just fucking go home, dude. Ocean's bein' a fuckin' dick tonight anyway. I fucking *hate* it when he does too much coke," he mumbled, urgently typing on his phone.

"What're you doing?" I asked.

"Calling an Uber," he said, with a grimace. "*Fuck.* Says it's gonna be here in like fifteen minutes. *Completing a ride nearby.* Fuck you, *Cody,* and your gay-ass Prius."

Beau started pacing again and suddenly grabbed a rock he found on the side of the street and hurled it through a car window that shattered with a loud crash.

"*Fuck!*" he yelled.

"Dude!" I shouted, cupping my ears.

Beau stood completely still, panting in silence.

"Dude!" I repeated. "What the fuck! That's somebody's *car*, man."

Beau turned to me, oblivious to what I'd said, and smiled, "Remember when we'd drive around in middle school and smash windows?"

"What?" I asked, still rattled.

"Yeah," he turned to me vacuously, his face a mesh of emotions. "Remember? And we peed on that homeless kid," he laughed.

"Yeah…" I said hesitantly. An image flashed before me of the three of us behind the wheel of Ocean's Range Rover, racing up and down the Palisades, smashing car windows, and the sound of piss splashing on a homeless kid who didn't look to be much older than us, sleeping on the corner of Pico and 16th.

"That was fun," he said, slipping into a dream. I cautiously scanned the area, seeing if anyone had heard the noise and come out of their house, but we were alone.

Finally, I saw a pair of headlights, and noticed a car pulling towards us, and Beau said that that was our Uber so we got in and took off.

I looked over at Beau who was silently staring out the window and I put my hand on his arm comfortingly, but he quickly snatched it away, so I left him alone.

"Can you stop at, like, a McDonald's drive-thru, or something?" Beau suddenly barked at the driver.

"I can't deviate from the path, it's Uber. It's already—"

"—I'll pay you!" Beau snapped. "I just—please, just stop at

McDonald's. Or, like, Jack in the Box. I don't care," he pleaded. "Whatever's open. I'll give you, like, a thirty-dollar tip."

I must've fallen asleep while we had stopped at the drive-thru, but I woke up from the smell of grease and oil, and looked over and saw Beau fiendishly stuffing French fries into his mouth, but I don't think he noticed me staring in the darkness. I slipped in and out of consciousness, the continuous lights of the freeway being my only indicator of motion, along with the occasional, scattered image of Beau next to me, the sound of his incessant chewing bleeding into the silent hum of the engine.

I woke up in a furnace.

My eyes struggled to regain focus until I noticed that I was outside lying on a sunbed, completely dressed; even for an L.A. winter, it was unusually hot. I rubbed my eyes and saw Beau lying across from me, curled up in a fetal position, a pair of black sunglasses folded next to him. I reached over and grabbed them.

The blazing sun bounced off the pool, and I checked my phone, but it was dead, so I had absolutely no idea what time it was or how long we'd been out there. The wind was calmly blowing through my hair and, on the inner reflection of the glasses, I saw a single pearl of sweat slowly descending the side of my face. The vast blue ocean stared at me from afar, and the sound of the waves thundering in from below the cliffs eventually blocked out the violent ringing inside my head.

Feeling sick and dirty, I picked myself up and dragged my feet across the warm, marble tiles and dipped my toes in the pool. I looked around and figured that it must've been the early afternoon, and then I took off everything but my underwear, grabbed an inflatable mattress, and dove into the water.

Underneath the surface everything went completely quiet, and I heard nothing but my heartbeat and then the ringing returned, so I held my breath for, what felt like, forever, and effortlessly ran my fingers through the soft locks of hair quietly dancing on top of my head.

I poked my head through the surface and climbed on top of the mattress and tried to get comfortable but noticed that both of my nostrils were completely clogged so I blocked the left with my thumb and exhaled out the other, a thick projectile of snot and blood splashing next to me in the pool. I tried with the other nostril, but it was no use, so I laid flat on my stomach and dangled my arms off the side, struggling to piece together the previous night, but it made my head hurt, so I just closed my eyes and drifted along the surface, thinking about all those other times I hadn't felt this bad, and how I'd taken all of them for granted.

I heard a faint shout, and then I opened my eyes and saw Beau standing at the edge of the pool, his bony shoulders poking through his t-shirt.

"I'm going to bed," he called, and then he quietly walked inside.

XII

Beau and I were sitting inside Carney's in Sherman Oaks, which is this old burger place built inside an old train cart. I wasn't that hungry, but I struggled to force feed myself a couple of fries; Beau showed no interest in his food either. We hadn't said much since the day before, but that morning I heard him throwing up in the bathroom. I asked him about it on the way over, but he said he didn't know what I was talking about.

"How did all of it get started?" I pried, referring to Ximena.

Beau let out a long, helpless sigh.

"We made out a few years ago, and every time I see her, she's always so flirty and acts like she's super down, but if I look away for *one second*, there she is making out with some dude who she usually ends up fucking later that night," he paused, his tone weak and dispirited. "And she's always talking about all these, like, *rockstars,* or whatever, who keep texting her and asking her to come over, and she'll like *show* me the texts and we'll make fun of them together. Like, she always makes it seem like she's not down for any of that—and, like, when she says it, I believe her, you know?—but then like a week later she'll show up to a party with, like, some Jonas Brother type guy, or something. And then she'll come over holding hands with him and introduce him to me and just treat me like I'm just some guy she barely knows. But then like a week later I'll get a text at like three in the morning saying she misses me and asking if I have any coke. It just drives me crazy, man. I dunno what to do," the desperation was pouring out of him.

"She just always dates older dudes, and every time we're out with them, Karen—you remember, Ocean's girlfriend?—always pulls me off to the side and tries to have some, like, deep talk with me about how Ximena actually *does* like me, it's just not the right time… which is fucking *bull*shit, because I *hate* it when girls act like that and try to be all reassuring, just to pretend like they know what they're talking about?"

"Yeah, that Karen girl kinda sucks."

"Oh, don't worry. I know, man. She's the worst. She always acts so high and mighty and thinks she's so cool even though she comes from some small shithole in Kentucky, but now, thanks to Ocean, she gets in to all these Hollywood parties and can brag to her friends back home. Ocean even said that one night he found her Googling herself. She's a loser."

"Jesus," I said. "She's not even cute."

"Yeah. She's pretty gross. I dunno what Ocean sees in her."

We poked at our food a bit longer, neither of us eating anything, so eventually we just threw out our trays and left.

In the car, Beau reached into his glove box and pulled out another orange pill bottle and, unscrewing the cap, threw a few in his mouth.

"What's that?" I asked.

"What?"

"The pills," I said.

"Oh," he paused, screwing the cap back on. "Adderall."

"Adderall? Why the hell do you take that?"

"My dad—well, the *doctor*—said I have, like, ADD, or *ADHD,* or whatever, and told me to take these."

"*And* you're taking pills for depression?"

"Yeah, so?"

I paused, shaking my head.

"Do you even have ADHD?"

"I dunno. I mean, like, *probably*. It seems like everyone does."

"I was on those for a while, man. You shouldn't ta—"

"—Okay, okay," he sighed irritably, throwing his hands up.

"Dude, I'm serious. Those things aren't good—"

"*Okaaaay*," he groaned. "Just leave it, all right?"

"All right," I sighed.

Apparently, it's not popular to bring customers into the dispensary who are without a club card, so I waited in the car as Beau rushed inside, promising that he'd *only be a minute*.

After what must've been close to forty-five minutes, Beau finally came running out with, what looked like, a grocery bag filled with stuff. Judging by the look on his face you would've thought he'd just won the lottery.

"Dude!" he shouted enthusiastically, like a kid proudly showing off his new bike. "Look at thiiiiis," he began, opening the white paper bag in his lap. I looked down, and to my surprise, there was literally *just* weed in there.

"What, the *weed*?" I asked, unimpressed. Beau's face soured.

"The *weed*? Dude, do you see how *much* this is? He gave me so much more than he usually does. Like, *look at* how *much* that is."

"Yeah, you're right. That's a lot of weed," I said, sarcastically.

Beau sneered. "Whatever."

He snatched the bag from me and started the ignition.

When we were driving down Ventura, Beau's phone started ringing and he asked me to pick it up.

"Hello?" It was Ocean, and he asked if Beau and I wanted to come to this party in Beverly Hills. Beau silently shook his head, until Ocean revealed that Ximena would be there, to which Beau immediately pulled an illegal U-turn, and headed towards the freeway.

"What're you doing? I thought you didn't wanna go?"

"I mean, I dunno, dude. It *could* be fun."

"Did you change your mind because of Ximena?"

"What? *No,*" he said defensively. I didn't say anything after that.

Beverly Hills is one of the few areas I hadn't spent much time in, mostly because the idea of fun for the standard Beverly Hills male was fucking unconscious, drugged-out, girls at parties.

I was at a Bar Mitzvah once, off of Coldwater Canyon, and I came in on four guys jerking off on an unconscious girl in the bathroom. When one of them noticed me staring, he said, '*It's chill, bro. She's a shiksa.*'

The house was right off Sunset on the north side, where the mansions get really big, but the street was so packed with cars that we had to park almost three blocks away. I had taken a couple of hits in the car, and I could tell that I was high, but when I passed the piece to Beau, he put out his hand and said *no.* The music was getting louder and louder as we approached the house, and at the entrance, standing in front of the huge, iron gate, were two security guards in matching black polo shirts; each with an earpiece, that they definitely thought made them look official and intimidating.

"List?" one of the guys grunted officiously, puffing out his chest, praying that one of us would make a run for it inside, so that he could put his two weeks of high school football practice to good use, and tackle us. I had to bite my tongue to prevent myself from saying something snarky, but thankfully Beau interjected and told him we were friends of Ocean's. The guard checked his little clipboard, leaned over to his colleague—his gorilla-like posture alluding to a strictly all-chest-no-legs regime at the gym—and nodded reluctantly, and let us enter.

What felt like hundreds of half-naked Persian dudes were running through the house radiating chlorine and Armani cologne. One group was crowded into the kitchen passing around a bong; another group was snorting coke off the coffee table in the living room; and when we got outside, the remaining kids were reinventing new ways to consume beer: beer pong, keg stand, shot-gunning, whatever.

"Do you see Ocean?" Beau asked.

"No, let's go find him."

On the side of the Olympic sized pool, there was a set of stairs that descended onto the backyard to a basketball court, a tennis court, and a big grassy lawn. When we walked down, I heard coughing, and I turned and saw Ocean, sitting next to Karen, Ximena, and a bunch of other kids I didn't recognize, some of whom looked *much* older than us, sitting in a circle on the tennis courts, snorting coke, and passing a joint around.

"There they are," Ocean shouted, as he stood up and hurried over and hugged us both. As he leaned in, I heard the anxious sound of his teeth grinding together. I said hi to Karen, who smiled blithely, and when I sat down, I began to recognize some of the other faces in the crowd.

"Abby Wallace?" I asked, addressing an affected, leopard clad girl who Ocean was sitting next to.

"What?" she replied.

"You're...you're Abby, right? Didn't...we had science together, right? Mr. Bradford's class?"

"Oh. Uhm, *hey,*" she began, noticeably uncomfortable. "Actually, it's uh, it's *Arabella Salt,* now," she said condescendingly, avoiding eye contact. I tried not to laugh, but I remembered that her dad was some rich guy in Malibu, and I could only assume she was trying her hand at a music career based on her appearance and dismissive entitlement. Later that evening I found her Instagram profile, which consisted of nothing but black and white photos of her smoking cigarettes and sticking her tongue out and licking guitars, with French song lyrics as captions. What a poet.

Ximena was sitting next to some dude who looked forty, and I subtly glanced over at Beau who was seething with jealousy. Ocean was passing his phone around—neat lines of coke spread out across it—along with a rolled-up bill; everyone snatched at the phone like ravenous animals clawing at raw meat. When the phone finally got over to me, I just didn't feel like it, so I passed it to that forty-year-old that Ximena was talking to.

"Thanks, little man," he chuckled with a wink, as he took the phone and vacuumed three lines.

"Hey!" Ximena yelped, playfully hitting him on the shoulder. "Now there's only one left, *asshole!*"

The guy began to laugh, fingered the final line with his pinky and smeared it on his tongue, then licked the tip of Ximena's nose.

"That better?" he asked.

"God, you are *such* an asshole!" she repeated, wiping her face. Ximena took the phone and snorted up the last smidgen of coke that was left, and handed the phone back to Ocean, who was preoccupied with rolling a joint.

"How long have you been on Zoloft?" Karen asked Abby.

"Like, forever."

"Yeah, same. How many milligrams?"

"Oh, I'm, like, super depressed, so I need, like, one fifty milligrams a day."

"Yeah, *same*. I'm also *super* depressed, so I take, like, such a strong dose. Like, yeah, about one fifty."

"I was prescribed Xanax for a while, but then, like, my depression got so bad, so they gave me Prozac and Zoloft at the same time, and that's when I turned to music. That's the only way I can deal with my pain."

"Oh my god, I know exactly what you mean. It's, just, like, so difficult, dealing with everyone, you know?"

"I know. I'm just surrounded by fakes."

"I *know,*" Karen mimicked, grabbing Abby by the arm. "That's what I always tell Ocean. I hate feeling so lost, you know? It's, like, nobody I meet ever understands what I'm going through, you know?"

"Exactly. They're just so, like…inauth—"

"—*Inauthentic,*" Karen interrupted, beaming. "Oh my god. I can't believe we're just, like, literally the same person."

"Yeah."

"Do you still get Xanax?"

"No, but I just steal my mom's now," Abby said, pulling out a little bag of white pills from her purse.

It felt like I had somehow walked into the wrong theatre, and to a movie I didn't want to see, but was now forced to sit and watch.

Finally, I stood up because I needed to pee, and walked around the stairs and peed behind a bush, and then I heard someone shout, and I craned my neck and saw Ximena floating towards me.

"Hey," she said.

"Uh," I muttered nervously, quickly zipping up my pants before turning around completely. "Hey."

"What's your name?"

"Uhm," I paused. "Alexander."

"You know something?"

I shook my head.

"You haven't even introduced yourself to me," she said coyly. "That's pretty rude."

"Oh... sorry," I said, extending my hand. "Hi."

"Aren't *you* formal," Ximena chuckled, staring at my hand. "You wanna *shake* my hand?"

"Uhm..." I retracted myself. "No. I guess not."

"So, you *don't* wanna shake my hand? What's wrong with my hand?"

"N-no, nothing. I just—"

"I'm teasing."

I let out a breath of relief and tried to smile. She eyed me up and down.

"What're you doing over here?"

"I had to pee," I stuttered.

"Hmm," she paused. I felt myself getting tense. "So, you're, like, pretty good friends with Beau, huh?"

"Yeah, why?"

"Seems like it."

"Yeah, we've, uh... we've known each other since middle

school," I said, struggling to find the words.

"Yeah, he said you're, like, off at Hogwarts now, or something?"

"Well," I laughed nervously. "Sort of. I guess. I go to boarding school in England."

"*England.* That's fun. Do you like it?"

"Yeah, you know. It's, uh, it's a bit colder than here," I could feel the words clumsily pouring out of me. "But I uh, well, it's pretty different, but it's not bad and—"

"—Did you shake it?" she interrupted.

"What?"

"Did you *shake* it?"

"Shake *what?*"

"Your *dick,*" she moved closer, pointing to my crotch. "After you peed. Did you shake your dick dry?"

"Uhm…" I stammered. "Yeah. W-why?"

"Hmm. Just wondering."

Ximena smiled lewdly and walked away. I felt a sudden wave of guilt crash over me. I hadn't felt that powerless in a while.

Suddenly, Beau appeared out of thin air and asked, "Hey! Where were you?"

"Sorry I just…I had to pee."

"Oh, okay."

"Yeah, I wasn't doing anything," I said.

"Okay," Beau laughed. "Have you seen Ximena?"

"What? *No,*" I said defensively. "*Why?* "

"Okay, okay," he replied. "I was just *wondering.*"

"Sorry," I said. "I think I'm just…hungry."

"Do you think that dude's handsome?" he asked, biting his nails.

"Who?" I asked, my mind still distracted.

"That guy who licked Ximena's face."

"What? No way," I said, snapping out of it. "He's uh…he's a loser."

Beau smiled, "Yeah…yeah, I guess you're right. Fuck that guy," he said, consoling himself. "He *is* a loser."

"Let's go," I said.

"What?"

"Yeah, come on. This party sucks."

"Yeah…yeah you're right. Ximena didn't even say hi to me. She's so hard to read. It drives me crazy."

"Yeah," I said.

"Have you ever talked to her?" he asked.

"Huh?"

"Have you ever talked to Ximena?"

"Uhm… no," I said. "I haven't."

"So typical of her, you know? Like, I told her you're one of my best friends, and she doesn't even say hi to you. She's such a bitch."

"Yeah," I said distantly.

Suddenly: "If she tried to get with you, would you?"

"What?"

"Never-mind," he said quietly.

As we walked towards the entrance, I turned and saw Ximena sitting on some guy's lap, and I could tell Beau noticed, as his slow walk turned into an aggressive march, nearly sprinting out of the house, forcing me to run after.

I caught up to him outside, but Beau stayed silent as he stormed off towards the car.

After we got in and he started the ignition, he sped down to Westwood village where he pulled into In-N-Out and ordered four double-doubles, three fries, and two milkshakes, all of which he inhaled almost instantly. When he was done, he sat quietly, panting, as if having awoken from a dream, and then he looked over at me with guilty eyes, as if I'd just caught him in the act of murder.

"Are you o—"

"—Did you see Abby Wallace?" Beau interrupted. "She's such a fucking loser. Remember she filmed herself shoving a carrot in her vagina and then it leaked and got sent to everyone."

"Oh yeah," I said, my mind instantly hijacked by the image of a large carrot entering a young girl. "Wasn't that in, like…when *was* that?"

"That was, like, seventh grade. I remember Ocean saved it on his computer. He still has pictures of every girls' tits."

"He *does*?"

"Yeah, remember when they used to flash us on iChat?"

"Who?"

"I don't remember *every*one. I just remember Ruby Blackwood had like the grossest tits ever. Remember that picture *also* leaked, and she had to switch schools?"

"Oh, yeah," I said, trying to remember, my thoughts constantly shifting between the carrot, Ruby's tits, and Ximena.

"Yeah, Ocean has like a folder with all those tits in it. He should probably delete those though or else he'll get charged for being, like, a paedophile, or something," he laughed. "Those girls were all, like, twelve at the time."

XIII

I woke up to four missed calls from Ocean the next morning, all between three and five a.m. I called him back several times and when he finally answered it took him forever to become even re*motely* comprehensible, but eventually he got to the point and asked me to come over, and I said I would, after I'd eaten.

After I was done with my cereal, I left my unwashed bowl on the counter, purposely leaving it there for Esmeralda to find, knowing that when she saw it she'd start arguing with my dad about how terrible my manners were, and then I went into her bathroom, rubbed her toothbrush against the inside of the toilet bowl, got dressed, and called an Uber.

Ocean was lying on his couch covered in a cloud of smoke with an opened bag of Cheetos in front of him glaring at the TV when I arrived.

"Wassup," he said distractedly through a mouthful of Cheetos. "You want a hit?"

"I'm okay," I replied.

"All right."

After watching TV for about half an hour he asked if I'd come with him to do this '*thing*' real quick, and I didn't think much of it so I said yes, and then we put on our shoes and left.

We took Malibu canyon over towards the valley and headed south on the 101 until I finally asked him where we were going.

"I just need'a pick up this thing from this dude who I owe

money to."

"*Okay...*" I said, suspiciously. "Why do you owe him money?"

"I was supposed to sell some coke for him, but I accidentally did all of it myself."

"Is he shady?" I asked nervously.

"Nah, he's chill," he paused. "I asked you to come because we haven't really hung out that much since you've been back."

I smiled. "Yeah, I know."

Ocean lit up a joint as we sped down the freeway, got off on Reseda Boulevard, and began driving down areas I'd never been in before. Like I said earlier, the valley really has such an ancient vibe to it. I swear, driving down Reseda, you wouldn't even guess that you're in L.A. any more. It really feels like you've gone back in time to the days of roller rinks, XXX theaters and bellbottoms.

We passed a guitar shop, and I remembered how much Ocean and I used to play in middle school.

"When was the last time you went to Guitar Center?" I asked.

"Huh," he said absently. "I dunno."

"We should go after," I said enthusiastically. "That'd be fun. You down?"

"I'm good," he said, and suddenly I felt stupid for asking, and then we didn't talk any more until we arrived.

The house we pulled up to looked like something straight out of *Boogie Nights*: rock-wall exterior, blue Chevy parked out front, and the smell of chlorine luring us in, as we approached the front door.

Ocean stopped and turned to me before he rang the doorbell, and I could tell right away how uneasy he was, which instantly made me nervous.

"All right, dude, so, uhm," he stuttered. "He can be kinda gnarly sometimes, but I swear, he's chill. He just does that because he thinks its... intimidating."

I'd never seen Ocean nervous before which only enhanced my own anxiety, so all I did was forge a smile and shut up. Ocean knocked on the door several times, until, finally, a Mexican girl wearing nothing but underwear and a baseball cap, opened up, big, fake tits bouncing as she giggled at the sight of us.

"Well, heeell*loooo*," she said suggestively. "You must be *river*, or whatever," she said, imitating the noise of the ocean and running her hand through the air.

"Yeah, it's uh, it's Ocean," he said mechanically, struggling to keep eye contact.

"Well then, *Ooocean*, make yourself at hooome," she said, swinging the door open. I was so nervous that I barely even registered that there was a hot girl with her tits out standing right in front of me. We sat down on a plastic covered couch in the living room, and when we turned around the girl was gone, but from the other side of the house two guys came walking over: one short Mexican guy with face tattoos; the other very tall, white, with a shaved head, and a 13 tattooed under his right eye.

"Wassup, pimp," the short one barked.

"Heeey man," Ocean replied meekly. "How you been?"

"Been good, playboy. I been good."

"Cool, man," Ocean said.

"Yeah, man. It *is* cool," he said sadistically. "It's *real* cool, man."

The tall one didn't say anything, he just stood there quietly, staring at us.

"You know what'd be even cooler though, man?" the short one said.

"Wh-what?" Ocean asked hesitantly.

"If you could tell me," he stood up and turned to me, "Who the *FUCK* this motherfucker is!" He took out a switchblade and began coming towards me; I felt my body go limp. "You a fuckin' narc, huh, pretty boy? Some captain America lookin' pendejo. You tryna' get me arrested? S'that what you doin'?" he continued, as he got on top of me, straddling me, holding the knife a centimeter away from my eye, his pungent breath forcing its way down my nostrils.

"Dude, dude! He's cool, what the hell man!" Ocean pleaded. "He's not a narc, he's my friend! He's only seventeen!" Ocean shouted. I shut my eyes and waited for my life to end, until, finally, I felt him get off and then I heard him laugh.

"I'm just fuckin' with you's twos!" followed by another fit of hysterics. "You should'a seen ya'll faces! God *damn*, lil homie! That shit was hil-*air*-iouz!"

He turned to me, demanding eye contact, and effortlessly threw the knife into the table, the blade plunging into the wood like a flag on conquered terrain.

"You muss'a thought I's some kind'a faggot, huh, white boy?"

"What?" I choked.

"Well, I got on top'a you, din't I? So, you muss'a been thought to yo self, '*damn*, this nigga some kind'a faggot,' *huh*?"

"No, no," I said, my voice trembling. "I didn't think you were gay."

He paused, turned to Ocean, then back to me.

"*No*? Well," he tilted his head. "Why not? You got something a*gainst* faggots, white boy? That shit make you—" he got in my face, "—un*com*fortable? You *homophobic?*"

"No, sir. No, I—it doesn't—I just didn't think you were gay,

218

that's all. But, if you were, I wouldn't have cared either, it's—"

Something interrupted me—vicious pain; a bomb—and exploded in my stomach. I keeled over, struggling for air, and tumbled to the ground. He retracted his fist and laughed.

"You *act* like a bitch," he bent down and glared at me. "I'm'a *treat* chu like a bitch," and stood back up.

I struggled to breathe through intervals of coughing, and I looked over at Ocean who stood arrested in the middle of the room, petrified.

"Now, homie," he said, addressing Ocean. "You ain't been 'round in a minute, so I be thinkin' to myself, *damn*. This nigga don't give no *fucks* 'bout me or my bidniss. This white boy just gon' walk *aaaall* ova me and not give no fucks, huh? Guess the jokes on me. Guess that makes *me* the silly nigga."

"No, no, it's not like that, man," Ocean pleaded. "That's why I came today, I told you, I promised I'd drive—"

"—Shh," he hushed, bringing his finger to his lips. "Since it *is* the holidays, I'm'a letchu off, and you'ont owe me no money. Feel me?"

"What?" Ocean said, surprised.

"Like I said, homie: You'ont owe me no money. But," he paused. "That don't mean I ain't tryna get mine, *too*, feel me?"

Ocean hesitated, "What, uh… what do you… *want*?"

The guy looked down at me, as I was finally starting to prop myself up on my elbow, still struggling for air.

"S'been a *while* since I had me some white boy pussy. And I ain't *eva* had me no white boy pussy like *that*, homie," he began rubbing his hands together and licking his lips.

I swallowed, sweat running down my spine.

"And white boy pussy like *that* be lookin' so mu'fuckin sweet, it almost be lookin' *dangerous*, you feel me?" He turned to me. "So's that whatchu is, huh? Some dangerous-ass, white-boy pussy?"

He walked over to a cupboard and pulled out a big, black plastic bag and started towards me. I looked to Ocean for help, but he looked as helpless as me.

"Mister Dangerous," he repeated, laughing to himself. "I like that, homie. *Mister Dangerous.*"

"What do you want?" I mumbled anxiously, his mouth a millimeter from my face.

He laughed maniacally, and turned to Ocean, and then back to me.

"What I *want*? Shit," he began shaking his head. "*Maaaaan,*" and then he threw me to the ground, pulled something out of the bag and began shoving it down my throat. "I just want you to have a good *time,* Mister *Dangerous!*" he barked through his teeth. "I just want *every*body to have a good mu'fuckin' time!"

I started coughing, gagging, struggling to breathe, gasping for air, but his hand was in my throat, cramming whatever he was holding into my mouth, leaving no option but to swallow. I was kicking and squirming beneath him, trying to get him off me, but he wouldn't budge.

"Get off'a him, man!" Ocean begged, and then suddenly the guy quickly stood up and climbed off of me.

I laid on the floor—coughing, spitting, nearly puking—holding my throat, struggling to breathe.

The guy was panting, and finally regained his breath.

"I'm a nice guy, dawg. I'm just tryna make sure *all* my niggas have a good time, thassall. Happy New Year, and all that *bull*shit. Now get the fuck outta here, 'fore I change my mind and get me that white boy pussy like I asked for."

Ocean ran over to me and urgently hoisted me up to my feet, threw one of my arms over his shoulder, and we booked it out the door, gagging and coughing as I ran.

"Get in, get in, get in!" Ocean yelled, as we both jumped in the car. "Fuck, man. I'm so sorry. I'm so sorry," Ocean cried, his voice breaking.

As Ocean pulled out the driveway the nausea started getting even worse than when we were inside, and I told him to pull over so I could throw up but he insisted on driving for another block so we could get as far away as possible, and he handed me an old Sprite bottle that looked like it had been rotting in that car for weeks. I opened up the window and started spitting, and then I forced the warm, flat Sprite down my throat, which was almost as bad as whatever it was I'd just eaten. I gargled, gagged, and kept spitting out the window, the wind battering against my face as we sped down the freeway. Finally, still panting, I brought my head back in the car.

"What the *fuck,* man!" I shouted. "What the fuck is wrong with you! Who the fuck were those guys? I thought they were gonna kill me!"

"Man," he said, rapidly shaking his head. "I'm so sorry, I'm so sorry," he kept repeating. "I had no idea—I didn't even—I just thought I just had to drop something off for him because I owed him money and—"

"—What the fuck did he just feed me? That tasted like shit!" I shouted, still gagging.

"Okay, well, don't freak out, okay?"

"*Don't-freak-out*? What-the-fuck-was-in-the-*bag*, man!"

"I just think it was shrooms. That's what it *looked* like."

Fuck.

A wave of angst washed over me as I felt my body begin to

crumble.

"Dude, dude, it's gonna be fine, at least he didn't *stab* you. Duke Hamilton said that once he was buying coke from him and he saw him stab a dude right in the—"

"—At least he didn't stab me! What the fuck is wrong with you, man? Fuck Duke Hamilton, I don't *care* what *he* said! I've never taken shrooms! This isn't fucking funny! Am I gonna be okay? Did you see how much he gave me? Man, I'm gonna die, I'm gonna die," I cried, my voice shaking. "What if I have a bad trip? I've read about this shit, man. That's what happened to the guy from the fucking Beach Boys. He had a bad trip, and he went insane and never recovered."

"First of all, that was *acid.* And you're gonna be *fine.* Just trust me, I'll take care of you. I promise."

"Did you *see* how much he gave me?" I repeated.

"Was it a lot?"

I turned to him judgmentally.

"Haaa," he laughed, awkwardly. "Okay, all right. Uhm— *fuck...*" Ocean scrunched his face and began anxiously teething his fingernails, before bringing his open palm down through the air. "You're gonna be fiiine, man. He did the same thing to me, once. I was fine. Here, I know what to do." He took out his phone. "Just listen to this and trust me. Like under the pier, remember? You're gonna be fine." Ocean scrolled through his phone, eventually landing on a song that sounded familiar, patted me on the leg, as I just sat there anxiously, waiting for my life to crumble.

After ten minutes, or maybe an hour, everything started to get a bit fuzzy...

'...we sail through endless skies...'

222

Ocean and I glide down the valley streets and the sun glares at me through the windshield.

The driving becomes smoother and smoother; the car is hovering over the cement.

Ocean lights a cigarette; exhales purple smoke. He looks over at me and begins to laugh; his teeth look like velvet pebbles. I feel my brain attempt an escape through my forehead; I bring my hands up, and push it back in.

I look down at my hands; the wrinkles in my palms dance and coil like drunken snakes.

The sky changes colors rapidly; my hands continue to increase in size. I try to talk to Ocean; my mouth won't obey and remains shut. I feel myself begin to laugh; it's unclear if I'm making any noise, or not.

I don't know how or when we got here, but we're at the beach. Ocean takes my hand and leads me to one of the sand dunes. He lays out a blanket; the blanket stretches out its arms and invites me in.

I can see the noise emitting from the crashing waves of the ocean; I can touch the smell of the sea; I can hear the sight of dolphins jumping through the surf.

We're in a house; I'm in a pool. Parrots everywhere. I tell Ocean I'm allergic to parrots; he says he doesn't have any parrots. There are parrots everywhere.

I'm out of the pool, standing on the grass. The grass offers a hug; I lie down and reciprocate with my own embrace. The earth loves me; I love the earth.

Suddenly I'm clothed again, my head hanging out the window of a speeding car. Soft, delicate fingertips blow my hair back and tickle my cheeks. I open my eyes; a sea of pelicans soaring high above us.

Slender, pretty girls change colors as they swim down the street. One by one, their ribs detach from their bodies and drift off into the wind. Please do not feed the models, I hear someone whisper.

The sounds from the speakers slowly pour over me, melting into my skin. I bring my head back inside the car, my face refrigerated from the wind. I smile at Ocean; he smiles at me. Right here, right now, I do not care about anything…I feel so very, very happy.

* * *

I woke up on the couch, completely disoriented, wearing nothing but jeans, but I felt surprisingly fine. I walked around the house, completely lost, until I finally found Ocean, sitting with his feet in the pool with a bowl of cereal in his lap. He hadn't heard me yet, so I just stood there, on the other side of the glass door, and observed him sitting there all alone, and began wondering what he was thinking about. After seeing the bowl of cereal, I quickly realized that the only thing I'd eaten—or saw anybody *else* eat— during the entire time I'd been back home, was cereal. With the few exceptions of the occasional hamburger, that's all anybody ever seemed to eat. Before I went outside, I noticed a box of Apple Jacks, and a carton of milk, sweating on the kitchen counter, so I poured myself a bowl and walked outside.

"Hey," I said gently, as I approached him. He turned around with a staggered gaze, clearly having interrupted his train of thought.

"Hey," he said quietly, before staring back down into the water. I sat down next to him and dipped my feet in the pool. We were both shirtless, and I looked at my body, and then over at his, and noticed how gaunt and frail we both looked. I don't think I could've weighed any more than one-twenty, one-twenty-five, tops; neither could he. Ocean had this badly done Apache chief tattoo on his shoulder that was more gray than black, but somehow it looked kind of cool, and, above his nipples, he had, TROUBLE MAKER, written in small, childish font. It was messy and carelessly done, but it suited him. His long, wavy hair hung in front of his face like a curtain, a shield of protection to keep the outside world at bay, and the rings on his fingers looked more organic than the skin he lived in. I looked down at his cereal and noticed that he had barely touched it, and he was now just spooning the soggy, inflated pieces floating around; looking down at my own I realized I hadn't touched mine either.

"My dad's not coming home for, like, another two months," Ocean said, shattering the silence.

"What?" I asked.

"Yeah…his assistant left me a voicemail this morning saying my dad had to stay in Australia until the end of February."

"So, who's gonna be here then with you?"

"Well…" he paused. "Whenever my dad's gone for a while, the maid usually sleeps here until he comes back."

"So, it's just you and her in this entire house?"

Ocean let out a sick laugh, "Yup."

"That sounds pretty lonely."

"Eh, whatever. I don't really give a shit."

I looked out at the massive backyard in front of us—the infinity pool, the guest house, the tennis court further down, the outdoor sauna—and turned around to stare at the abandoned, white castle sitting behind me, and all I could think of was what a giant waste of space this place was. Ocean's dad had cameras across the entire driveway, so having more than a couple of friends over at a time was nearly impossible—the *thought* of having a party was complete lunacy—so Ocean was literally trapped in his own house with nobody around to talk to except for a maid who barely spoke English.

Ocean eventually stood up, walked into the house, and came back out with a joint. He took a few puffs and passed it over; I inhaled deeply and passed it back.

"Come on," Ocean said, slowly raising himself, before walking towards the edge of the pool. When I went over, I looked down below my feet and saw the infinity pool spilling over, what looked like, a hundred foot drop down a cliff. The water continued endlessly, waves crashing into the cliffs beneath us, the salty breeze blowing in from below tickling my damp feet.

"You know something, man?" Ocean said, followed by a deep inhale of his joint.

"What?"

"This view fuckin' sucks."

I sat down next to him in one of the lawn chairs and stared out over the billion-dollar view, thinking about how jealous the entire universe was of us today, and how we couldn't have cared less.

"You know what's funny?"

I shook my head.

"I always thought grownups were such idiots. But then I realized that I'm the one who keeps getting played by them, so I guess the only real idiot here is me."

"I don't think you're an idiot."

"That's only because you're an idiot, too," he said with a quiet chuckle.

You're probably right, I thought.

We sat in silence for a few moments.

Suddenly: "It's New Year's today."

"It is?" I asked, completely oblivious.

"Yeah," he said. "There's this party somewhere on Crescent Heights tonight. You wanna go?"

"Sure."

"Cool."

Ocean finished the last of the joint and threw the roach off the cliff and headed back towards the house. I stayed outside for another few minutes absorbing the view and, as I turned around to get one final glimpse, the fog had nearly swallowed the lawn chairs entirely; the edge of the cliff having completely vanished, like a mirage. As I approached the house, I stopped to look at my reflection in the sliding glass door: exposed collarbones, indented groove in the middle of my chest, sunken cheeks and apathetic, dark circles under my eyes. I thought about my sordid reflection in The Viper Room mirror a few days prior; I didn't recognize *this* person either.

Karen came over a few hours later unannounced, and then Beau joined shortly after, and the four of us sat on the couch, blazing and drinking a bit.

"Do you dye your hair?" Karen asked unprovoked.

"What?" I asked. "No."

"Are you sure?" she snickered, unconvinced. "I'm *just* saying. I'm a girl, so I notice that stuff, and it *really* looks like you dye your hair."

"Okay, well I don't."

"If you did that'd be *super* gay."

"I get that, Karen, but I *don't*, okay?"

She laughed and submissively raised her hands. "Okay, okay. Calm down. You don't have to get so sensitive. It was *just* a question."

I got so frustrated I stood up and went to the bathroom. I checked my phone and thought about texting Bardot, to ask what her New Year's plans were, but then I saw my reflection in the mirror again and felt guilty about texting her when I looked like this, so I decided not to.

When I returned, Karen was moaning again.

"Honestly, people who get star struck just amaze me. Like, *what* is the big deal, they're *just* people," she preached, as I sat back down on the couch. Despite being together, I never once saw Ocean and Karen talking to each other, and whenever she was around, Ocean looked more distracted than I was: always on his phone, in another room, talking to someone else, but never once getting close to Karen.

"You seem pretty close with Arabella," I interjected, deliberately baiting her.

"That's so funny. Everybody always says that," she boasted. "I guess people can just tell that we're both, like, on the same vibe, or whatever."

"Both of you seem pretty misunderstood. Especially her, as

an artist, I mean," I continued, Karen oblivious to what I was doing.

"Oh my god, she *is*. That's what we always talk about, how the media, people, *society,* just gets everything wrong. The direction she's going in, like, with her art, it's just, like... *so* frustrating expressing yourself, not just as a person, but as an artist, too. And, like, you never know who to trust—you're always gonna be surrounded by fake friends who only like you because of who your parents are or how much money you have, it's pathetic—so that's definitely why Arabella and I clicked. We just both know what it's like," she continued sanctimoniously. "Plus, she's a taurus, and I'm a virgo, and earth signs are known for being, like, super compassionate and, like, just really authentic."

"I'm a taurus," I said.

"Really?" she asked, offended.

"Yeah," I grinned. "That's probably why Abby and I have so much in common."

"It's Arabella now. And do you even *know* her?" she taunted.

"I've known her since third grade."

"*Oh,*" she hissed. "Okay, but like, *that* doesn't really count. That's just, like, being an *acquaintance* of someone. You only *know* her because you grew up in the same area. Like, Arabella and I *found* each other. I think that's a *little* different."

"Yeah, you're totally right," I said, and I heard Beau chuckle.

Karen pulled out a little bag of coke from her purse and extended her hand towards Ocean, one of the few times I ever saw them interacting.

"Babe," she said discreetly.

Ocean looked up from his phone, saw the bag, and glared up at her.

"What?"

"*Here,*" she insisted, like trying to feed a toddler vegetables. "Take some."

"Karen, your coke sucks."

"No, it *doesn't,*" she sneered.

Karen sighed irritably, got up and left the room.

When she was gone, Ocean turned to me, "Want a Xanax?"

"Uhm," I hesitated. I turned to Beau, who shrugged in agreement.

"I'll try half," I said.

Ocean snapped the oblong bar in two pieces and handed me one of them. I swallowed it, and after about thirty minutes, I wasn't nauseous any more.

After finishing a twelve pack between us, Ocean suggested that we should probably get showered and head over since it was New Years and there would be traffic and then I realized I didn't have a change of clothes, but Ocean just laughed and led me into his father's room and although I've never been all that fashion conscious it was hard not to be overwhelmed when he opened the doors of his dad's closet. It looked like a museum.

His father and I were the same height, so he told me that pretty much anything would fit me. Ocean pulled out a black suit hanging in the closet, and when I put it on, he said, "Now you're worth more than a year's tuition at UCLA," and chuckled.

The two of us stood in the bathroom fixing ourselves in the mirror, and Beau entered, obliviously wearing a suit five sizes too big, and just the sight of him looking so clueless made me anxious.

"You can't wear that," Ocean mocked, and I could tell it made Beau self-conscious, but Ocean grabbed him another jacket out of his dad's closet that fit much better, which instantly calmed me down.

"Who picked out the last suit for you, Helen Keller?" Ocean snickered.

"Was it bad?" Beau asked timidly, his cheeks blushing.

"No," I lied. "It was just the shoulders that were a bit too big."

"Oh," Beau paused. "Do I look okay, now?"

"Much better," I said reassuringly, and patted him on the back.

Beau furtively glanced at himself in the mirror, and then quickly turned away and sat down on the couch.

Karen walked in, wearing spiky heels, completely out of harmony with the rest of her dull outfit, and her nails were dipped in a fresh coat of thick, white nail polish.

"What are you guys *doing*?" she barked.

Ocean ignored her.

"Are those Skechers?" I asked.

"Are you stupid?" she grimaced. "These are Diane von Furs—."

"—*Really*?" I interrupted. "I thought they were Skechers."

"Well, unlike you, I don't shop at *Skechers*."

Karen walked over to the marble faucet and poured out a little bit of coke on the surface, subtly dabbing at it with her pinky, before scooping some up into her nostril.

Ocean turned to her and grimaced, but she didn't notice.

We got in the Uber and headed over to the Chateau Marmont, which is this anciently decadent hotel where literally every single rich kid hangs out, desperately trying to enhance their social status through Lana Del Rey inspired Instagram posts, in hopes of one day being known as a regular, and getting snapped by TMZ. Even though the drinking age is twenty-one, Ocean and Beau's dads *were,* in fact, regulars, so they didn't ask any of us for I.D. Instead, they quickly sat us down at one of the best tables in the house.

"Oh my god, so the other night I was with Ximena, and Jimmy Franco just kept calling her but we just kept sending it to voicemail and..." Karen began, but the second I heard her say *Jimmy Franco,* as if they were best buds, my brain immediately signed out.

Most of the people there were probably twice our age, but everyone is so surgically preserved in this town, that you'd never guess. The waiter came out with a pitcher of Sangria and immediately tried to make conversation with Ocean about his dad—a regular occurrence for Ocean, something he despises—but when he finally realized that the conversation was heading south, he ended with, "Tell your dad that Scotty from the Chateau, says hi." Being the dick that he is, Ocean replied with, "Will do, *Sammy.*" I don't really blame him for his callousness, though. Everywhere Beau and Ocean go, people are always telling them to tell either of their dads that so-and-so *'says hi,'* and I can only imagine how tiring that must get after a while.

The sangria was way too sweet, and tasted like cavities and bad decisions. We quickly drained the pitcher and then the four of us went to the bathroom to do coke. When we sat back down, Ocean ordered a pizza but, when the food arrived, none of us touched it. We ordered another pitcher, but after about half a glass each, Ocean suggested that we dip to the party. He threw six twenties on the table, and then we all stood up and left.

The Uber driver was some Jamaican dude who had moved to L.A. to play soccer, which was a pleasant contrast from literally *every* other driver who's an 'actor/musician', and tries to hand you their head shot as soon as you enter the car, telling you about their acting methods, and how they'd love to work with Spielberg one day.

When we pulled up to the party, I could hear the music pulsing through the windows even before I stepped out of the car. When I turned around and looked at the party in front of us, I realized we were by far the youngest kids there; everyone must've been at least thirty-five. Ocean confidently led us up towards the front door where a florid, little bouncer was standing officiously with a clipboard.

"Name?" he grunted, as we approached him.

"Ocean Mulwray, plus three."

The bouncer scanned his list, and when he realized that we actually *were* on the list, he frowned diagonally, as it was obvious how thrilled he would've been to deny our entry.

Neon streamers slithered up and down the walls, disco balls hung from the ceiling, and '80s music pulsated throughout the cavernous hallways, echoing with lewd intentions. Two gay guys spray-painted in leopard print walked past me and winked; I awkwardly smiled back, trying my hardest to stand in a way where my heterosexuality was unmistakable.

Even though everyone there was a lot older than us, it was pitch black, so I doubt anybody could notice how much younger we really were.

"Ximena just texted me, she said she's out by the pool,"

Karen squealed, and immediately headed towards the back of the house, pulling Ocean closely behind her. Beau instinctively started following them like a loyal dog but I grabbed his arm and stopped him.

"What're you doing?"

"Why don't we just hang back and get a drink, or something?"

"What're you talking about? They're all going outside."

"Look," I paused, raising my voice over the music. "I know Ximena's out there, but why don't you let her come to you."

Through the flickering lights I could tell he was insulted.

"I'm not just going out there for *her*."

"Okay, okay. Sorry. I just... I don't really like being around Karen, so is it cool if we just hang back and find a drink, or something?"

He hesitated, and then, finally, said "Okay."

We walked up a long, spiny staircase and entered a room similar in size to the one downstairs, except the noise was a bit more tolerable. I started getting heartburn as we approached the bar in the corner of the room, and I could feel my teeth grinding together and then I felt myself start to worry if we were going to find more coke.

"Drink?" I shouted over the music, pointing towards the bar. Beau nodded. A couple of girls, couldn't have been much older than us, were slow dancing awkwardly and I reached in between them and grabbed a vodka bottle on the counter behind them. When I retracted my arm, it slightly brushed against one of them who had a blonde pixie cut and death colored lipstick and she snatched my arm and asked me how old I was.

"Thirty-six," I said. They both smirked, and pixie-girl hit my arm.

"You are such a little punk," followed by another giggle. "How old *are* you guys?"

"Fourteen," Beau said, in a surprising spell of confidence. "Got any coke?"

"Shut *up*," one of them replied. "You two are *not* fourteen."

The girls looked at us suspiciously, both mechanically tilting their heads to one side.

"*We* don't. But our *friend* does."

"Where's your friend?" I asked.

"Follow us," they said, and pixie-girl grabbed my arm and started leading us down the hall, further and further away from the party…

… Until we came to another staircase leading down to, what I assumed was, the basement, but when we came down, we walked into, what looked like, a recording studio. Several guitars, big black speakers fastened in the ceiling, a couple of keyboards and microphones, and a bunch of those sound mixing tables with all the flickering lights and switches on them. Four people—all of whom looked as if they'd just been pulled out of an Urban Outfitters window display—were hovering around a tiny little coffee table, loudly snorting. When the door shut behind us, one of the guys with a Skrillex haircut looked up and shouted, "Jenny—*babe*—what the *fuck*! Who the *fuck* are these guys?" before rubbing his nose.

"Lance, *babe,* it's chill," she replied. "They're *cool*. They're with me."

"Yeah, *Lance*. Chill out, *babe*," Beau quietly mimicked under his breath.

Lance, neutralized, stood up and brushed his hair behind his ears and straightened himself out. He reached for a wide

235

brimmed fedora and donned it proudly, before dusting off any remaining coke in the embarrassing mustache that was growing on his upper lip.

"So," he began, approaching us. "You guys cool, or what?" Lance asked, crossing his arms.

"Yeah, man. We're cool," Beau said.

"Cool, man," he replied. "Have a seat."

He cut us up like five or six lines each on a large, rectangular mirror, and handed us a rolled up twenty. I hate when people insist on doing coke off of a mirror. Not just because it's cliche, but also because I don't like staring at my own druggy, bug-eyed reflection. The thing is though, coke makes you feel like caring about any of that stuff is pointless, and I was about two more lines away from never caring about anything ever again.

Lance snorted a caterpillar of a line, and threw his head back, "Woo! Happy fuckin' new year!"

Jenny, her friend, and the rest of the people—who hadn't even looked up from their own coke-a-palooza—laughed, and continued vacuuming away. Lance must've snorted his lines ten times faster than us, because when we finished all of ours, he had already poured out another bag in front of him and had almost finished that one, too. I felt my nose start to burn and the drip was really kicking in at the back of my throat, so I sat up and leaned back into the leather couch we were sitting on and found myself staring at Lance in order to keep myself steady, noticing what a mess he was. After he finished both of his bags he stood up, removed one of the guitars from the wall and started playing, completely unaware of how bad he was.

Suddenly, loud, distressed footsteps echoed down the

staircase, revealing a short, skinny, pig-nosed white dude covered in tattoos, wearing a large chain and a black wife beater with bleached hair.

"*Lance,* homie," he yelped with urgency. "Listen, dog, I need some—" and then he saw us and pointed, suddenly infuriated. "Who the fuck are these guys?"

"Whoa, Joey. It's cool man, it's cool. They're cool," Lance said calmly, holding up his hand.

"Oh, it's cool? You think it's cool to give out my coke like fuckin' Halloween candy to a couple'a dildos I've never seen in my life before? Is that fucking *cool* to you? Huh, Lance?! 'Cause I don't think that's fuckin' *cool*, bro!"

Then, encouraged by a wave of coke-fueled confidence, I stood up and raised my hands.

"Dude, dude. Just chill—"

"Don't fuckin' put your fists up at me, motherfucker! I'll fuckin' kill you!" he shouted.

Then he lunged at me, and I felt myself wince, but he came up short, and landed on the glass table, instantly shattering it, launching a massive coke cloud up into the air.

Everyone in the room screamed, but Joey screamed louder, "My fucking coke! Fuck!" The girls cowered in the corner, and Joey rolled over on the floor, his black top resembling a powdered donut. He continued screaming and, although I should've been nervous, I felt myself begin to giggle. I looked over at Beau who still looked too petrified to move, but the laughing wouldn't stop.

"You fuckin' laughin' at me, nigga? I know fuckin' 50 Cent, nigga! I have his number in my phone! I can get twenty homies over here right now to fuckin' merk your ass, you little faggot!"

Joey struggled to get up, but this time Lance grabbed him

before he could attack me. I saw that as my only opportunity to bail, so I booked it up the stairs, ran back out through the hall, and dissolved into the glittery, sweaty mesh of people dancing.

"Fuck," I said, but when I turned around Beau wasn't there. He must still be downstairs, I thought, but then I felt someone grab my shoulder.

"Hey stranger," I heard a warm voice whisper in my ear. Ximena's eyes were wrapped in thick mascara, but I could hardly see her, except for those big white saucers staring straight through me. "When did *you* get here?"

"Uhm," I stuttered. "We've been here for like... I dunno, really."

"Nice *suit,*" she said, and fingered my lapels.

"Thanks. It's uh... its Ocean's dad's."

"You *stole* his dad's suit? "

"No, no. No, Ocean let me borrow—"

"—I'm just teasing, you know. And I know who his dad is. It's not like he'd notice, anyway."

"Oh," I said, and laughed awkwardly.

"Do you smoke?"

"Uhm," I paused. "Sometimes."

"Good. Come on."

She grabbed my hand, and I couldn't help but feel guilty as her cold, slender fingers wove into my own, as she effortlessly pulled me through the crowd.

She led me up a separate staircase in the back of the house, which seemed to go on forever and I asked where she was taking me and she just giggled and said, "Come on, Malfoy."

At the top of the stairs, we took a turn into a small dark room, and walked out onto a balcony, which had a view stretching out across the entire city.

"Wow," I said, staring at the endless sea of lights. "What a view."

I felt her hand poke my shoulder and when I turned, she was holding a lit cigarette an inch away from my nose; when I put it in my mouth, I could taste her lipstick.

"Are you really from L.A.?" She asked suddenly.

"Yeah," I said, feeling defensive. "Why?"

"I dunno," she shrugged. "Doesn't seem like it."

"Why not?"

She stared at me silently, studying my face, and I felt myself get nervous.

Then, finally: "You're too observant."

"I am?"

"Mhmm."

She inched closer and pinched my ear. "Does your girlfriend ever get jealous over how green your eyes are?"

"I d-don't have a girlfriend."

"You don't?"

"N-no," I choked.

"So, why have you been running away from me, then?"

"What? I h-haven't been—"

"*Hey!*" Beau shouted, startling the two of us. He was panting but tried to pull himself together as he came closer, catching his breath.

"Hey, *Beau,*" she said seductively, and kissed him on the cheek.

"What were you guys doing on the roof?"

"I uh—" I stuttered. Beau glared at me.

"How long have you guys been up here?"

"Not long, just, like—"

"Beau," Ximena said maternally. "Where have you *been*? We've been looking for you all night. Alex was just telling me he couldn't *find* you," she pouted. "He was getting worried."

"Really?" Beau's voice went up.

"Uhm. Yeah, I uh... I just couldn't find you and then Ximena came up and started talking to me and—"

"You guys *know* each other?" I could feel the nerves bleeding through.

"What? No, no," I began reassuringly. "She came up to me and asked—"

"—So, you *do* know each other?"

"*Beau*," Ximena interrupted. "Am I not allowed to be friends with Alex?"

"What?" He blushed, defensive. "No, I didn't say that."

"Beau, sweetie," she pulled him in and kissed him. "Come on."

"Okay," he said, and disappeared down the stairs with her, leaving me on the balcony.

Drunk and alone, I walked outside trying to find Ocean, but as soon as I saw Karen sitting next to him, I wished I hadn't. They were sitting on a couple of lawn chairs on the grass, their faces illuminated by the turquoise glow from the pool light, but as soon as I got closer, Karen shook her head and said, "I just *can't* get over it. Are you sure you don't dye your hair?"

"Karen," I said. "What is your problem?"

"*Excuse* me?"

"Why are you always on my ass? What have I done to you?"

"Ugh, Alex," she began, disgusted. "I'm sorry you feel that I'm *on your ass,* but it was literally *just* a question. If you don't feel comfortable talking about your highlights, that's *fiiiine.*"

I rolled my eyes and sighed.

"No, Karen. I do not have highlights."

"Are you sure?" Karen grimaced with uncertainty. "I guess I've just never seen natural hair look like that. It's so… I dunno… *yellow*. Maybe you *should* get highlights, you know? I mean, you want the girls to like it, don't you?"

"Karen… if having yellow hair means repelling girls like you, then I can't begin to tell you how happy I am with the way I look."

"Ugh," she scoffed, standing up. "You're pathetic." She threw her glass in the pool and stormed off.

"Sorry about that," I said, but Ocean seemed amused.

"Don't be. She's been super annoying all night," he paused. "Where's Beau?"

"Inside with Ximena. I uh…" I hesitated. "I don't like her."

"Dude, I know," Ocean said, unfazed. "She's hot, but, like, a total slut. Apparently, she walked barefoot all the way down Doheny just to give some club promoter head, and then afterwards he made her walk back. I tried telling him, but he doesn't wanna hear it. He says they have a *special connection,"* he rolled his eyes. "So fucking gay."

"Yeah," I said dismally, and sat down next to him, my ears quietly thanking me for sparing them of the inside noise.

Ocean lit a cigarette and made eyes at some girls sitting across from us. He coolly brushed his hair back as his rings glistened in the pool light.

"You having fun?" he asked.

"Yeah," I said, my voice going up.

Ocean laughed, "Me either," followed by a long exhale. "Just wish we had some more fuckin' coke."

"That'd be nice."

"See those things over there?" he asked, pointing at the girls. I nodded, awkwardly making eye contact with one of them.

"How many blowjobs you think are in there?"

"I dunno," I said. "Probably a few."

"I'm gonna ask," he said, and flung his cigarette into the pool. "*Hey!*" he shouted, waving his hand. "You two—yeah *you*—come *here!*" he continued, waving them over.

The girls rose, and walked over to us.

"Hey," one of them said as they got close. Since there were no more chairs, they were forced to lean at an awkward angle when they spoke, and I could tell it made them uncomfortable.

"Question."

"Okay," one of them replied nervously.

"Which one of you sucks the best dick?" he asked.

They laughed awkwardly, unsure of how to react.

"*What?*" one of them asked.

"It's just a question," Ocean said.

"Uhm... *I dunno?*" the brunette, with a spray-on turtleneck accentuating her implants, asked.

"Never-mind. My friend was right. He said, '*I bet those girls over there are fucking boring,*' and I was like *no way*, but he just proved me right. So, I guess you should fuck off so we can find somebody *cool*," he said, and flicked his wrist dismissively.

"We're not *boring*," the blonde one said defiantly.

"Yeah, we're *not*," the brunette said, fishing in her purse. "*Look*," she said, proudly flaunting a little white bag. "We have *coke*," she continued, shaking it between her thumb and index finger.

"You're not from here, are you?" Ocean said, unimpressed.

"Are *you*?" the brunette asked.

242

"Actually, I'm from Oklahoma. I'm an actor."

"Oh my *god*!" she said, naively. "Me too! Are you *really*?"

"*No,*" Ocean laughed sarcastically. Their faces simultaneously dropped with embarrassment. "Don't worry, turtleneck. Just give me some coke and I won't make fun of you anymore."

She smiled sheepishly. "There aren't any chairs."

"So? Sit on the grass."

"I don't wanna ruin my—"

"—Shh, sit down," he repeated, and slowly brought his palm down.

Both of them—high heels and short, skinny little dresses—sat down hesitantly, trying to cross their legs.

"What do you do?" Ocean asked the blonde.

"Uhm," she began meekly. "I'm a model."

"A model," Ocean repeated, with an eye roll. "So, you use Instagram filters for a living. Impressive."

"No," she scoffed, offended.

"How many followers do you have?"

"Uhm... I dunno. Like, a hundred thousand?"

"And what about you?"

"Like, forty—maybe fifty—thousand?"

Ocean laughed, "So why're you two at this party?"

"What do you mean?"

"I'm just surprised you're not in Dubai, licking the balls of some fat, oil billionaire," he smiled. "Isn't that how you insta-models pay rent?"

"Fuck you," the blonde one growled, and the two of them got up.

Ocean started laughing, "I'm just teasing. Don't be so sensitive. Sit down."

243

"You're a fucking asshole," she said, both now standing; but not walking away.

"I know, I know, I'm sorry," he moaned theatrically. "I can't help it. Mommy didn't love me. Come on. Sit back down"

The girls hesitated, looked at each other and, if not a bit shamefully, sat back down again.

The girls had practically forgotten that I even existed at this point, but I really needed to pee, so I took that as an opportunity to leave.

"Yo, go find a bottle, or something, and bring it back out," Ocean called, as I stood up.

"Okay," I said, and walked off, hearing the girls now giggling behind me as I got further away.

Re-entering the house was like walking into a wall of sweaty bass thumping. I quickly found a bathroom, but as soon as I opened the door I came in on a half-naked guy bent over the faucet, with another guy in a leopard onesie and a pink, feathery boa coiled around his neck, fucking him from behind. I locked eyes with both of them and the humping suddenly stopped, and everything went quiet. We stood there for a minute, all of us completely frozen, until the bottom shouted, "Get the fuck out you little perv!" But then the other guy shouted, "*Wait!* You're kind of cute!" But I quickly stumbled backwards out of the room and slammed the door behind me, the faint sound of, *"he looked like fun,"* trailing out from inside as I ran away.

Beau was in the living room dancing with Ximena, a drunk, wishful smile wrapped around his head, and then I saw her whisper something in his ear and leave. Beau saw me and ran over, his feet nearly levitating.

"Dude, I think we're gonna have sex," he said innocently.

"Really?" I said, trying to hide my skepticism. "No way."

"Yeah, man! I-I just—I just think it's finally gonna happen. She's been saying all night how much she likes me, an-and how she's so happy that I came and how she can't wait to kiss me again at midnight."

Beau's eyes were rolling back into his own head as he sunk deeper into his own fantasy, seemingly unaware that I was standing right next to him.

I patted him on the shoulder reassuringly. His eyes turned back and stared at me: a silent, hopeful gaze.

"She just kept apologizing over and over for what a *bitch* she's been, and she kept saying sorry, saying how no guy means as much to her as I do."

"Really?"

"I dunno why, but Ocean really hates her. He says she's a slut, but she's *not*," he said. "I really like her, man."

"I know," I said. "I believe you."

"You know how I know?" he asked, rhetorically. "Earlier—like, on the dance floor—they were playing *All I Want for Christmas,* and she whispered in my ear and said that all *she* wants for Christmas is *me,*" his eyes sparkled. "And then she kissed me and said she couldn't wait for tonight and I'm the most special person she's ever met."

"You *are* very special," I said, meaning it.

"*No*, not like *that*," he giggled bashfully. "But you know what I mean."

I *know*, I thought. I know what you mean.

A voice thundered over the speakers: "*Five minutes till New Years!*" And people immediately started pouring into the living

245

room. Beau and I got squished in the middle of everyone, and then he turned to me, "I'm gonna go find Ximena," but I grabbed his shoulder and convinced him to stay for a minute.

I saw a bottle of Jaeger and grabbed it and handed it to him and he took a quick, painful swig, his face squirming with disgust, as thick, brown syrup leaked out of the corners of his mouth.

"Three minutes till New Years!"

Beau looks worried. I take a few more swigs; I start to gag, and my head starts spinning.

Lance from downstairs comes up and hugs me and apologizes for his friend and offers me another bump; I take several.

I turn around but Beau is gone. Ocean enters, with his arm around the blonde, from outside. He hands me a glowing joint.

"Two minutes till New Years!"

People assume their positions. Ocean starts making out with his new girl; I can't find Beau.

"One minute!"

Ocean wraps his arm around me and blows smoke in my face; he says something but the music's too loud and I'm about to throw up.

"10...9...8..."

I feel a tongue being forced into my mouth. The leopard man with the feathery pink boa from the bathroom is holding me by the shoulders, grabbing my crotch. I push him off; he slaps me and spits in my face.

"...1... HAPPY NEW YEAR!"

The entire room erupts in unison; the ear-splitting bass resumes; the room goes wild; my head's buried in the sink and I'm puking my lungs out.

I wrapped my lips around the tap and sprayed water in my mouth, trying to kill the taste of puke, alcohol, and coke in my mouth. I straightened myself out, but the room was still spinning, and for some reason I just needed to find Beau. I grabbed Ocean and asked him if he'd seen him, but Ocean just winked and shot finger guns at me before resuming his kissing, so I went off alone.

I struggled to make my way down the hallway, and I kept stumbling into the wall, eventually bumping into a couple making out against a wall, the guy shouting, *"What the fuck!"* and pushing me to the floor, kicking me in the leg. It took me a second to get up, but I pulled myself together and continued down the spinning corridor.

Every footstep took much longer than it should've, as moving in a direct line was nearly impossible. As I managed to drag myself towards the back of the hall, I heard a faint moan coming from one of the rooms and I approached the door from where the noise was coming and slowly pried it open and saw, what looked like,

Ximena, topless, grinding back and forth with a pair of legs sticking out from underneath her. It must be Beau, I thought, and although I was happy for him, I couldn't shake the feeling of envy. I couldn't stop staring.

But then I heard someone shout, *"Alex!"* and I instantly recognized the voice, but prayed my ears were betraying me. As I turned, I saw Beau, from the corner of my eye, moving towards me, and I felt my body go limp.

"Dude, have you seen Ximena?"

Before I could react, Beau heard the noise and hesitantly pushed the door open. Although he was witnessing it for the first time, the image in front of him was one he'd fantasized about so often that it had almost become familiar to him, and that symphony he'd heard in his head so many times before, the one he was so sure would belong to him tonight, was now being performed for another man right in front of him.

"Don't fucking stop," she moaned through heavy panting. Her breathing grew faster; her cries louder.

Like a dandelion dissolving into the wind, I watched the life inside him slowly vanish.

"...it's getting faster, moving faster now, it's getting out of hand..."

.

He just stood there, frozen, and watched as she got fucked by a guy, who, in that moment, she deemed more significant than him. I tried to pull him away, but he pushed me back and remained fixated, possessed, as if purposely begging for the pain. Beau turned and looked at me for a minute, his face begging for an answer, as if there was something I could've done to have prevented this. His bottom lip began to quiver, and I felt my mouth begin to form a word—an apology, *some*thing—but I had nothing.

His wet eyes blinked twice and, without another word, he took off running. I looked back into the room, the moonlight piercing the blinds and illuminating her tits as they bounced with each thrust; thick, tattooed hands emerged through the bed sheets and fondled them. I stood there for another minute, unable to look away, until Ximena craned her head and shouted, "Close the fucking door, pervert!"

Back in the living room the party was still booming but now my mind was way too hazy, and the spins were so gnarly that all I could do was focus on not throwing up. Blurred faces whizzed by me and I'd stare at them intently for a few seconds to see if I knew them or not. Everyone who saw me looked disappointed, and I was falling into everything at this point: knocking over things in my path, bumping into people, completely incoherent.

"Alex, you good?" I heard a voice ask me. I turned around and saw Ocean, in a green mist, staring down at me. "You're trippin' dude, go sit down. I'll get you some water." Not sure if I said anything, but I stumbled outside and sat down in one of the lawn chairs by the pool. I remember feeling cold, and suddenly I felt my throat open as my head slumped over and then I began puking over my shoulder. Ocean came back out with a glass of water and handed me something.

"Take this, man." Ocean placed the pill on my tongue and helped my trembling hands bring the glass up to my lips.

* * *

I woke up from something pounding in my ears until I recognized

249

the noise as police sirens. I opened my eyes, completely disoriented, realizing that I'd fallen asleep in that lawn chair. People were desperately running in and out of the house, and then I saw the red and blue lights illuminate the trees in the backyard as they came closer. I tried to stand up, but my head was throbbing so bad I could hardly even sit up without puking.

"Alex! Alex!" I heard someone shout. "Where the fuck are—*there* you are!" Ocean shouted, running towards me. "We gotta go, man! We gotta fuckin' go, the fuckin' cops are here, dude!"

Ocean hoisted me up from the chair and grabbed my wrists and started pulling me.

"Where's Beau?" I asked, coming to.

"What?" Ocean said, not stopping.

"Where's *Beau!*" I asked again, louder.

"*Beau?* How the fuck should *I* know?! We gotta fuckin' bail, *dude!* Come *on!*"

Cops were pouring in through the front door, flashlights shining everywhere. People were getting frisked, cuffed and tackled all around me.

"*Fuck,* dude!" Ocean shrieked. He turned back towards the kitchen, but cops were piling in from the back; there was no choice but to jump out of one of the windows. Ocean quickly snagged a beer bottle and hurled it at one of the windows; it shattered with a loud crash, glass flying everywhere.

"Okay, *jump!*" he shouted. He gave himself a running start, then dove through the window, landing on the grass outside. *Fuck,* I thought. I gave myself some room, and then took off sprinting, launched myself through the opening, but completely missed the grass, and painfully landed on the concrete. I felt Ocean grab my arm and bring me to my feet, but as soon as I stood up, a sharp, heavy blow slammed into my ribs, and I felt myself soaring through the air, two cops firmly wrapped around me.

"Get the fuck off'a me, faggot!" Ocean shouted, flailing his fists and elbows, trying to break free. I tried to push them off, but hard, sharp knuckles dug into my liver, followed by a leathery elbow plunging into my throat; metallic cuffs coiled around my wrists, cutting off my circulation—I couldn't move or breathe. Ocean kept kicking and swearing until one of the cops pulled out a taser and shot him; a quick succession of silent, epileptic jolts followed, before he finally stopped moving.

The cops aggressively jerked me to my feet, painfully dug their elbow in between my shoulder blades, and lead me outside and threw me into the back of their car, headfirst, slamming me against the other side.

I groaned painfully, throwing up in the seat in front of me.

I don't know if you've ever been in the back of a cop-car, but it's not so much a backseat as it is a hard, plastic cage, its discomfort amplified when both of your hands are tightly cuffed behind your back, cutting off your circulation. I guess that's the point, though, to make this ride as painfully memorable as possible so you don't ever wind up there again.

I managed to squirm into an upright position and, as the car drove down the side of the mountain, I looked out at the view, and the seducing lights of Los Angeles, asking myself what the hell I was doing wearing this stupid suit, handcuffed, and all messed up, riding in the back of a fucking cop car.

As we descended the canyon, we merged onto Sunset Boulevard, and I pressed my face against the glass and saw all the drunk, smiling faces passing by on the street, and I thought of all the people around the world celebrating tonight with their friends, family and loved ones, and then I thought of Bardot, and what she would think of me if she knew what I was doing right now.

* * *

As soon as we got to the station, they chucked me in a cell, and locked the door. After, like, twenty minutes, two guys pulled up with Ocean—who was still completely out of it—and threw him in the same cell as me. Ocean slumped over when the cops let go of him, but I grabbed him and propped him up against the wall and cocooned him in some ratty old blanket that I found in the cell that smelled like piss. The coke had almost completely worn off, and now I could only feel the Xanax aftertaste calming me down. There was one bench in that cell and, since Ocean was already finished, I pulled myself up on it, and slowly closed my eyes.

"Wake up!" I heard someone shout, followed by the loud tinkering of metal against metal, rattling my skull. I opened my eyes and saw the pale brick ceiling staring back at me. When I finally sat up, I noticed Ocean hadn't moved.

"Which one of you is Ocean?" the cop barked through the cell bars.

"*He* is," I said quietly, pointing to Ocean.

"Yeah, well, tell him to wake the hell up. Daddy's here and he bailed you out."

"What!" I rubbed my eyes, unsure if I'd heard him correctly. "His *dad* bailed us out?" I asked again. Before I'd fallen asleep, I was slowly coming to terms with spending the rest of my life in an orange jumpsuit.

"That's what I said," the cop sneered. I sprung up in the air and ran over to Ocean and started shaking him.

"Dude! Wake up, wake up! Your dad bailed us out! We get to go home! Come on, dude, wake *up*!" Ocean grunted in his sleep, until I slapped him across the face and then he finally opened his eyes, completely disoriented.

"Why are you screaming at me, man? What the fuck?" he moaned, rubbing his eyes. "What the fu—" he looked around, confused, "—Where the fuck *am* I?"

"The cops, you *idiot*. We're at the police station. They tasered you," I said, with a slight giggle.

"They *tasered* me?" Ocean asked, his eyes expanding. "What the fuck, I got *tasered?*"

"*Yeah*," I laughed. "But *dude—listen*! Your *dad* is here! He bailed us out!"

As soon as I said *'dad,'* Ocean's demeanor immediately shifted.

"W-what? M-my... *dad*?" he asked, his breathing getting shakier.

"*Yes*, dude! He's *here*, come on!"

"H-he's *here*?" Ocean asked again, still in disbelief.

"Dude, *yes*. For the *last* time: he's *here*. Now, get up! Let's get the fuck outta here," I repeated, both of my hands tightly gripping his shoulders, shouting in his face.

Ocean began stretching his eyeballs and I could tell he was embarrassed, but I helped him to his feet and brushed him off.

"Okay, man. Okay, okay. *Fuck*. Okay. Uhm. *Fuck*! Do I look fucked up?" he asked self-consciously.

"No, dude. You're fine," I lied, but whatever: Ocean always looked fucked up. He dusted off his shoulders and nervously brushed his hair behind his ears, trying to look as presentable as possible, as if preparing for a job interview, or meeting an ex-girlfriend.

"*Now*," the cop began austerely, as we approached the cell door. "Before I let you boys go, I should tell you that the way you boys behaved tonight is completely unacceptable." An image flashed before me of every teacher, principal, cop, parent or therapist sitting in front of me, reciting the same sentence. "You boys are still in high school! What were you two even doing at a party like that in the first place?" the cop continued with assertion, his voice bleeding into my father's. "When you get home today, you should take a long hard look in the mirror and ask yourselves what the hell you think you're doing with your life. I don't wanna have to find you two in this cell again, you understand? You keep this up and you're gonna end up somewhere you *really* don't wanna be, somewhere *daddy* can't bail you out of," he said smugly. "Such entitlement has no place in this world or the next. Your entire generation—you goddamn *millennials*—have no respect for *any*body. Every single one of you," he sighed. "You're all so goddamn entitled."

Ocean callously stepped forward, and stared straight through him.

"We just take some getting used to, man."

The cop sighed hopelessly, but he opened the gate anyway. Ocean winked at him victoriously before leaving the cell.

I followed him out the front door, expecting none other than Ocean's dad waiting there for us, a guy I hadn't seen since elementary school, but when we got out to the front of the station, he wasn't there. Instead, there was some pasty little dweeb in a suit, with way too much hair gel, smiling unctuously.

"Whoa! Let me guess: the names *Bond*, James Bond?" he said awkwardly, pointing at our clothes. "Hey guys, name's

Justin," he continued, hesitantly stretching out his hand towards Ocean. Ocean didn't budge, he just stared at it hatefully, until Justin nervously retracted his arm.

"So... rough night?" followed by another nervous laugh.

"Where's my dad? Ocean asked sternly.

"He's—"

"—Not here," Ocean interrupted, his head dropping.

"Well... *no*, he's not. But *I* am, and I've heard a *great* deal about you, and I've been instructed to come pick you guys up so," he stuttered. "Maybe if you *want*, we can get some food on the way home and—"

"—D'you have a car?"

"What?" Justin asked, his voice shaky.

"Do-you-have-a-*car*, Jus*tin*?" Ocean repeated.

"Well... yeah, I *drove* here."

"Where is it?"

"*What?*"

"Where's the car?"

"It's... over... *there*," Justin replied weakly, pointing to a black Mercedes parked a few feet away.

"Give me the keys."

"What?"

"The *keys*. Give them to me."

"Ocean, dude, he's just—" I said, trying to intervene, but Ocean raised his hand at me to be quiet.

"Ocean, I—I can't just *give* you th-the—"

"*Actually*... you *can*, and you *will*, because if you don't," Ocean moved closer. "I'll make sure you don't have a fucking job by tomorrow morning."

Ocean held out his open palm, patiently waiting.

Justin looked completely helpless. Shaking, he turned to me

for support, but I just shrugged at him. I thought he was going to cry.

Justin walked over and placed the keys in Ocean's hand, and Ocean's fingers slowly closed over them. He smiled, and walked over to the Mercedes and got in. I gave Justin a final look of remorse, before getting in the car.

"What am I supposed to do?" Justin cried.

Ocean rolled down the window, "You got a phone on you, man?"

"Yeah," Justin yelped.

"Then call a fucking cab, *Justin*," Ocean snarled, as the car roared past him.

* * *

Ocean drove silently, firmly gripping the steering wheel, and keeping the speed limit for once. I looked out of the window at all the stereotypical palm trees, trees that aren't even from California in the first place.

It was still dark out, and it was weird thinking about how just a few hours prior, we were submerged in lights and music, but now, suddenly, it was just the two of us driving silently through the forlorn L.A. streets.

I watched as we sped past the Christmas trees and the sleigh bells and the wreaths hanging from the street lights and the unconscious homeless men dotted up and down Sunset Boulevard and the fake snow painted on all the store fronts and then I listened to the birds begin to invite the start of a new day and I found myself getting envious of them because they could fly away whenever they felt like it, but I knew they never would because the weather's too seductive here. I could feel the hangover slowly creeping up on me, and the congestion in my nostrils was only getting worse by the second.

Ocean asked if I wanted a ride home and I said yeah, so we took a right on the 405 right after Westwood and headed north over the hill towards the valley.

Driving on the 405 felt unnatural, because I'm not from the valley, but *now*, heading in this direction meant that I was heading home, and I sat there struggling to make sense of it all.

We stopped in front of my dad's house and Ocean put the car in park and waited a few minutes before turning off the engine. He was still wrapped in that blanket they gave him at the station, but it actually looked sort of cozy, despite the smell. I was staring at him, and it looked like he was trying to say something, but each time he was about to, he'd fidget with his hair or bite his nails.

Finally, I asked, "You good, man?"

"What?" he jumped, and quickly snapped out of his thinking. "Yeah, why—why wouldn't I be good?"

"Just wondering. I mean…it's been a pretty hectic night, after all."

"Yeah… it has."

Then I heard the faintest sound of a sniffle, and I looked over and saw Ocean hunched over, heavy teardrops propelling off the tip of his nose into his lap.

"Are you crying?" I asked.

"No," he choked.

"Dude, you're crying. What is it?"

Ocean sniffled some more but stayed silent.

"Ocean!" I said loudly, and grabbed him. His eyes were red and puffy, and tears were trickling down his cheeks and then he quickly threw his arms around me and began sobbing, like a scared kid being shipped off to war.

"Wh-what," his voice shaking. "What did I ever do to him?"

"Who?"

Ocean tried speaking through the intervals of dry heaving.

"My *dad*, man! What did I ever do to him besides being born?" he sniffled. "I never fucking asked for *any* of this. It's so fucking unfair, I fucking hate him!" Ocean slammed his fists on the dashboard. "And, like, earlier when that fucking cop said he was outside waiting for us, remember? Like... I *really* thought it was him. I *really* thought he was gonna be outside waiting for me. I've never felt so fucking stupid before in my life. I can't believe I actually *thought* he was gonna be there," he said, shaking his head. "I'm so fucking gullible it's pathetic. But, like, I wouldn't've even cared if he was pissed. I wouldn't even have cared if he fuckin' *hit* me! Because at least that would show that he cared enough to even be upset with me in the first place... that he cared enough to *no*tice and be mad at the fucking mess I am... that I've *become*... that he cared enough to show up at *all*... instead of sending some fucking faggot named Justin to come and pick me up." Ocean wiped the snot and tears from his face. "And, like, remember when you were a kid and you'd be in the supermarket and you'd lose your parents and you'd freak out for a few seconds because you couldn't find them, but then when you found them, you'd be super relieved, and you'd hug them and you could finally relax? Well, I still feel like that kid. I'm still fucking lost, man! And day in and day out, I feel like I'm lost in that fucking supermarket, running down aisle after aisle... looking for them... for *any*one. And the supermarket has anything you could ever need, but it's still so cold and empty in there... just like me."

I didn't know what to say. We sat in silence for several

minutes, until I heard what sounded like a laugh.

"Wanna hear something funny?" he said, wiping his eyes with the blanket.

"Okay."

"I tried to kill myself."

"*What?*" I gasped. "*When?*"

Ocean quietly giggled some more. "Last year."

"That's not *funny*."

"No, listen. It was the day my dad was coming back from some premiere—it should've lasted a weekend, but he was gone for weeks, same time around my mom's funeral—and I'd planned it all out and everything. So, I had this noose tied around my neck—it was just some stupid tie I grabbed from his closet—and it was wrapped around the ceiling fan, and when I kicked the chair out from underneath me," he started giggling, "the fuckin' noose gave out, and I fell over and broke my thumb," he said, now laughing. "The only thing I killed was my ability to jerk off for the next month. I was *so* pissed. *Man,*" he laughed again, letting out a long sigh. "That's when you know you're a real fuck-up. When you can't even fuckin' kill yourself."

I watched as his eyes got lost in thought, and I just sat there looking at him. Then he brought up his hands, and pulled on his right thumb with his left, proudly displaying the damages.

"See? Can't move it back any further. And you know what the funniest part is? Lupé drove me to the doctor, and when I got back my dad hadn't even come home. Apparently, he came back, like, four days later, but he'd already left before I got home from school, so he wouldn't even have seen me hanging there. Instead, I would've killed myself in front of my fucking maid who can't even speak English." He laughed and shook his head. "Talk about wasting your performance on the wrong audience."

"You're not gonna try that again, are you?" I asked hesitantly, after a long pause.

"No," he said coldly. "And for what? So a bunch of people I never even spoke to, can post RIP Ocean on Facebook, and tell people we were best friends? Fuck that," he paused. "When people die, everybody only makes it about themselves, and if I died, it'd be no different...especially for my dad."

He started raking his bottom lip with his teeth, before letting out another sigh.

Then he turned to me, humorlessly, "Remember when you fucked Lucy Stewart?"

I felt a sudden pain shoot through my entire body, as Ocean titled his head, and glared at me. I began to open my mouth, trying to think of something to say, but his expression quickly shifted again.

"I'm just kidding, man."

"What?" I stuttered.

"I don't care about that."

"You... don't?"

"No."

I stared into my lap, the shame making it hard to breathe. "I've never felt so guilty over anything in my life. You didn't talk to me for two years."

"Yeah, I know," he turned away from me and stared out the window. "Because you left me. And I hated you for it."

"What do you mean?"

"You just... *left*. You didn't say anything. No Facebook status, no phone call, no nothing. Just... *gone*. On the first day of school after the summer, when the teachers were taking attendance, a lot of them called your name, and everyone looked around the room when there was no answer because no one knew where you were except me, but I didn't say anything. I just sat there… quietly… hating you in silence," he sniffled. "When you left, I had no one."

"I didn't think you wanted anything to do with me," I said, shrinking into the car seat. "I thought you hated me. That's why I didn't call."

"I *did*!" he turned to me and shouted. "I did fucking hate you!" He turned back towards the window, his voice lowering again. "You… you could've fucking told me, man. *You* got to leave! *You* got to get the fuck out of here! *You* got to escape when *I* had to fucking stay. I had no one!

"What about—"

"—*Beau*?" he scoffed. "Come *on*, man. You think I like listening to that Bulimic bitch cry over girls out of his league all day?"

"I got sent to boarding school," I said, cowardly turning away from him. "It wasn't my choice."

"So?" his voice suddenly turned weak and bashful. "Maybe *I* wanted to go."

"To *boarding* school?"

"I dunno. Maybe."

"But… man, it was my punishment. It wasn't a reward. I thought I was gonna *hate* it."

"I know," his tone dropped to a whisper. "But we could've gone together. I wanted to get out of here *too.* "

"I didn't… I'm sorry—"

"—It doesn't matter. It's too late now, anyway."

He exhaled through his nose. I watched him brush his hair back behind his ears, several locks disobeying him as they fell back in front of his face.

261

Then he looked up again. "Remember when we got arrested for slicing Mr. Humphrey's tires?"

It made me laugh.

"Yeah. And you told that cop that you'd *'consider a lifetime guarantee of no pussy'* before my dad grabbed you and told you to shut up."

We both started laughing.

"I said that?" he asked in between a fit of giggles.

"Yeah, you did."

"Man... I was such a dick. Shame your dad saved us. I should've been locked up."

I looked over at Ocean and, as he smiled, it felt like I was looking back at that same kid from all those years ago; wet, sandy haired and a dripping wetsuit down at his waist, with bits of burrito spilling out of the edges of his mouth. I remembered the first time I ever spoke to him, it was in fourth grade, and we were on the school bus on the way to the LaBrea Tar Pits for a field trip. Some girl behind him laughed at him and he turned around and peered over his seat and said, 'what're *you* laughin' at, *freckles*?' After that day we were hopelessly inseparable, all the way up until the day before I fucked Lucy Stewart at a party, right before I left. We didn't speak for two years up until about a week ago when I saw him come out of the bathroom at Mason's place in Venice and, suddenly, a part of my life that I thought was closed forever was instantly ripped back open.

"What should I do about the suit?"

"Keep it," he said carelessly.

"*Really?*" I asked, pinching the expensive lapels. "You sure?"

"You really think my dad's gonna notice anything missing? Keep it, man. Looks better on you, anyway," he smiled.

"Thanks."

He began rubbing both of his arms and pulled the blanket tighter around him.

"Listen..."

"I know, I know."

"Okay... yeah."

I hugged him once again before I got out of the car, real long and hard too, and he tried his best to hug me back. As I stepped out and watched him pull away, I got this weird feeling that I wouldn't see him again, at least not for a very long time. I don't know why, and I couldn't explain it to you, even if I tried, but as those red taillights slowly dissolved into the early morning darkness, I tried to cement the outlines of his face in my memory, because I knew that would be the last time I'd get a proper glimpse of it.

When I got inside it was still dark and toys covered every inch of the floor, so I took out my phone to shine a path for me, and as I was tiptoeing through the living room, I saw this big bookcase covered in framed photographs of my dad, Esmeralda, and their new kids, in different places, glowing with joy. Multiple shelves with photos of them: on the beach, eating food, at the park, holding hands, cutting cake, and every other image you project to the outside world to display your impenetrable happiness. I scanned every shelf until finally, way at the bottom, I came across an old, faded photo of myself, probably about the same age their kid was now, sitting on a tricycle, smiling, wearing a Batman t-shirt. I picked it up and tried to remember what it was like back then, before my dad made it big, and when my mom, him and I lived a very simple life in that tiny little apartment over on Venice Boulevard. I put the photo back but turned it around so that it faced the wall, and then I walked back into my room and took off all my clothes and got under the covers.

The valley's a lot colder during the winter than the west side, and although I usually prefer sleeping shirtless, I opened my suitcase and put on my attic wolves hoodie. It smelled just like Durnford Hill.

I laid in bed, shivering, and the events of the last two weeks repeatedly playing before me like some movie I couldn't turn off, and suddenly I felt like crying but, for some reason, I just wasn't able to.

* * *

Two days later, the same day I was going to leave, I took an Uber to Malibu, got out at Cross Creek, and stared at that big, stupid hammer statue Ocean and I would always try to climb when we were younger. I must've stood there for a good thirty minutes just glaring at it until, finally, my nausea got so bad that I had to run and find a bathroom so I could go throw up.

I left the park and spent the rest of the day on top of Point Dume looking out over the water, observing the surfers scattered across the waves below me. I was staring at all the million-dollar houses and, as I did, I was reminded of that quote about a bee drowning in honey and, for a brief moment, I think I finally understood what it meant.

I thought about all the people around the world who were bleeding themselves dry just to get a taste of that intangible slice of paradise, unaware that behind those vast green lawns with the infinity pool and wide-windowed houses, the bed of roses that awaits has just too many thorns. But then again, maybe the thorns don't sting as much when you have a nice view to wake up to.

As I walked down the mountain, some skinny, rat-faced kid who I recognized from my old high school with blue hair and covered in ugly tattoos, asked if I was a *Val,* and shouted that this was a *Malibu locals' only* area. I didn't acknowledge him, but as I got further away, I heard him yell, "Go back to the valley, you fucking faggot! M-L-O!"

Later that night, when I got out at the airport—after I'd checked in my bags and everything—I tried calling Beau and Ocean a few times, but it went straight to voicemail. I thought about leaving each of them a message or sending a text, but I couldn't think of anything to say, so instead I just hung up and waited in front of my gate. Across from me was a brightly lit tourist shop that sold those oversized sweatshirts with *California/Los Angeles/Hollywood* plastered across the chest in an obnoxiously loud font. I even saw a family, all of them smiling, go in, and buy a couple of hats and sweaters before they walked over to their gate.

The dad was fat, bald, wearing socks and worn-out sandals with a hefty camera dangling around his neck; the mom was sunburnt on the front of her chest with tits so saggy she could've tucked them into her cargo shorts; and the kids were half a donut shy of obesity, wearing matching Disneyland t-shirts, both glittering with childish naivety. I remember thinking how unattractive that family was and how I'd rather die than wear something like that, nevertheless *look* like them, but then I realized that it didn't really matter what they were wearing or what they looked like, because they looked genuinely happy, whereas everyone I saw in L.A. had perfect teeth and glowing skin, and yet, I doubt any one of those people had had a day even *half* as good as the ugly family in front of me was having. It made me wish that I were ugly because, maybe then, you stop caring about all that other superficial stuff—like how your hair looks and whether a certain color highlights your eyes, or not—and only bother with genuine happiness. But then again, maybe if you peeked behind the curtain, you'd find that that family was miserable as hell, and they just happened to be having a good day on the one rare occasion when I happened to be sitting in the audience. Even sad people have good days *too,* sometimes. One of my therapists once told me that.

XIV

When I got back to England it felt like I had just woken up from a long dream, the last few weeks feeling like they hadn't actually occurred, and everything was all just a fragment of my imagination.

The first few days back in school seemed odd, and every passing face I saw in the hallway, even those of my close friends, seemed so distant, like people I had previously only seen in photos, who I was now seeing in person for the first time.

It was great seeing Patrick and Archie and the rest of my friends but, somehow, I just felt so disconnected from everyone and everything, and when I'd be hanging out with them, I found myself constantly zoning out of their conversations; thankfully they didn't bother me about it, though. Anyone who I'd stop and chat with was livid to hear about how *awesome* my break had been and, just to satisfy and get them off my case, I'd fabricate some new story each time to adhere to whatever fantasy they'd constructed of how I lived my *amazing* life in Los Angeles. Naturally, everyone was amused, even my teachers.

Bardot came up to me after class one day and asked if I wanted to go for a walk, and I said sure, so after school we met up outside Highland. The weather wasn't nearly as cold as it had been before I left, so all I needed was a thick sweater and I was good, no Antarctica parka, or anything. Bardot told me she missed me and asked me how my Christmas had been, and I told her it'd been fine, and asked about hers, and she began telling me all about Sweden and getting to see her family and old friends and how white her Christmas had been and how they went ice skating and all that cute, childish stuff that I didn't feel entirely familiar with, but I didn't care, because I just liked listening to the purity in her voice. Finally, when she was finished, she asked me how it was going back home in Los Angeles, and although a thousand images flashed before me from the past few weeks— getting molested, dealing with my dad, seeing my mom, getting high almost every day, and helplessly witnessing my friends' descent into hell—all I said was, "It was fine, but I don't think I'm gonna go back there for a while," and I didn't.

I walked Bardot back to her dorm later that night, and although I could tell there was an invitation lingering in the air for a kiss—due to the way her eyes were sparkling when she looked at me—I just couldn't do it. Instead, I just stood there looking at her and, as she was looking back at me, I—for the first time in my life—felt that unknown feeling start to boil inside of me, and all of the happiness, pain and fear that would undoubtedly come with it. I saw the authenticity in her eyes that I didn't think existed any more, the unfledged mind that I once carried, the one that I now knew would never come back after everything that had happened over the past few weeks.

I didn't know what to do, and all I wanted was to tell her how I felt about her and how much I had thought about her when I was away and how special I thought she was and how she was the most real and genuine person I'd ever met before in my life and how I wished that everything and everyone would just go away and how all I wanted was to build a castle for us to live in to keep the outside world at bay where there would be nobody allowed inside except for Bardot and I... but nothing came out. All I did was give her a quick hug, and then I quietly walked back to my room.

The next day Bardot came up to me again after school and told me she could tell that something was wrong and said that if something was bothering me, I could always talk to her if I needed to, and even though I could tell that she meant what she said due to the sincerity in her voice and the way she leaned her head in and looked at me when she said it, I just knew it wasn't fair to pollute her with any of it.

After class, when it had turned dark, I was walking back up to Highland and Bardot came running up from behind and stopped me.

"Hey!" she demanded, grabbing my arm.

"What?" I said, avoiding eye contact.

"What is it? Why won't you talk to me?"

"What do you mean?"

"Oh, *stop* it! You know what I mean, Alexander. What's the matter? What happened?"

"Nothing's *happened*, I'm fine," I said, hearing the forgery in my tone. "I'm just jet-lagged, and I'm tired."

"No, you're not, you're *lying*."

"And how would *you* know that, even if I was?"

"Because you made the same face when you told me why that boy hit you... or when you lied and said you were excited to go home for Christmas. Everything else you've said has been true... except for that, and now this. So, what *is* it?"

"Listen, I don't know what you think you know about me, okay? But—"

"—*Alexander*," her voice cracked. "I—I know I haven't known you for very long, but—" she hesitated. "—Alex, you don't understand. I finally feel like I've found someone I can talk to. Someone I can talk to about... about *every*thing. Someone who listens, someone who understands. Someone who knows what it feels like. I don't know what *it* is, but I know that you know what I'm talking about. And... when... when I'm with you, I can say more in just a few seconds than I've said in my entire life... and now," she took a deep breath. "I don't know what's happened, or... or if I've *done* something wrong or... or if you're mad at me but... just please talk to me... please, Alex. I don't know what's wrong, but I can *tell* when you're lying to me. But I don't care! I just... I just want to know what's wrong, and what*ever* happened, I promise, I am not going anywhere. I just..." her voice dropped. "I don't want *you* to go anywhere. Please."

"Bardot. It's—"

"—*What*!" she snapped. "If you don't like me any more just *say* it!"

"It's not that... I'm sorry it's just... it's not fair to you."

"*What's* not fair to me?" she yelped, tears building.

"I don't *know*! All of it! Okay?! It's none of your fucking business and it's not your fucking burden to carry, *all right*? So, stop fucking asking!" I shouted.

"Alexander," she whispered, and grabbed my face in her hands and pulled me towards her. "You don't have to carry all of your burdens alone," she said. "I could help you carry them, too."

"Okay, you wanna know what's wrong? You *really* wanna know?!" I pushed her away from me. "You said you want honesty, right? Honesty's the most important thing, right? Okay, let's go, then. You wanna know that I lied about my mom being dead? Yeah. She's alive, and she's a fucking addict who can barely even remember the name of her only fucking child. My dad's an asshole, I have a stepmom who got me sent to correctional therapy for years, I snorted coke, smoked weed, I even sold drugs here at Durnford and, oh, best of all, I paid for an old Thai lady to suck me off!" I shouted, nearly panting.

"What?" she asked, stunned, in disbelief.

"Yeah. I paid for sex."

"What're you talking about?"

I leaned in, "I paid for a little old lady to suck... my... fucking..."

"Stop it!" she shouted. "Stop it! That's enough!"

"Why? I'm being honest. That's what you want, isn't it?"

We stood there, in silence, looking at each other, and I saw her eyes water.

"What is wrong with you?" she yelped. I said nothing.

Bardot was perfect. I didn't deserve someone like her, but, then again, what if I ended up being wrong about her? What if she turned out to be just another Karen, or Ximena, or Esmeralda? But the second those thoughts came, I knew just as instantly that none of them were true.

"Alexander," she said quietly. "Why do you do things that you know are going to hurt you?"

"I don't know," I said quietly. "I don't know why I do anything."

"Why are you trying so hard to push me away?" she choked. "What are you so scared of?"

"I don't know, Bardot," I said, looking away. "But I think I should go now."

We didn't speak much after that, and not because I didn't want to, but really just because I had nothing organic to say and, eventually, I think she could tell. So many nights passed where I'd sit at my computer with Facebook open, wanting to write her something, asking how she was doing or *any*thing, but as soon as

I started typing my hands would start to tremble, and eventually I'd get so frustrated that I'd just slam my computer shut. Every time I'd see the green dot next to her name I'd always wonder if she was thinking about me as much as I was thinking about her…but who knows?

I always prayed I'd see her at a party, or something; hoping that I'd have the courage to say something to her when I was drunk, but she didn't hang out with the same people I did, so that never happened.

Eventually, we just became passing strangers in the hallway, occasionally shooting the other a wistful smile, a brief glance that painfully reminded me of when that smile could have been the start of something more.

A few months later, right after my birthday, when I was packing up my stuff for the summer, Fergus came up to my room with a sealed envelope and told me—in an incomprehensible manner not unusual for Fergus—that a pretty girl with a weird accent had come by, and had told him to give it to me, and when I opened the letter, it said:

Happy birthday Alexander,

I hope you find what you're looking for.

Yours forever,

Bardot

I heard her voice in my head as I read it and, after rereading it for the hundredth time and getting every last whiff of her perfume buried deep within the ink in which the letter was written, I folded it and delicately tucked it in my wallet.

Bardot's mother got sicker, so she was forced to move back to Sweden after the summer to help care for her, so I never saw her again.

* * *

The following spring, two days before graduation, I got an email from my dad saying he wasn't going to be able to make it because of a 'sudden work conference,' and the next morning I woke up to eight hundred dollars in my bank account, with a text reading: *happy graduation*. My dignity wanted to reply with a 'fuck you, keep it' text, and send all the money back, but who am I kidding? Nobody says no to money, no matter how proud they tell you they are.

On the day of my graduation—after I'd shaken the hands of all my teachers and said my final goodbyes, to the people I was slowly realizing that I'd probably never see again for the rest of my life, except for when scrolling through my Facebook timeline—I took a second to look around and ponder over the last few years I'd spent in that place, and how, just like that, it was suddenly all over.

It felt like such a trip, and I just couldn't understand that it was finally finished. I walked around the campus grounds—past the main school building, past the dorms I'd spent countless hours in, and the other dorms that were completely foreign to me—and then I walked up to the top of the hill just above my own dorm, past the Highland entrance that I had run into every day for the past three years, and looked out over the quaint little town that I'd grown to call home, and looked down at the long windy road that slithered down to the school entrance, and I remembered sitting in a cab with two heavy suitcases in the trunk—my clothes smelling of airplane food, and my skin still warm from the L.A. sun—sitting in the backseat, nervously looking through the windshield at the lights approaching in the distance, ready to start my new life in a *boarding* school, my only reference to such a place being Hogwarts. I stood there thinking about all the memories I'd made over the last few years, and then I was interrupted by the sound of running in the near distance, and then I was reminded of Bardot, and running home from my dorm to make it in time for dinner.

Bardot had deleted her Facebook not long after she moved back home, so I couldn't contact her, but later that day I went up to the front office to ask for her Swedish address so I could send her a letter. At the bottom I wrote my phone number, but about a week later I got a phone call from some lady, who could barely speak English, telling me that the previous tenants had moved out about seven months ago, and she was sorry to inform me that she had no idea where they lived now, but tried to assure me that Gotland was very small, and if I ever came to visit, it probably wouldn't take long until I found somebody who knew her. The woman hesitated before she hung up, before finally telling me that she'd do her best to find the address of the previous tenants and, if successful, she'd give them my letter. The kindness of strangers is never something I've found to be remotely reliable, but I guess sometimes you have no other choice but to invite some optimism into your life. I told Vera about the letter right before I sent it, I even let her read it too, and when she did, I saw a tear shimmy down the edge of her face before she reached over and grabbed me by the cheek and said, in that thick Russian accent I didn't realize I was going to miss so much until after I left, "If you can make old Russian woman cry, Sasha, you can do anything."

When I got back to my room, which was now all packed up, I sat down at the empty desk and looked at that chair Bardot had sat in when she came over that one time, and thought to myself how, in a few months after summer, there'd be someone new living in here, and everything that I felt was mine, would now belong to someone else. He'd have his own Patrick, his own Fergus and, hopefully, for him, maybe even his own Bardot, too. My therapist told me not to dwell on the past too much because it'll drive you crazy but still, every once in a while, I'll take out that letter Bardot wrote me all those years ago and wonder to myself if I'll ever truly find what I'm looking for.

After I'd said my final goodbye to Durnford, I was taking a train into London—to Patrick's house, where I was going to stay for the summer—and my phone was dead, so I found some gossip magazine crammed in between the seats, and on page four, in small font at the bottom, I read: *Tragedy In La La Land. Hollywood Royalty Crashes Under The Influence*, and they didn't even have to say the name, because somehow I already knew.

I tried reading the article some more, but the truth is I hadn't spoken to Ocean once since I saw him driving away in his car after New Year's over a year ago. As I started coming across some of the details in the article about the crash and his condition, I couldn't stomach it anymore, so I stopped reading. I felt so guilty, and no matter how many times they repeated '*accident*', I just knew it wasn't, so, finally, I ripped out the page and threw it behind me. I wasn't sure whether to feel sad or not, because in some fucked up way, I really wasn't all that surprised; instead, I just became angry more than anything. Angry at the abandonment by his father, and how he could let his son continuously get so close to darkness until it finally swallowed him whole, leaving him barely alive after a drunken car crash that could've been completely preventable if he'd only spared five minutes to talk to his own kid.

Fucking parents, man, I'm telling you. As soon as they start making *real* money and getting *real* power, any prior devotion to parenthood goes right out the fucking window.

I felt a sudden urge of curiosity inside me and couldn't help but reach for the crumpled paper again just to check the date of the article—it had been printed over three months ago.

* * *

Several years later, after I'd graduated from L.S.E., Patrick and I moved into this apartment—or *flat,* as they like to call it in Europe—in the Ennismore Gardens in London. It was super expensive, but Patrick's father paid the rent and had agreed to help us out until we both had a steady income. As expected, Patrick decided to follow in his father's footsteps and pursue a career in politics, but no matter how persistent he *or* his father were in their attempted convincing, I could never bring myself to take them up on any of the job offers they sent my way.

No, I wanted to find something on my own and, after a few internships, I finally secured a job at a consulting firm in Canary Wharf, the only helping hand I'd gotten from *any*one being my own tenacity, and that really made me proud as hell. When I got back to the apartment after my first day at the office, Patrick, Archie, Chilly, and even Fergus, jumped out from behind the door with two boxes of pizza and a cake that said *white-collar wanker,* with a big heart around it. Nobody had ever done anything like that for me before in my entire life. It's funny—if you want to know the truth, I even began to cry.

As work progressed, I started working with this company over in Shanghai, and some of their guys were coming to the city and it was my duty to show them around and keep them happy. Mind you, that these guys were loaded, but when they got to London, they told me that they had been there so many times already and they'd grown bored of the city, but some of *my* guys had been planning a trip for all of the new, valued, employees, so where do you think they had planned to go? You guessed it: Los Angeles. I hadn't been back home since I was seventeen, and when all the Chinese guys found out I was born, *and* raised there, they looked at me like I'd just invented fire, insisting they come along, paying for everyone's first class airfare, hotel, transportation, everything.

We only had about three days to spend in the city because they wanted to hit New York on the way back, so when we landed at LAX, they insisted on getting a hotel on the Sunset Strip, so I managed to get a few rooms at The Mondrian.

That night we headed further down Sunset to check out some of the new clubs that had opened, and everyone kept turning to me for advice on what to do and where to go in the city, and although I told them I hadn't been 'home' in nearly a decade, they still turned to me with all their questions.

When we finally arrived at the club, I saw the long line of people waiting to get in, and it suddenly made me feel old and out of place. While standing in line I noticed someone familiar a few heads in front of me, and when she turned around, I noticed it was Karen, who, to my dismay, immediately made eye contact, and enthusiastically ran over, trying to make conversation.

The second her lips began moving I got a bad taste in my mouth, and I thought about saying everything I'd wanted to say all those years ago and how horrible I thought she was, but her chapped lips, the deflated bags under her eyes, and the battered Michael Kors purse she was self-consciously carrying over her shoulder suggested that she was probably a bit more down and out than she'd like to admit, so I figured I'd just leave it alone. I started zoning out almost immediately from whatever it was that she was saying to me, and I couldn't stop thinking about how after all these years, Karen was still standing in the exact same line, desperately trying to get in to some stupid club with some of her obsolete Instagram-famous friends, wearing the same outfit with the same makeup, having probably snorted a couple of lines with that Zeus guy, no less than an hour earlier. She told me her and Ocean had broken up right before his accident, after he had apparently beaten her and put a cigarette out on her arm— a scar she proudly insisted on showing me, like some masochistic art exhibit—and then I tried my best to quickly end the conversation after that, without giving away anything too personal about myself, or what I was doing with my life. She insisted on a hug, so I reluctantly obliged with one arm and my butt out, before she returned to her friends and squeezed back in line, continuing her pursuit of entry by desperately flirting with the bouncer.

Seeing her made me think of Ocean and Beau, and how they'd both been so ruthlessly raped of a stable, conventional life simply because of who their parents were, what they represented, and where they had grown up. I remembered all the times Beau, Ocean and I had been running around Los Angeles as kids, fantasizing about how we'd be rock stars and movie stars one day, and that we'd all live on Mulholland Drive—like Jack Nicholson, Marlon Brando and Warren Beatty—and we'd rule the city and get more girls than anyone could've ever imagined, and one day our kids would grow up and be best friends, just like we were.

Last time I heard, though, Beau had gained a bunch of weight, changed his last name and moved up north to Salinas; Ocean was a quadriplegic confined to a wheelchair, with a permanent speech impediment who ate through a tube; and I was working in an office, combing my hair, and putting on a suit every day before I left for work, and playing golf on the weekends. *Christ.* Ain't that a trip?

Acknowledgements

I wrote this book many years ago and had it not been for my mother's insistent encouragement it would've remained as nothing more than a file on my computer. To my father, Emma, Alex, and all of my friends, for your love and support. To everyone at Olympia Publishers, for breathing life into these pages and thereby fostering my first child. To J.E., for being the first friend to read it. To The White Stripes, for your distortion and validation.

To B.B.L., for your friendship, and in whose apartment on Wilcox Avenue I first started writing.

And lastly, to S.D. Having loved you made me a better writer; having lost you made me a better person.